IMPROVED HOLLOW CATHODE LAMPS
FOR ATOMIC SPECTROSCOPY

ELLIS HORWOOD SERIES IN ANALYTICAL CHEMISTRY

Series Editors: Dr. R. A. CHALMERS and Dr. MARY MASSON
University of Aberdeen

APPLICATION OF ION SELECTIVE MEMBRANE ELECTRODES IN ORGANIC ANALYSIS
G. E. BAIULESCU and V. V. COȘOFREȚ
EDUCATION AND TEACHING IN ANALYTICAL CHEMISTRY
G. E. BAIULESCU, C. PATROESCU and R. A. CHALMERS
HANDBOOK OF PRACTICAL ORGANIC MICROANALYSIS
S. BANCE
ORGANIC TRACE ANALYSIS
K. BEYERMANN
FOUNDATIONS OF CHEMICAL ANALYSIS
O. BUDEVSKY
INORGANIC REACTION CHEMISTRY Volume 1: Systematic Chemical Separation
D. T. BURNS, A. TOWNSHEND and A. G. CATCHPOLE
INORGANIC REACTION CHEMISTRY Reactions of the Elements and their Compounds Volume 2, Part A: Alkali Metals to Nitrogen and Volume 2, Part B: Osmium to Zirconium
D. T. BURNS, A. TOWNSHEND and A. H. CARTER
AUTOMATIC CHEMICAL ANALYSIS
J. K. FOREMAN and P. B. STOCKWELL
FUNDAMENTALS OF ELECTROCHEMICAL ANALYSIS
Z. GALUS
LABORATORY HANDBOOK OF PAPER AND THIN LAYER CHROMATOGRAPHY
J. GASPARIČ and J. CHURAČEK
HANDBOOK OF ANALYTICAL CONTROL OF IRON AND STEEL PRODUCTION
T. S. HARRISON
ORGANIC ANALYSIS USING ATOMIC ABSORPTION SPECTROMETRY
SAAD S. M. HASSAN
HANDBOOK OF ORGANIC REAGENTS IN INORGANIC CHEMISTRY
Z. HOLZBECHER, L. DIVIŠ, M. KRÁL, L. ŠUCHA and F. VLÁČIL
GENERAL HANDBOOK OF ON-LINE PROCESS ANALYSERS
DAVID HUSKINS
QUALITY MEASURING INSTRUMENTS IN ON-LINE PROCESS ANALYSIS
DAVID HUSKINS
ANALYTICAL APPLICATIONS OF COMPLEX EQUILIBRIA
J. INCZÉDY
PARTICLE SIZE ANALYSIS
Z. K. JELÍNEK
OPERATIONAL AMPLIFIERS IN CHEMICAL INSTRUMENTATION
R. KALVODA
METHODS OF PROTEIN ANALYSIS
Edited by I. KERESE
HANDBOOK OF CHEMICAL EQUILIBRIA IN ANALYTICAL CHEMISTRY
S. KOTRLÝ and L. ŠUCHA
ATLAS OF METAL-LIGAND EQUILIBRIA IN AQUEOUS SOLUTION
J. KRAGTEN
GRADIENT LIQUID CHROMATOGRAPHY
C. LITEANU and S. GOCAN
STATISTICAL THEORY AND METHODOLOGY OF TRACE ANALYSIS
C. LITEANU and I. RÎCA
SPECTROPHOTOMETRIC DETERMINATION OF ELEMENTS
Z. MARCZENKO
LABORATORY HANDBOOK OF CHROMATOGRAPHIC AND ALLIED METHODS
O. MIKEŠ
STATISTICS FOR ANALYTICAL CHEMISTRY
J. N. MILLER and J. C. MILLER
SEPARATION AND PRECONCENTRATION METHODS IN INORGANIC TRACE ANALYSIS
J. MINCZEWSKI, J. CHWASTOWSKA and R. DYBCZYŃSKI
HANDBOOK OF ANALYSIS OF ORGANIC SOLVENTS
V. SEDIVEC and J. FLEK
ELECTROCHEMICAL STRIPPING ANALYSIS
F. VYDRA, K. ŠTULÍK and B. JULAKOVÁ
ANALYSIS WITH ION-SELECTIVE ELECTRODES
J. VESELÝ, D. WEISS and K. ŠTULÍK

IMPROVED HOLLOW CATHODE LAMPS FOR ATOMIC SPECTROSCOPY

Editor:

SERGIO CAROLI, Ph.D.
Research Director and Head of Physical Chemistry
Applied Toxicology Department
Instituto Superiore di Sanita, Rome

ELLIS HORWOOD LIMITED
Publishers · Chichester

Halsted Press: a division of
JOHN WILEY & SONS
New York · Chichester · Brisbane · Toronto

First published in 1985 by
ELLIS HORWOOD LIMITED
Market Cross House, Cooper Street, Chichester, West Sussex, PO19 1EB, England

The publisher's colophon is reproduced from James Gillison's drawing of the ancient Market Cross, Chichester.

Distributors:

Australia, New Zealand, South-east Asia:
Jacaranda-Wiley Ltd., Jacaranda Press,
JOHN WILEY & SONS INC.,
G.P.O. Box 859, Brisbane, Queensland 4001, Australia

Canada:
JOHN WILEY & SONS CANADA LIMITED
22 Worcester Road, Rexdale, Ontario, Canada.

Europe, Africa:
JOHN WILEY & SONS LIMITED
Baffins Lane, Chichester, West Sussex, England.

North and South America and the rest of the world:
Halsted Press: a division of
JOHN WILEY & SONS
605 Third Avenue, New York, N.Y. 10158 U.S.A.

© 1985 S. Caroli/Ellis Horwood Limited

British Library Cataloguing in Publication Data
Improved hollow cathode lamps for atomic spectroscopy. –
(Ellis Horwood series in analytical chemistry)
1. Atomic spectra   2. Hollow cathode lamps
I. Title   II. Caroli, Sergio
535.8'4   QC454.A8

Library of Congress Card No. 85–900

ISBN 0–85312–707–7 (Ellis Horwood Limited)
ISBN 0–470–20209–2 (Halsted Press)

Typeset by Ellis Horwood Limited
Printed in Great Britain by The Camelot Press, Southampton

Table of Contents

Foreword

Although the basic properties of hollow-cathode discharges have been known for about seventy years and a number of applications have been reported in the course of time, their use as spectroscopic radiation and excitation sources has been rather limited. Their use as primary sources for atomic-absorption and atomic-fluorescence spectroscopy is well known. The high efficiency of excitation, low background intensity and the narrow line-width of the spectral lines are promising properties for their application as excitation sources in atomic-emission spectroscopy, but they have never gained a popularity similar to that of arc and condensed-spark discharges, irrespective of the fact that, under favourable circumstances they are particularly well suited for trace analysis, analysis of small samples, determination of gases, and efficient excitation of elemental lines of high excitation potential.

The ever increasing need for more powerful analytical methods, especially in the field of simultaneous multielement trace determinations, has brought about a significant revival of interest in the use of such discharges. This has been further enhanced by the recognition that customary excitation sources, in which local thermal equilibrium prevails, cannot be further developed to such a degree as sources not in thermal equilibrium. If, in the latter case, means can be found to increase the power of detection for many kinds of application in the analysis of metals, non-metals and liquids, by an order of magnitude, much simpler analytical procedures can be developed, in which, for example, pre-enrichment can be avoided. If, at the same time, the precision and accuracy can be kept at a high level, as with some of the low-pressure discharges, it will be all the better. An answer to these requirements may be in many cases hollow-cathode discharges in their present, most modern form. It is indeed amazing, how much progress has recently been made by using pulse techniques, additional excitation with the help of electric and magnetic d.c. and RF fields, combination with thermal vaporization etc.

Therefore, a critical and comprehensive review of the current state of development, offered by experts in their respective fields and well chosen and matched by the editor of this book, is most welcome and deserves urgent attention by everybody concerned with improving old techniques and developing new methods in any branch of optical analytical spectroscopy. The editor has aimed at and succeeded in providing a wealth of information relevant to many kinds of application. The literature cited in the various articles is extracted from many sources which otherwise would be difficult to trace. It should be particularly helpful to those who might wish (and who should be encouraged) to enter this field by joining the research work in progress elsewhere.

I am sure that the book will serve its purpose well, and stimulate not only further work on hollow-cathode discharges, but perhaps also on plane-cathode discharges which in many aspects are quite similar, but in other aspects different, regarding the field of optimum application.

I congratulate the authors and editor for the result of their combined efforts and sincerely hope that excitation sources of such power, versatility and promise should definitely be made available to the general analytical problic by some enterprising instrument-making firms.

K. LAQUA
Institut für Spektrochemie
Dortmund, FRG

Preface

Most of the popularity gained by the hollow-cathode discharge stems from its utilization in atomic-absorption spectrometry, the discovery and exceptional development of which was greatly influenced by the availability of this source of sharp and stable spectral lines. On the other hand, the remarkable properties of the hollow-cathode discharge have not yet been fully exploited. Discovered by Paschen at the beginning of this century, it is obviously far from being the latest novelty in the spectroscopist's shop. It is only over the last two decades, however, that it has really come of age, thus significantly contributing to the renaissance of emission spectroscopy.

Besides its innovative applications in fields such as laser technology and mass spectrometry, from a purely analytical point of view the hollow-cathode discharge could be used as a radiation source in atomic-emission spectroscopy, with direct profit from its characteristics, to a much wider extent than is actually the case. Its properties in fact make the hollow cathode something unique, equally suitable for the determination of trace, minor and major elements in a variety of matrices such as metals and alloys, electrically non-conducting powders, gaseous mixtures, and residues from evaporation of solutions.

Recently, renewed interest in this type of low-pressure discharge has prompted further research, particularly in order to increase the intensity of spectra emitted by the hollow cathode, since these are generally less intense than those obtainable with other more conventional sources.

This multi-authored book, written by well-known specialists, attempts to give a comprehensive account of the progress made so far in developing new versions of the hollow-cathode lamp to promote enhancement of radiation output. Such points as coupling with a magnetic field, superposition of micro-wave irradiation, separation of atomization and excitation processes in the so-called furnace atomic non-thermal excitation spectrometry system, boost by means of an auxiliary discharge, modifications in the hollow-cathode geometry (essentially by modifying its bottom or by reducing its diameter so as to operate in a microcavity), as well as variations in the operative mode of the lamp through a burst of radiofrequency energy or by application of a pulsed current, are thoroughly discussed and considered for their analytical potential in both emission and atomic-absorption spectroscopy.

The editor hopes that this book will not only outline the state-of-the-art in this field, but also mark future trends in stimulating fashion.

Finally, the editor wishes to acknowledge the professional assistance of Alessandro Alimonti, Oriano Falasca, Francesco Petrucci, Oreste Senofonte and Nicola Violante, whose co-operation and efforts greatly facilitated the compila-tion of this book. Gratitude is also expressed for Giovanni Briancesco's skilful technical assistance in the preparation of a large part of the drawings and schemes.

Sergio Caroli

1

Analytical potential of the microwave-coupled hollow-cathode discharge

S. Caroli, A. Alimonti and F. Petrucci

1.1 MICROWAVE-INDUCED PLASMAS

1.1.1 Introduction

There has been considerable renewed interest over the past few years in low-pressure microwave-supported (MW) discharges as a means for generating plasmas, which in turn are capable of exciting chemical species introduced into them. Not only atomic-absorption and fluorescence spectrometry (AAS and AAF, respectively), the analytical potentials of which were appreciably expanded by the availability of electrodeless discharge lamps, but also atomic-emission spectroscopy (AES) have taken advantage of the many attractive features shown by plasmas for elemental analysis. This is extensively documented in numerous scientific papers (see for instance an excellent review by Zander and Hieftje [1]).

The gases most often used for sutaining the plasma are He and Ar, which provide a medium energetic enough for the excitation of almost every element in the periodic table, including the halogens and many other non-metals that are difficult to determine. The higher ionization potential and energy of metastable helium species result in detection limits better than those obtained with argon, though the higher atomic weight of argon greatly simplifies the problem of nebulization of liquids. The relatively high degree of excitation peculiar to MW plasmas, the sharpness of the emitted spectral lines, together with reduced background emission, as well as the relatively low installation and running costs of MW generators (powers of 200 W are seldom exceeded and noble gas consumption is as a rule less than 1 litre/min), constitute important properties, the exploitation of which is still far from complete.

On the other hand, sample introduction procedures are not yet entirely satisfactory, the plasmas are not very stable to liquid aerosols or sample injection, and the atomization step also remains a critical point simply as a consequence of the low power available. Matrix interferences are often severe and further limit the wider applicability of the MW discharge radiation source in AES. Notwithstanding, the significant advances reported in the recent past (see e.g. [2] and [3]), show that the limitations may be circumvented, at least to some extent, for example by combination of the MW radiation source with other excitation devices less prone to the disadvantages listed above. In this respect the MW-coupled hollow-cathode discharge (MW-HCD) is of promise for various analytical purposes. This will be demonstrated in more detail after some general considerations on the mechanism of MW plasma breakdown and stabilization.

1.1.2 Microwave plasma formation

The application of an electric field at a frequency of 10–2500 MHz to a noble gas, ordinarily contained in a closed tube, generates a plasma with characteristics that may vary considerably with the experimental conditions. The MW frequency most commonly adopted is 2450 MHz, because several power generators commercially available as medical diathermy units operate at this frequency, in accordance with international regulations. The ultimate consequence of energy transfer from the applied electric field to the electrons in the plasma is excitation and ionization of the gas atoms through their collisions.

The breakdown and stabilization of the MW plasma are conditioned by an appropriate choice of noble gas pressure (p), and the maximum amplitude (E_o) and frequency (ω) of the electric field. At constant E_o and ω, the number of collisions undergone by an electron increases with p until the gas particle density becomes too high to allow the attainment of sufficient electron momentum for the ionization of an atom. Ignition of the plasma, on the other hand, takes place at too low values of p since adequate power (P) cannot be transferred from the field. For one electron the power absorbed from the field is given by Eq. (1.1) [4]:

$$P = \frac{e^2 E_o^2}{2m(f^2 + \omega^2)} \tag{1.1}$$

where e is the charge and m the mass of the electron, and f the frequency of collision.

The ionization of the gas atoms through collisions with electrons continues until a dynamic equilibrium state is reached; this is characterized by the partition of the energy supplied by the MW field, between electrons and ions. Balance between the energy supplied to the plasma and that dissipated from it through, for example, inelastic collisions and impacts on the tube walls, is essential for obtaining a steady-state plasma.

The pressure of the supporting gas determines whether the plasma is in local thermodynamic equilibrium (LTE) or not. It can be assumed in fact that plasmas at atmospheric pressure are in LTE as a consequence of the high particle density.

In this instance both the Boltzmann equation describing the population of a given atomic level and the Saha equation accounting for the ionization equilibrium are valid, and the thermodynamic temperature is therefore sufficient to characterize the plasma. There is no need to examine in detail the processes occurring at microscopic level, to exploit them analytically. A much more complex situation arises when the gas pressure is decreased to some hundred Pa or even less. Reduction of the particle density changes the overall character of the deactivation mechanism of excited states from collisional to radiational. As a consequence of the smaller number of collisions per unit time a significant portion of the energy transmitted to the plasma is converted into electron motion and excitation of electronic states. If the plasma is assumed to be optically thin, as is often the case, energy is lost mainly by emission of photons. This means that the plasma can no longer be described as being in LTE and the interpretation of the microscopic processes resulting in excitation requires the determination of quantities such as spectroscopic temperature, electron temperature and concentration, and concentration of metastable noble gas species [5].

There is strong experimental evidence that, under such conditions, two distinct groups of electrons exist [5-7] — one with low density and high energy and the other with high density and low energy. Whereas the electron temperature is essentially determined by the first group, the second group is considerably more abundant, constituting the major part of the overall electron concentration. The fraction of high-velocity electrons responsible for the ionization process is, however, large enough to counterbalance the loss of ions caused by recombination and ambipolar diffusion to the walls. The electron temperature required to sustain the plasma is, as a consequence, directly related to the ionization potential of the noble gas employed to generate the plasma. For argon and helium the electron temperatures span the ranges of 26000-53000 and 50000-130000 K, respectively, depending on the operating pressure and the applied power [5,8,9].

1.2 METHOD FUNDAMENTALS

1.2.1 Characteristics and drawbacks of the hollow-cathode discharge

Among sputtering sources, the HCD has gained wide popularity not only because of its fundamental role in AAS, but also as a powerful excitation device directly applicable to AES. From this point of view it is particularly worth mentioning the stability and reproducibility of the emitted spectra, the lines of which are notably sharp and narrow, as well as the low effects of matrix composition, the limited spectral interferences, and reduced background intensity [10,11]. The versatility of the HCD for analytical purposes makes it equally suitable for the determination of trace, minor and major elements in dry residues from solution [12,13], metal alloys [14], electrically non-conducting powders [15] and gaseous mixtures [16]. The pretreatment of samples that is almost always necessary and the inadequacy of HCD in the direct analysis of liquids (injection into the discharge zone perturbs plasma stability) to a certain extent limit a more generalized use of this source. Furthermore, in spite of the prolonged residence time of analyte atoms (depending on the particular cathode configuration) and the absence of LTE (which enhances the signal-to-background ratio by two or three orders of magnitude with respect to sources in LTE [17]), the absolute emission intensity as well as the detection power of the HCD cannot be considered entirely adequate for trace analysis. In order to maintain its advantages, this discharge must be operated at relatively low direct currents. An excessive increase in current would lead to broadening (by self-absorption) and even self-reversal of the atomic resonance lines.

1.2.2 Main physical processes in the hollow-cathode discharge

It can be stated that HCD and MW plasmas share some important features, thus justifying the assumption that their superposition could lead to a sort of mutual reinforcement. The question is whether this can occur without compromising any of their more attractive properties. Both discharges are characterized by a marked insensitivity of the spectroscopic temperature to working conditions and, just as in the MW plasma, at least two groups of electrons with very different energies and densities can be identified in the HCD. A unique feature of the HCD, however, is the effect of the cathode geometry, in that a fraction of the electrons released from the cavity surface and accelerated across the dark space can undergo a limited number of collisions with plasma particles, reverse direction and repeatedly cross the glow region. This possibility of making multiple passages greatly increases the ion- and photon-producing effectiveness of these electrons, with energies up to a few tens of eV, which form part of the non-Maxwellian energy distribution [11,18]. The presence of a group of very fast electrons which make very few or no collisions is also predicted and agrees with the high discharge currents found in an HCD.

Figure 1.1 illustrates schematically the zones formed within the cathode cavity when the discharge is operated.

The atomization and excitation mechanism characteristic of the HCD can be broken into the following main steps: ionization of the carrier gas under the influence of the applied electric field; impact of the ions thus generated, as well as of metastable and neutral species, on the sample, where they partly dissipate their kinetic energy by extracting atoms or clusters of atoms from its surface; and transport into the plasma with subsequent excitation. The amount of sputtered material Q has been found [19] to obey Eq. (1.2):

$$Q = \frac{CL^2 t}{hFp} \qquad (1.2)$$

where L is the applied power, t the sputtering time, h the depth of the cavity, F the frontal surface area of the cathode, p the gas pressure, and C a constant depending only on the carrier gas and the nature of the cathode material. The role of the photons originating in the dark space or in the glow region in the generation of electrons is still open to debate. The nature and extent of the phenomena occurring in the HCD plasma depend strongly on the working parameters and also on the type of rare gas used to sustain the discharge. It can

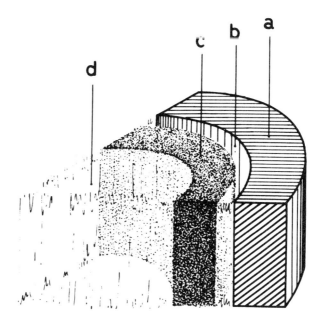

Fig. 1.1 – Cross-sectional view of an HCD. a, Cathode wall; b, cathode layer:
c, Hittorf dark space; d, negative glow.

be said, however, that direct electron collisions such as $X + e^- \rightarrow X^* + e^-$ and $X + e^- \rightarrow X^+ + 2e^-$, as well as recombination $X^+ + e^- \rightarrow X^*$ (X = inert gas atom and * indicates the excited state) are mainly responsible for the excitation of the gas. The sample atoms (M) ablated from the cavity surface can undergo direct electron collisions of the type $M + e^- \rightarrow M^* + e^-$, $M^* + e^- \rightarrow M^{+*} + 2e^-$, $M^+ + e^- \rightarrow M^{+*} + e^-$, and the like. On the other hand, metastable states are possessed by all noble gases and can be generated through the sequence excitation–collisional deactivation or ionization–recombination excitation. The lifetime of these lowest triplet states is about three orders of magnitude longer than that of normal excited states. Metastable species can store a large amount of energy and are of primary importance in the excitation of foreign atoms through Penning ionization reactions $X^m + M \rightarrow X + M^+ + e^-$ and $X^m + M^+ \rightarrow X + M^{2+} + e^-$ (where m indicates the metastable level). Excited species can subsequently be originated by radiative recombination $M^+ + X + e^- \rightarrow M^* + X$, and finally emission through decay to the ground state $M^* \rightarrow M + h\nu$. Moreover, it is self-evident that Penning ionization is successful only when the energy of the metastable level is higher than that required for ionizing M or M^+. Helium and argon each have two important metastable levels, at 19.73 and 20.53 eV and 11.49 and 11.66 eV, respectively, enough to ionize quite a number of elements. Although the complexity of the processes which take place in an HCD has been only briefly touched on, the information provided here is sufficient to highlight the effects which are likely to ensue from the combination of an HCD with an MW field.

1.2.3 Interaction of the microwave and hollow-cathode discharge mechanisms

Various consequences of the superposition of an MW field on an HCD can be hypothesized from theory, for example that the sample vaporization rate is enhanced, or that the excitation of a given amount of analyte atomic vapour is effected more efficiently, or even that both phenomena occur simultaneously. The first hypothesis, however, seems unlikely since the sampling mechanism is, in the case of cooled HCDs, mainly physical ablation due to the bombardment by inert gas particles producing a pseudo-vapour at a temperature much lower than that necessary to generate it thermally. The vaporization process in MW plasmas is on the contrary essentially thermal, so that at the working temperature of the composite source ($500-600°C$) it would not contribute significantly for many solid materials. Experimental evidence of this assumption has been achieved for elements of different volatility, such as aluminium, copper, graphite and iron, for which the sputtering rates do not appear to be affected by the presence of an MW field. In this connection also, the residence time of the analyte atoms within the excitation zone would not be influenced, as it is dictated by the equilibrium reached between the sputtering and redeposition processes. Therefore, if mutual reinforcement of the two types of discharge occurs, it must arise in only the excitation process. It is conceivable that ionization of the carrier gas would be increased if both effects occurred together. The presence of a group of fast electrons in both types of plasma would lead to the simple conclusion that the concentration of fast electrons is increased. Since impacts with these highly energetic species play a fundamental role in the excitation mechanism, the ultimate consequence should be an overall increase in the intensity of the emitted spectral lines. Several investigations have shown that, with argon as the filler gas, this prediction is amply confirmed by experimental data [20-22]. In fact, under working conditions which permit an effective coupling of the two excitation types, not only is the emission intensity from the cathodic material enhanced, but also a decrease is observed in the intensities due to both noble gas and background. The background, being already very low for each discharge alone, practically vanishes. These facts offer the possibility of better detection limits and lower spectral interferences. A complete explanation of the mechanism responsible for this behaviour is not yet possible; even the HCD and MW are not completely understood theoretically. Nonetheless, it may be suggested that the higher density of fast electrons resulting from the increase in the degree of ionization of the noble gas produced by the simultaneous action of the two excitation modes implies a shift to the right of the reaction for metastable species formation, $X + e_{fast}^- \rightarrow X^m + e_{slow}^-$. The increase in the number of metastable species will lead to a higher contribution of the Penning ionization mechanism and consequently to greater excitation of the analyte species. The larger population of metastable species also means a depletion in the number of atoms of the rare gas available for conventional excitation and emission, thus accounting for the weaker intensity of its spectrum. The enhancement in metastable argon concentration has been confirmed by AAS measurements related to transitions involving the metastable levels themselves. The origin of the background may be attributed in general to four main factors; the occurrence of band spectra;

series limit continua; a continuum from non-quantized processes due to the free-free electron radiation; and a continuum from incandescent particles. Of these, only the third factor appears to play a significant role in low-pressure discharges in noble gases. The corresponding intensity is independent of wavelength and can be expressed by Eq. (1.3):

$$I = K \frac{n_e \, n_i}{kT^{1/2}} \tag{1.3}$$

where n_e and n_i are respectively the electron and ion density, k the Boltzmann constant and T the absolute temperature. Since the continuous background emission in these types of plasma is essentially caused by radiative recombination with slow electrons, such as $X^+ + e^- \rightarrow X^* + h\nu_{cont}$, a diminution in their number may well account for the observed phenomenon. To summarize, there is. a single plasma, in which the two discharge mechanisms must coexist, and there is an apparent enrichment in fast electrons and metastable argon species.

If the support gas is changed from argon to helium, superposition of the MW on the HED produces little or no detectable effect, but any effect observed is opposite in direction to those encountered for argon. When compared with the HCD in argon, the HCD in helium is characterized by a lower concentration of electrons, though the fraction with energy close to the whole cathodic drop and thus capable of penetrating the opposite dark space is much larger. In other words, the greater ionization potential of helium requires a high electron temperature to sustain the plasma. It is also generally accepted that the smaller total ionization cross-section of helium lowers by approximately one order of magnitude the frequency of impacts, and that the role played by metastable species in this gas is much less important, as excitation is mainly due to direct electron collisions. Therefore, the completely different behaviour of the coupled discharge in helium is not surprising. A tentative explanation consistent with experimental observations should incorporate the assumption that the superposition of MW irradiation under the operative constraints that make it possible (as detailed in the next section) can supply the plasma with a fraction of fast electrons that is small when compared with that generated in the HCD, and is often insufficient to produce clear effects. Hence, it would seem logical that the availability of a slightly larger number of high-energy electrons will cause reduced effects. This increase in the density of fast electrons is indirectly confirmed by spectral intensity measurements of the high-lying levels of helium.

We must point out that these considerations are valid for the total emission from the coupled discharge and that no attempt has been made to elucidate the radial distribution of the intensity of spectral lines; the entire cross-section of the cathode was viewed and focussed on the detection system. Exceptions to the general behaviour described above are also encountered and these show the need for a more detailed interpretation. At present, the parameters exerting a major influence in the MW-coupled HCD cannot be quantitatively and thoroughly assessed. Moreover, variations in the working gas pressure and applied current would certainly affect the extent and nature of the dominating processes.

Notwithstanding the lack of the further experimental information necessary for elucidation of the basic processes contributing to the observed characteristics of the coupled discharge, it is apparent that this device could have advantageous analytical applications; this will be discussed in Section 1.4.

1.3 MODES OF OPERATION

1.3.1 Instrumental facilities

Forms of apparatus for the generation of MW plasmas have been reported in many recent technical papers [e.g. 1,23,24], to which the reader is referred for a detailed description of power units and types of MW cavities. Although most MW power sources commercially available operate at 2450 MHz, there is a considerable variety of cavity structures, that can be used with either helium or argon at atmospheric or reduced pressure. A common feature is the need to match the impedances of the cavity and transmission line, and to tune the resonance frequency of the power supply to that of the cavity to optimize the transfer of power to the plasma. Slab-line, tapered rectangular TE_{013}, fore-shortened $\frac{1}{4}$- and $\frac{3}{4}$-wave coaxial, and foreshortened $\frac{1}{4}$-wave radial cavities can meet some of the different requirements. The last device mentioned, which has been much modified and improved and is known at present as the Beenakker TM_{010} cavity resonator [25], has excellent power-transfer efficiency.

Demountable HCD tubes for use in AES can be divided into two broad categories depending on whether or not there is cooling by means of a circulating fluid. The basic difference between the two operating modes is that the sampling process in the hot HCD version is dominated by thermal phenomena, whereas the excitation mechanism remains essentially unaltered. The experimental configurations devised and utilized so far are numerous, thus demonstrating the vitality and flexibility of this analytical tool. Detailed accounts can be found in the relevant literature [e.g. 10,26].

Coupling of the two discharge types within the same plasma-containment device requires that the conditions are satisfactory for both. The easiest way to accomplish this is to use HCD lamps with the anodic and cathodic blocks separated by a quartz cylindrical chamber with the double purpose of providing electrical insulation and ensuring adequate transfer of MW power to the noble gas within the discharge tube. Figure 1.2 represents schematically the lamp configuration best suited for this purpose.

One way of achieving superposition of MW radiation on the HCD is with an antenna placed perpendicularly to the main axis of the lamp (as shown in Fig. 1.3). In spite of its simplicity, requiring no physical connections with the lamp, this configuration has proved to be surprisingly good from the viewpoint of reproducibility of data [21,22], with only two serious limitations, (*i*) the utmost care is necessary when positioning the antenna, so that a standing electromagnetic wave is produced, with maximum electric field along the tube axis and (*ii*) the amount of power reflected backward or dissipated outside the lamp is considerable (up to 80%).

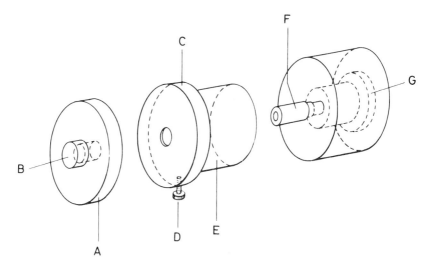

Fig. 1.2 – Details of an HCD lamp capable of MW coupling.

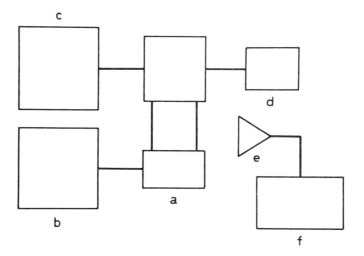

Fig. 1.3 – Schematic diagram of the antenna-mediated MW–HCD coupling.
a, Hollow-cathode lamp; b, vacuum pumps; c, current-stabilized unit; d, noble gas
supply; e, antenna; f, MW power unit.

Another method for MW coupling is to connect the generator directly to the
tube with coaxial cable. For this, the connector is inserted in the metal ring that
supports the quartz chamber. This ring, if adequately insulated from the cathodic
block, acts as a resonant cavity with some formal similarities to the one devised by
Beenakker. The assembly is shown in Fig. 1.4. This method permits the efficiency
of power transfer to be optimized, but its realization is extremely demanding
because complete electrical insulation of the various components is mandatory

and the geometrical requirements are particularly severe. Although it is not ideal from the standpoint of maximization of cavity quality-factor, stainless steel is the material of choice for the ring because of its high corrosion resistance and ease of machining.

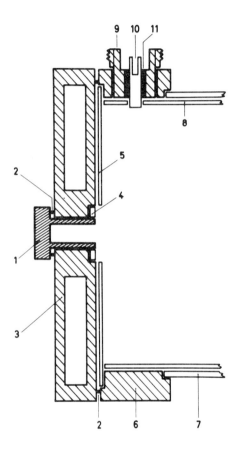

Fig. 1.4 – Cross-sectional view of the direct MW–HCD coupling. 1, Hollow cathode; 2, silicon O-rings; 3, water-cooled cathodic block; 4, insulating Pyrex ring; 5, insulating Pyrex disc; 6, cylindrical metal wall; 7, external insulating Pyrex chamber; 8, internal insulating Pyrex chamber; 9 and 10 coaxial cable connectors; 11, Teflon insulator.

From Fig. 1.4 it might be inferred that the position of the hollow cathode and cavity is not the best, as the MW plasma is located freely in the cavity itself. This is, however, valid for discharge tubes which simply act as containers of the sample [27]. In the coupled excitation source, on the contrary, this configuration is essential to guarantee the interaction of the two types of discharge, because the sample tube is now a metal hollow cathode and not a conventional MW plasma chamber.

The composite excitation source can be switched on in three possible ways: by igniting the MW plasma first and then the HCD, or vice versa, or simultaneously, the same steady discharge being attained by all three methods. If the MW plasma is ignited first, the cavity is seen to be filled with a homogeneous luminescence as a consequence of the application of the MW field. When the HCD is started first, this luminescence is concentrated almost completely within the hollow cathode. This can be explained on the basis of the small though not negligible voltage drop existing between the anode and the hollow cathode mouth, towards which the noble-gas positive ions generated by the MW effect are driven. The reverse procedure shows an identical phenomenon since the glow inside the cathode becomes more intense when the MW field is coupled.

1.3.2 Optimization procedures

In superposition of the two discharges there has to be a compromise in conditions in order to ensure optimum working of the combination. Fortunately, the similarities of the phenomena occurring in both plasmas justify the assumption that changes in some basic working parameters qualitatively affect the discharge behaviour in the same way. Thus it could be predicted that an increase in the total power (MW and electrical) supplied to the composite source would lead to higher electron concentrations, whereas increased pressure should decrease the electron temperature in each of the two discharges, and therefore also in the coupled one.

The general behaviour of the MW-coupled HCD in dependence on the basic working parameters is now described, on the basis of the available experimental data.

1.3.2.1 Effect of pressure

From a theoretical viewpoint, for each particular analytical case an optimal pressure range can be identified which corresponds to maximum emission intensity, because the biggest proportion of fast electrons is generated. This is so for both types of plasma. For a coupled lamp, the overall emission intensity output appears to be qualitatively affected in the same ways by variations in discharge gas pressure, as shown in Figs. 1.5 and 1.6. It is noteworthy that the patterns shown in these figures are valid for most elements, except for a few cases, such as Al or graphite, which do not show any appreciable difference when MW coupling is used. It is also clear that the differences between the intensities of a given line with and without MW superposition tend to be larger with increasing pressure, independent of the nature of the gas.

1.3.2.2 Effect of applied power

It is intuitively expected, and experimentally observed, that an increase in the power applied to either plasma results in increased emission intensity (at least up to a threshold value). It is more interesting to investigate what happens in the composite tube on variation of the ratio of the two forms of energy applied to it. The general pattern followed is exemplified by the behaviour of a copper cathode in argon, shown in Fig. 1.7.

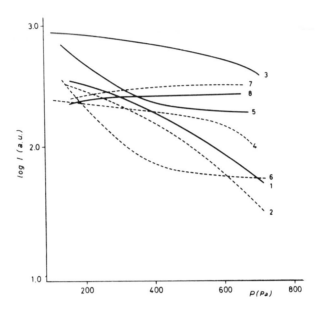

Fig. 1.5 – Dependence of emission intensity on gas pressure in the MW–HCD.
Current, 75 mA; MW power (effective), 50 W. Solid lines, with MW superposition;
dotted lines, without MW. 1 and 2, Cu(I) 299.7 nm; 3 and 4, Zn(II) 250.2 nm;
5 and 6, Fe(II) 238.2 nm; 7 and 8, Ar(I) 338.8 nm.

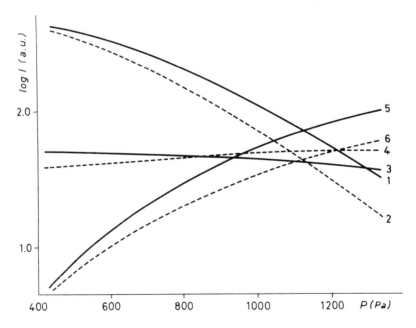

Fig. 1.6 – Dependence of emission intensity on gas pressure in the MW–HCD.
Current, 100 mA; MW power, 50 W (effective). Solid lines, with MW superposition;
dotted lines, without MW. 1 and 2, Cu(I) 327.4 nm; 3 and 4, Zn(I) 280.1 nm; 5
and 6, He(I) 276.4 nm.

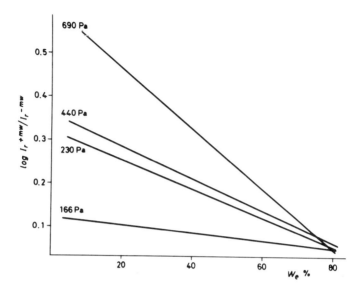

Fig. 1.7 – Effect of the percentage of electric power (W_e) on the overall emission from the coupled lamp. I_r^{+mw}, ratio of the intensities of the cathode material and carrier-gas lines in the presence of the MW field (50 W effective); I_r^{-mw}, the ratio without MW. Spectral lines, Cu(I) 299.7 nm and Ar(I) 338.8 nm.

It is usually found that the MW-HCD lamp is capable of emitting intense spectra when run at currents considerably lower than those normally used for the non-coupled HCD. The composite tube can thus be operated with optimum performance at a current of 50–100 mA, which for the simple HCD mode means that deleterious effects such as self-absorption are virtually absent, and the discharge stability is maximized (for both discharge modes, mild operating conditions minimize the undesirable effects, the extent of which rapidly increases with applied power). The advantageous features of both plasmas can thus be preserved in the combined discharge, at the same time as provision of an environment of energy high enough to generate an intense radiation emission from the composite tube. Generally speaking, this can be achieved when the power independently applied to each discharge does not exceed 40–50 W.

It should be recalled that, in an HCD, only two of the three main working parameters (carrier-gas pressure, current and voltage) can be set, because the third is determined by the values of the other two. Usually, the pressure is selected in advance and either the current or the voltage is set and the other allowed to change accordingly. Alternatively, the electric power may be kept constant.

1.4 ANALYTICAL APPLICATIONS

1.4.1 Analysis of metals

When electrically conducting materials have to be analysed by means of an HCD, the simplest way is to machine hollow cathodes directly from the sample mass or, when the amount of sample is limited, to prepare discs of suitable diameter and thickness to place at the bottom of supporting hollow cylinders of a different material, not containing the elements under investigation [14,28]. A recommended procedure for preparing samples requires mechanical and chemical cleaning by use of 600-grade emery cloth and several rinses in an organic solvent such as n-hexane, followed by predischarge for a short time (1–2 min is sufficient in most cases), in order to eliminate even the slightest trace of adsorbed impurities [22].

The determination of trace and minor elements in steel is a case where the application of the coupled discharge instead of a simple HCD is highly beneficial. Recent findings [22] have shown that a gain of at least one order of magnitude in the determination limit can be achieved. The compositions of the steel specimens are listed in Table 1.1.

Table 1.1 — Analytical parameters for BSC steel reference materials (Middlesborough, UK)

Analyte	Analytical wavelength (nm)	Concentration range (wt %)
Cr	(I) 425.4	0.044-3.07
Cu	(I) 307.4	0.090-0.495
Mn	(I) 403.5	0.016-1.42
Mo	(I) 386.4	0.007-1.41
Ni	(I) 305.4	0.048-5.15

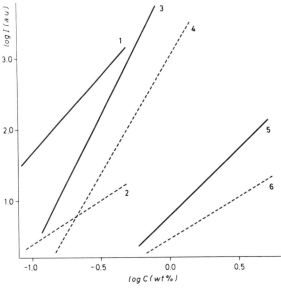

Fig. 1.8 — Plots of the dependence of intensity on the concentration of trace elements in steel. Solid lines, MW–HCD source; dotted lines, HCD source. 1 and 2, Cu(I) 327.4 nm; 3 and 4, Mo(I) 386.4 nm; 5 and 6, Ni(I) 305.4 nm. Argon pressure, 440 Pa; current, 100 mA; MW power (effective), 50 W.

The behaviour of three of the elements listed in Table 1.1 is illustrated in Fig. 1.8. The increase in emission intensity is accompanied by an improvement in sensitivity, as the slope of the analytical plot is clearly and constantly steeper. This tends to support the proposal that self-absorption, often overlooked in hollow-cathode-generated spectra owing to the line sharpness, can be eliminated or significantly reduced by using an MW–HCD tube. Linearity of the graphs does not appear to be altered by the MW irradiation, but a slight but definite improvement in precision is apparent, since the relative standard deviation drops from around 3% to about 2%. The calibration ranges found for various elements in copper samples [29] are detailed in Table 1.2.

Table 1.2 – Analytical data for trace element determination in copper

Analyte	Analytical wavelength (nm)	Concentration range (μg/g)
Ag	(I) 338.3	1–15
Al	(I) 396.1	1–5
As	(I) 235.0	1–10
Bi	(I) 306.8	1–5
Fe	(I) 373.7	1–20
Mn	(I) 403.1	1–5
Ni	(I) 352.4	1–4
Pb	(I) 283.3	1–10
Se	(I) 196.1	1–3
Sn	(I) 317.5	1–3
Zn	(I) 307.6	1–10

Table 1.3 – Comparison of the normal and MW-coupled HCD for the determination of trace elements in copper.

Analyte	Detection limit (μg/g)		Correlation coefficient	
	HCD	MW–HCD	HCD	MW–HCD
Ag	0.3	0.1	0.97	0.98
Al	0.06	0.01	0.97	0.99
As	0.5	0.08	0.95	0.97
Bi	1	0.4	0.98	0.98
Fe	0.5	0.07	0.99	0.99
Mn	0.08	0.01	0.98	0.98
Ni	1	0.2	0.99	0.99
Pb	3	1.2	0.95	0.98
Se	1	0.4	0.97	0.99
Sn	0.2	0.1	0.96	0.97
Zn	0.5	0.1	0.96	0.98

When argon is used as the filler gas, both the slopes of the calibration graphs and the net emission signals for the trace elements as well as for the copper matrix show an appreciable increase. The detection limits, calculated according to Aziz *et al.* [30] are also appreciably improved, normally by one order of magnitude (Table 1.3).

With helium as the carrier gas the effects are similar but very much weaker. Systematic evaluation of the effect of MW coupling on representative spectral

Table 1.4 – The variation in spectral intensity with the MW–HCD in argon

Element	Wavelength (nm)	Effect on intensity	Element	Wavelength (nm)	Effect on intensity
Al	257.5	**	Fe	(II) 235.2	*
	(I) 265.2	***		(II) 236.5	*
	(I) 266.0	***		(II) 238.2	*
	(I) 394.4	*		(II) 239.6	*
Cu	(II) 221.8	*		(II) 241.1	*
	(II) 224.3	*		(I) 304.8	*
	(II) 224.7	*		(I) 305.9	*
	(I) 299.7	*		(I) 344.4	*
	(I) 301.1	*	Cr	(II) 286.3	*
	(I) 328.0	*		(I) 302.2	*
C	(I) 247.9	**		(I) 427.5	*
	(II) 392.1	****		(I) 429.0	*
Mo	280.8	*	Ni	(II) 226.4	*
	(II) 281.6	*		(II) 227.9	*
	(II) 284.8	*		(I) 300.4	*
	(I) 379.8	*		(I) 305.1	*
	(I) 386.4	**		(I) 344.6	*
Zn	(II) 202.6	*		(I) 345.3	*
	(II) 206.2	*		(I) 346.2	*
	(II) 210.0	*		(I) 347.3	*
	(I) 213.9			(I) 349.3	*
	(II) 250.2	**	Ar	235.8	****
	(II) 255.8	**		279.7	****
	(I) 260.9	**		(II) 302.9	****
	(I) 328.2	*		(II) 303.4	****
	(I) 330.3	**		306.1	****
	(I) 334.6	**		(I) 338.8	****

   * Increase in intensity is greater than 10%.
  ** Effect is positive up to 100 mA, then the line is practically unaffected.
 *** Effect is slightly positive up to 100 mA, then progressively negative.
**** Decrease in intensity is greater than 10%.

lines emitted in the HCD by pure conducting materials has confirmed that it can be generalized, and to a reasonable approximation is independent of the wave length used and the state of ionization of the element in question; this is summarized in Table 1.4. Although not comprehensive, the data reported show that there is a tendency towards considerable enhancement in emission intensity of practically all the spectral lines that are analytically usable in the HCD. There are two significant exceptions, however, namely aluminium and graphite. The anomalous behaviour of these two elements is in part contradictory and so far has found no acceptable explanation.

1.4.2 Analysis of non-conducting powders

Samples resulting from the combustion of biological materials, airborne dusts, minerals, etc., are not readily analysed directly, because they are non-conductive. However, the HCD does have some advantages for such analyses, provided that the powders to be analysed are adequately mixed with conductive binders [15,31]. Since such a pretreatment normally necessitates a three- or fourfold dilution of the original sample, the MW-HCD might prove advantageous for this kind of determination. The powder to be analysed is mixed with a 1:4 graphite-copper mixture in order to make it electrically conductive. The final mixture can be pressed into hollow cylinders and discs so that the internal surface of support-ing cathodes can be completely lined with the material to be discharged. Alternatively, the sample, pelleted in the form of a disc, can be placed at the bottom of the supporting hollow cathode [32]. To be effective in this case, the ion bombardment must be concentrated on the cathode bottom by optimizing the discharge conditions. The mean size of the sample particles is critical for the reliability of the determinations and should not exceed 40 μm for optimal and reproducible discharge. Moreover, a pulse mode should be applied to the HCD,

Table 1.5 — Comparison of detection limits with the HCD, with and without MW superposition, for powdered samples

Element	Wavelength (nm)	Detection limit (ppm)	
		MW–HCD	HCD
Ag	(I) 338.3	0.6	2
Al	(I) 396.1	1	2
Cr	(I) 357.9	1	5
Ga	(I) 417.2	0.08	1
Mn	279.5	1	3
Ni	(I) 346.2	0.5	5
Pb	(I) 283.3	1	5
Sn	(I) 284.0	1	1
Ti	(I) 365.3	3	5
Zn	(I) 307.6	2	6

since this helps to circumvent polarization of the insulating particles of analyte oxides in the powders [33]. As a consequence, the average power available per unit time further decreases. Since the amount of sample available for discharge is limited because it is only at the cathode bottom, it is evident that this type of analysis might greatly profit from superposition of an MW field.

Some results obtained for this type of sample are given in Table 1.5. In this case, there is a slight improvement in the precision and in the linearity and slope of the calibration plots. The utilization of the MW-coupled HCD can thus be recommended when powdered samples are to be analysed without preliminary dissolution.

1.4.3 Analysis of solution residues

If solutions are directly injected into an HCD, considerable instability of the plasma results, thus making the determination unreliable. Therefore, with an HCD, what is generally called solution analysis involves, in practice, the dispensing of small aliquots of the liquid sample into the bore of suitable hollow cathodes, removing the solvent by drying in an oven or under infrared irridation, and then exciting the solid layer deposited on the cavity surface. Thus, this type of analysis has much in common with that of solid non-conductive materials. The main difference is that, because the salt film in most cases is extremely thin and therefore easily pierced by the discharge, no preliminary treatment is needed to make it conductive and facilitate its transport into the discharge zone. A recent survey investigation [21] has pointed out that the general pattern is the same for solution residues as for elements discharged at massive electrodes or as compressed powders. However, there may be a delay before the analyte signal reaches its maximum; it then decreases rapidly as the cathode load is consumed. It is important to stress that the MW-HCD produces a higher analytical signal over the entire duration of the discharge (see Fig. 1.9).

Table 1.6 summarizes the result obtained for some representative elements in solution.

Although helium-based systems normally do not show any noteworthy increase in emission, a very advantageous application of the MW-HCD recently reported [34] deserves special mention. The determination of phosphorus in an HCD with argon is unsuccessful because the ionization potential of argon (15.76 eV) is too low to produce excitation of phosphorus. Helium has a higher ionization potential (24.58 eV), with the disadvantage, however, that under the operating conditions that give a steady and reproducible discharge (current not exceeding 150–200 mA), the intensity of the spectra emitted is very low. When the coupled discharge is applied the four analytically usable lines of phosphorus – (I) 178.287, (I) 178.768, (I) 185.891 and (I) 185.943 nm – are enhanced, so become usable even at the low current used. The helium lines are also enhanced but this does not cause any inconvenience in the determination. Moreover, spectral background is virtually absent in both operation modes. A typical analytical curve is shown in Fig. 1.10. The detection power thus achievable corresponds to approximately 0.5 ppm.

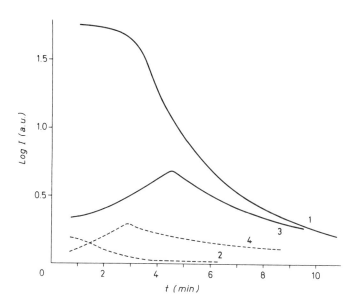

Fig. 1.9 – Burn-off curves with HCD in argon. Solid lines, with MW superposition;
dotted lines, without. 1 and 2, Pb (I) 405.8 nm; 3 and 4, Zn (I) 334.5 nm. Current,
100 mA; MW power, 50 W (effective); argon pressure, 690 Pa.

Table 1.6 – Effect of MW superposition on the HCD analysis of solution residues

Analyte	Wavelength (nm)	Effect on intensity
Al (as nitrate)	(I) 394.4	**
	(I) 396.1	**
As (as pentoxide)	(I) 228.8	**
	(I) 235.0	**
Cu (as nitrate)	(II) 224.7	*
	(I) 276.6	*
Pb (as nitrate)	(II) 220.3	*
	(I) 368.3	*
	(I) 405.8	*
Zn (as nitrate)	(I) 328.2	*
	(I) 334.5	*

 *   Increase in intensity is greater than 10%.

** Effect is slightly positive up to 100 mA, then the line is practically unaffected.

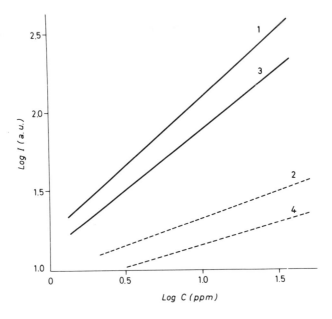

Fig. 1.10 – Calibration plots for phosphorus. Solid lines, with MW superposition; dotted lines, without. 1 and 2, P(I) 185.94 nm; 3 and 4, P(I) 178.77 nm. Current, 100 mA; MW power, 50 W (effective); helium pressure, 1130 Pa.

1.5 FURTHER PROSPECTS AND CONCLUSIONS

Despite the limited number of applications yet reported, and the numerous gaps in theory, the MW-coupled HCD has much analytical potential. In AES, for instance, trace and ultratrace analysis for toxicologically relevant and essential elements in biological matrices will benefit more and more from this technique, not only for the reasons mentioned in Section 1.4, but also because non-metals are in principle equally readily determined. In AAS, this composite source may have uses where hollow-cathode tubes and electrodeless discharge lamps are limited in their capabilities (because of weak emission intensity or inadequate performance for particular elements). The life of hollow-cathode lamps is mainly determined by the applied d.c. current, to which emission output is ultimately related. The advantages of the MW–HCD from this standpoint are obvious.

The HCD has occasionally been used to generate emission spectra from organic compounds excited in the discharge positive column (see e.g. [35,36]. The MW–HCD could allow such an organic vapour to be subjected to more energetic excitation conditions without fragmentation reaching unacceptable levels. However, there is as yet no experimental confirmation of this.

The freedom from, or at least the dramatic drop in, self-absorption phenomena should be of great practical value. The analytical dynamic range should be appreciably expanded, and the composite source should be better for use in wavelength and intensity calibration than the normal HCD [37].

However, there are some basic technical problems to be overcome. First, more efficient and flexible coupling systems between the MW generator and the lamp are required. These must cope with the difficulties that arise from the fact that the connection involves parts of the lamp at different electric potentials. Secondly, the lamp geometry and the gap between the hollow cathode and the anodic block still require extensive investigation, to clarify the role played by these parameters and allow their optimization.

REFERENCES

[1] A. T. Zander and G. M. Hieftje, *Appl. Spectrosc.*, 1981, **35**, 357.

[2] J. W. Carnahan, *Am. Lab.*, 1983, **15**, No. 8, 31.

[3] S. R. Goode and K. M. Baughman, *Spectrochim. Acta*, 1983, **38B**, 75.

[4] G. Francis, *Ionization Phenomena in Gases*, Butterworths, London, 1960, Chapter 4.

[5] K. W. Busch and T. J. Vickers, *Spectrochim. Acta*, 1983, **28B**, 85.

[6] H. Schlüter, *Z. Naturforsch.*, 1963, **18a**, 439.

[7] H. W. Drawin, *Ann. Phys.*, 1966, **17**, 374.

[8] P. Brassem and F. J. M. J. Maessen, *Spectrochim. Acta*, 1974, **29B**, 203.

[9] E. O. Johnson and L. Malter, *Phys. Rev.*, 1950, **80**, 58.

[10] S. Caroli, *Progr. Anal. Atom. Spectrosc.*, 1983, **6**, 253.

[11] M. E. Pillow, *Spectrochim. Acta*, 1981, **36B**, 821.

[12] N. J. Prakash and W. W. Harrison, *Anal. Chim. Acta*, 1971, **53**, 421.

[13] S. Caroli, O. Senofonte and P. Delle Femmine, *Analyst*, 1983, **108**, 196.

[14] S. Caroli, O. Senofonte, A. Alimonti and K. Zimmer, *Spectrosc. Lett.*, 1981, **14**, 575.

[15] S. Caroli, A. Alimonti and K. Zimmer, *Spectrochim. Acta*, 1983, **38B**, 625.

[16] B. Rosen, *Appl. Spectrosc.*, 1951, **5**, 26.

[17] H. Falk, *Spectrochim. Acta*, 1977, **32B**, 437.

[18] F. Howorka and M. Pahl, *Z. Naturforsch.*, 1972, **27a**, 1425.

[19] G. Knerr, J. Maierhofer and A. Reis, *Z. Anal. Chem.*, 1967, **229**, 241.

[20] S. Caroli, A. Alimonti and F. Petrucci, *Anal. Chim. Acta*, 1982, **136**, 269.

[21] S. Caroli, A. Alimonti and F. Petrucci, *TrAC*, 1982, **1**, 368.

[22] S. Caroli, F. Petrucci and A. Alimonti, *Can. J. Spectrosc.*, 1983, **28**, 156.

[23] R. L. Layman and G. M. Hieftje, *Anal. Chem.*, 1975, **47**, 194.

[24] R. K. Skogerboe and G. N. Coleman, *Anal. Chem.*, 1976, **48**, 611A.

[25] C. I. M. Beenakker, *Spectrochim. Acta*, 1976, **31B**, 483.

[26] G. Milazzo, *Appl. Spectrosc.*, 1967, **21**, 185.

[27] C. I. M. Beenakker, B. Bosman and P. W. J. M. Boumans, *Spectrochim. Acta*, 1978, **33B**, 373.

[28] S. Caroli, A. Alimonti and P. Delle Femmine, *Spectrosc. Lett.*, 1979, **12**, 871.

[29] S. Caroli, O. Senofonte, N. Violante, F. Petrucci and A. Alimonti, *Spectrochim. Acta*, 1984, **39B**, 1425.

[30] A. Aziz, J. A. C. Broekaert and F. Leis, *Spectrochim. Acta,* 1982, **37B**, 369.

[31] S. Caroli, A. Alimonti, F. Petrucci and K. Zimmer, in *Proceedings of the First Italo-Hungarian Symposium on Spectrochemistry: Environmental Protection and Spectrochemistry,* Rome, September 5-9, 1983.

[32] S. Caroli, A. Alimonti and F. Petrucci, *Spectrochim. Acta,* 1983, **38B** (Supplement), 58.

[33] A. I. Drobyshev and Y. I. Turkin, *Spectrochim. Acta,* 1981, **36B**, 1153.

[34] S. Caroli, O. Senofonte, N. Violante, F. Petrucci and A. Alimonti, (to be published).

[35] H. Schüler and M. Stockburger, *Z. Naturforsch.,* 1959, **14a**, 229.

[36] J. W. Robinson, H. P. Loftin and D. Truitt, *Anal. Chim. Acta,* 1968, **40**, 241.

[37] G. H. C. Freeman and W. H. King, *J. Phys. E,* 1977, **10**, 894.

2

The microcavity hollow cathode and its analytical potential

J. Czakow

2.1 THE MICROCAVITY EFFECT

The microanalytical technique that utilizes the 'microcavity hollow cathode' (MCHC) (whether the hot or the cold version), of all presently available spectro-chemical emission analysis techniques, shows the best attainable detection power in simultaneous multielement analysis, as summarized in Fig. 2.1. The term MCHC has been used at the Institute of Nuclear Research (INR), Warsaw, since 1972, to refer to cathodes having cavities 2 mm or less in diameter.

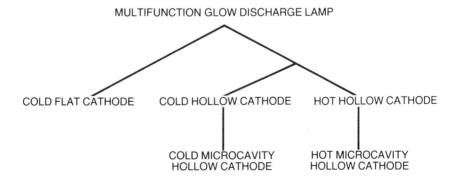

Fig. 2.1 – Application diagram for the multifunction glow discharge lamp.

The high relative and absolute detection power of the MCHC can be expressed by the empirical formula of Novosielov and Znamienskii

$$I_o d = k \qquad\qquad (2.1)$$

where I_o is the intensity of the spectral line, d is the diameter of the hollow-cathode cavity, and k is a constant.

The expression given above shows that the smaller the diameter of the hollow-cathode cavity, the greater the intensity of the spectral line, as confirmed by experimental data. The detection power for traces of Cd, Zn and Pb in indium antimonide [1], for example, was found to be improved by *ca.* two orders of magnitude, down to a threshold value of $10^{-7}\%$, when the diameter of the hollow-cathode cavity was reduced from 4 to 2 mm. This trend is confirmed by the results for Zn, Mg, Ni and Cr [2], the reduction in diameter resulting in higher intensity of the spectral lines. Current knowledge in this field cannot, however, explain the effect discussed above. The enhanced line intensity is probably the result of increased concentration of the vapour generated from the sample, and increased temperature of the hollow cathode, owing to the reduced mass. Simultaneously, there is an increase in pressure (p_o) within the cathode (since $p_o d = $ constant [1]) and a drop in voltage U and power W.

Furthermore, because the volume of the cavity is decreased, a smaller mass of sample is needed to provide a given atom concentration in the cavity. The electron energy is also reduced, since it is related to the free path λ, which in turn depends on the diameter d ($\lambda \leqslant d$) of the cathode bore. The overall effect of the factors mentioned above is that the emission intensity increases considerably.

It is interesting that the line intensity can be increased not only by reduction of the cavity diameter [3, 4], but also by making the cavity bottom conical instead of flat [5]. Alternatively, a graphite rod can be placed in the cavity (as recommended by Kolev [6]) or the cavity can be tapered. Another method is to reduce the diameter of the cathode from 4 to 2 mm at the cathode mouth only [4]. Tolansky outlined the construction of a hollow cathode with an axial 2-mm wide slot between two rectangular metal walls [7]. This cathode possesses a high glow intensity because of the closeness of the walls. A water-cooled microcavity hollow cathode gives similar effects, as described by Tölg [8] and Czakow [9].

Consequently, possible reasons for the improved detection power of the MCHC can be related to: (i) the small volume of the cathode cavity; (ii) the low weight of the cathode; (iii) the closeness of the cavity walls; (iv) the increased current density. All these factors are connected with the rise in cathode temperature and the increase in the concentration of the sample vapour, and also a greater effect of the electric field in the area of the cathodic drop, determined by the reduced cathode cavity diameter, resulting in a prolonged residence time of atoms in the plasma.

2.2 THE HOT MICROCAVITY HOLLOW CATHODE

2.2.1 Fields of application

The hot MCHC has a wide variety of applications in the field of spectral micro-analysis since the quantities of sample material required for excitation are very small (from several μg to 1 mg, depending on the diameter of the microcavity). Good results have been obtained with MCHCs having cavity diameters of 1, 1.5 and 2 mm. This type of analysis can be particularly useful in archaeology, criminology, examining works of art, detection of impurities and inclusions in materials, analyses related to environmental pollution control, and the like — that is to say in situations where very small amounts of sample material are available or almost non-destructive examination is required.

Reduction in the diameter of the cavity while the depth is kept substantial (about 15 mm, even in the case of hot MCHCs) permits attainment of a much higher emission intensity than is possible with an ordinary hollow cathode, and also a very high detection power for trace elements, with reduction of some undesirable effects resulting from fractional distillation of the sample. Owing to the shape of the cathode cavity, the sample within the cathode is consumed more slowly, and the residence time of excited atoms in the discharge area is prolonged.

In the hot MCHC some specific forces (of thermal, compressional and electrostatic nature) are produced which result in ejection of sample particles from the cavity with significant energy, especially when there is an excessive amount of sample. Therefore, a suitable sample-handling procedure should be selected for the type of material under examination. Because of the technical difficulties of introducing solid samples, the MCHC is most suitable for analysing solution residues or samples that are in solution [10].

Solution samples are introduced into the MCHC by means of a micropipette (for example 5- or 10-μl micropipettes of overflow type are ideal) in amounts from several to a dozen or so μl. Then the sample is dried by use of an oven or an infrared lamp. The dry analyte forms a thin film on the cathode inner surface. Powder and metallic samples dissolved in acids can be analysed in this manner. For example, 10-μg samples of steel dissolved in nitric acid gave good analytical precision and accuracy for components present at the 11% level. For solution analysis it is sometimes advantageous to pretreat the internal surface of the graphite MCHC with a solution of apiezon in petroleum ether or of a suitable polymer in a solvent.

Solid samples are most likely to be analysed successfully if they readily undergo pyrolysis (e.g. trace amounts of lacquers or other samples with an organic matrix). Very high detection power is then obtained. Solid samples that are not easily soluble can be analysed by using the graphite MCHC shown in Fig. 2.2 [11]. In this case the vapour of the sample diffuses through the wall of the MCHC into the excitation region. The sample is therefore uniformly dispersed and there is no danger of any surplus of vapour in the plasma (which would result in transition from glow to arc discharge). An arc discharge could also result from too much sample (e.g. for a 2-mm cavity MCHC, the sample weight should not exceed about 0.5 mg), or from the presence of free graphite particles within a graphite microcavity [12], or even from the presence of trace amounts of molecular gases.

In order to facilitate the placement of microgram samples on the bottom of the cathode microcavity, the cathodes are made in two parts. There are other

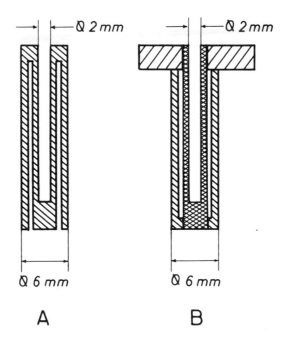

Fig. 2.2 – Microcavity membrane cathode suitable for multifunction glow discharge lamp: A, single graphite cathode; B, two-part cathode.

types of graphite MCHCs, where the volatilization and excitation regions are separate (Fig. 2.3A). This requires, however, very precise matching of the cathode components. The 'microcavity effect', i.e. the improved limits of detection, can also be attained by using a hollow cathode of the type shown in Fig. 2.3B, i.e. provided with a graphite capillary insert.

Metallic samples can be excited at various temperatures and currents (50-1000 mA) and time intervals, and because the spectral background is weak it is possible to excite the spectra of the components one at a time by changing the conditions (mainly the cathode temperature) and record them all at the same location on a spectrographic plate. The self-absorption of spectral lines is much less than in the case of excitation in an electric arc.

2.2.2 Operating conditions

A prerequisite for ensuring a stable glow in all the forms of cathode described is to provide an appropriate preglow sequence for a given analysis and stabilization of all the parameters of the glow discharge lamp. It is most important to keep all excitation-source elements clean. Preglowing of each MCHC, possibly at high temperature, is done to eliminate CO, NO, OH and CN, and prevent their molecular bands from showing in the spectrum. The C_2 molecular bands are always present, but those of CO appear only when there is oxygen in the sample to be analysed.

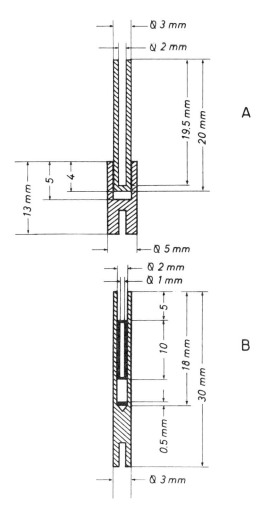

Fig. 2.3 — Graphite microcavity hollow cathode of various designs; A two-part; B, with membrane and capillary.

The hot graphite MCHC is an efficient excitation source, comparable to the d.c. arc. Its efficiency is a consequence of the high temperature of the cathode, which characterizes the hot MCHC. The temperature reached is 2000°C or higher (at currents of 1 A or more). This is of great importance in physico-chemical processes, particularly thermal, in contrast to the cold MCHC. First, in a hot MCHC, a reducing atmosphere prevails. Moreover, the cathode is very hot and this leads to fractional distillation of the entire sample volume. This effect can be utilized in the determination of elements of diverse volatility. Different cathode temperatures can be achieved by applying different currents, each suitable for a given group of elements present in the sample. The cathode temperature depends also on the electron work function of the cathode material (graphite possessing the highest). The sample temperature is higher than that of the cathode walls but lower than the maximum temperature of an empty MCHC. The time needed for total volatilization of impurities is directly proportional to the square of the sample-material film thickness and inversely proportional to the diffusion coefficient of the impurities in the sample [13]. This naturally imposes predetermined limitations on the amount of sample material to be introduced into the hollow cathode. The sample should not occupy too much space within the cavity, and the cavity volume should not be excessively large.

Argon is found to be the most suitable filler gas for analyses performed with the hot MCHC. Its main advantages are the fairly high atomic weight and ionization potential (15.7 eV), which enable the determination of a reasonably large number of elements. It is necessary to use an argon–helium mixture only for determination of fluorine, oxygen, hydrogen and neon. The disadvantage of argon as a filler gas is that it has an excessively rich spectrum. The argon used should be of very high purity. In particular, the presence of traces of oxygen results in highly irreproducible results.

The sample in the hot MCHC is excited by continuous stabilized d.c. discharge (for an MCHC of 0.5-2 mm bore). When pulsed direct current is used [14] it is necessary, to achieve stable glowing in cavities 1 mm or less in diameter, to select special excitation conditions (filler-gas flow, pressure, voltage, cathode-anode geometry, etc.). By use of a stabilized power supply capable of providing high-power pulsed discharges superimposed on continuous ones, it is possible to improve the attainable detection power [6, 15]. To stabilize the glow in the MCHC it is necessary to stabilize the supply voltage. This is done to keep the cathode in exact coaxial alignment with respect to the anode, as well as keeping the anode surface clean and ensuring that anode material will not form any refractory carbides. Also, in order to obtain reasonably good precision, it is necessary to place the cathode outlet exactly opposite the spectrograph slit.

2.2.3 Lamp design
The metal casing of the MCHC is formed by the corresponding components of an associated glow discharge lamp of any suitable design. The glow discharge is equipped with a suitable vacuum system (Fig. 2.4). Originally, glass discharge lamps with anodes in the form of metal sleeves were used; thereafter they were made entirely of metal with an earthed anode [18]. Recently, analyses have been done with shielded hot or cold MCHCs of the Grimm type (Figs. 2.5 and 2.6). The cathode material (graphite or metal), current, and cooling system will dictate whether the MCHC should be operated cool or hot.

The particular analytical task and the elements to be determined dictate the MCHC material to be chosen. All-metal hollow cathodes give better results for determining elements with high excitation potential. For example, for determining fluorine and chlorine or uranium oxides [16], steel cathodes are preferable, but for selenium and tellurium in ores, aluminium cathodes will give better results [17]. It is thought that the elements mentioned form solid compounds with the cathode material, which prolongs their residence time within the cathode. In the case of carbon cathodes, any CO present can result in poorer

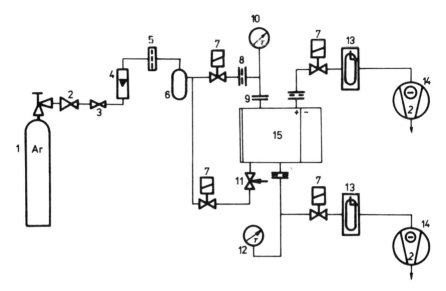

Fig. 2.4 – Schematic diagram of vacuum system for multifunction glow discharge lamp: 1, argon cylinder; 2, pressure regulator; 3, fine pressure regulator; 4, flow-meter; 5, dust filter; 6, cold trap; 7, solenoid valve; 8, flanged joint with orifice; 9, flanged joint; 10, constant-resistance vacuum meter; 11, needle valve; 12, constant-resistance vacuum meter; 13, cold trap; 14, double-stage rotary vacuum pump; 15, multifunction glow discharge lamp.

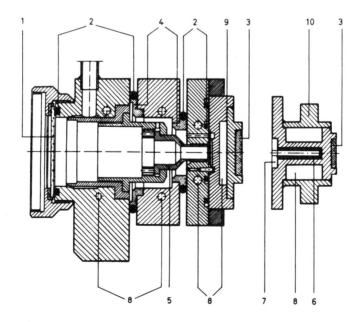

Fig. 2.5 – Multifunction glow discharge lamp made of iron: 1, quartz window; 2, O-rings; 3 and 4, insulators; 5, glow restrictor; 6, hollow cathode; 7, insulating ring; 8, water cooling; 9, flat cathode attachment; 10, hollow-cathode attachment.

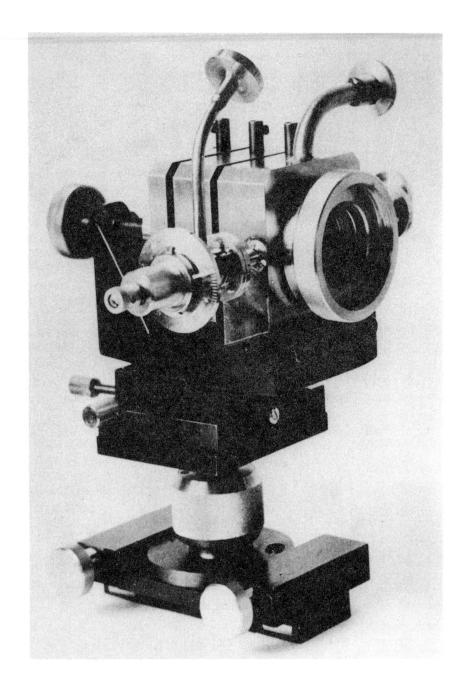

Fig. 2.6 – Multifunction glow discharge lamp [5].

detection power for these elements. Similarly, negative effects result from the presence of elements belonging to groups I and II of the periodic table. For most elements, the graphite MCHCs appear to be suitable and provide excellent results. It should be noted here that resonance effects take place in the MCHC, and these can improve the detection limits by at least one order of magnitude for some elements.

2.2.4 Analytical examples

The hot MCHC can be used in microanalysis for many tasks. This can be seen in Fig. 2.7, which illustrates the use of MCHC in the analysis of high-purity materials. As shown, it is possible to analyse not only concentrates (after removal of the matrices), but also to perform direct analyses of materials with detection limits down to the ng/g level for many elements. For example, solutions of high-purity gold and platinum [9] (20 μl, corresponding to 1 mg of metal) have been analysed for 12 trace elements present at levels down to $10^{-5}\%$. The determinations were done by the 'single addition' extrapolation method developed by Swietoslawska and Held [18]. This method gives good results (see Table 2.1) and is particularly useful for analyses done with the MCHC. In the same laboratory, comparable detection limits were obtained for microgram samples of lacquers, hairs, and paint samples from works of art, by means of MCHCs (1- and 1.5-mm bore). In soil filtrates, 10 elements could be detected in amounts as low as 1 pg [19] (see Table 2.2). According to Sabatovskaya *et al.* [20] 24 elements at 1 pg levels were determined by using the hot MCHC, with a precision of 12–15%. Kolev [6] also reported on detectabilities of 10^{-12}–10^{-8} g for 25 elements. Many elements present at ng/ml in concentrates were also determined.

The analysis of high-purity elemental gallium by means of a hot MCHC (2-mm bore) permitted the detection of traces of elements at levels as low as 10^{-11}–10^{-9} g and their determination in gallium oxide at concentrations of $10^{-5}\%$ [9]. Novosielov and Znamenskii [1] have described the determination, by means

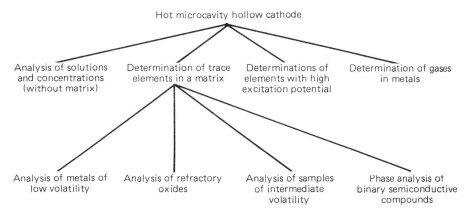

Fig. 2.7 — Use of the hot microcavity hollow cathode for analysis of high-purity materials.

of MCHC (2-mm bore) of impurities at the ng/ml level in the presence of a matrix. It is worth noting in this connection that the spectral source FANES (Furnace Atomic Non-thermal Excitation Spectrometry) developed by Falk *et al.* [21], which is actually a hollow cathode open at both ends, can be modified to a microcavity in order to improve its analytical capabilities.

Table 2.1 — Results for the analysis of high-purity gold and platinum.

Gold

Analyte	Spectral line (nm)	Spectrochemical analysis (ppm)	MCHC (ppm)	RSD
In	(I) 325.6	0.1	0.05	0.06
Ag	(I) 338.2	0.4	0.2	0.02
Pd	(I) 340.4	0.1	0.07	0.04
Ni	(I) 341.4	—	0.3	0.09
Cr	(I) 359.3	—	0.4	0.05
Pb	(I) 405.7	0.1	0.5	0.06
Al	(I) 396.1	0.4	1.2	0.04
Mn	(I) 403.0	—	0.2	0.04
Ga	(I) 417.2	0.1	0.2	0.04
Cd	(I) 326.1	—	0.3	0.06
Rh	(I) 343.4	—	0.2	0.07

Platinum

Analyte	Spectral line (nm)	Neutron activation (ppm)	MCHC (ppm)	RSD
Cd	(I) 326.1	—	0.3	0.03
Cu	(I) 327.4	0.6	0.6	0.02
Zn	(I) 334.5	2.8	2.1	0.05
Pd	(I) 340.4	0.6	0.2	0.03
Ni	(I) 341.4	—	0.2	0.03
Ir	(I) 351.3	0.9	0.7	0.03
Cr	(I) 359.3	—	0.6	0.04
Pb	(I) 368.3	—	0.2	0.04
Mn	(I) 403.0	—	0.1	0.03
In	(I) 325.6	—	1.0	0.04
Ag	(I) 338.2	1.3	—	—
Ga	(I) 417.2	—	0.2	0.05

Selected analytical conditions: hot MCHC of 1.5 mm bore and 20 mm depth, DFS–13 spectrograph, exposure time 1.5 min, 10-μl solution sample, current up to 450 mA, single-addition extrapolation method.

Table 2.2 – Detection limits for elements in soil filtrates

Element	Wavelength (nm)	Detection limit (pg)
B	249.7	4000
Co	344.9	1600
Cr	283.5	64
Cu	282.4	40
Mn	259.6	64
Mo	281.6	320
Ni	344.6	400
Sn	284.0	160
V	318.3	6400
Zn	328.2	160

Selected analytical conditions: hot microcavity hollow cathode of 1.5 mm bore and 20 mm depth, ISP-128 spectrograph, exposure time 1 min, 10-μl solution sample, current 400 mA.

2.3 THE COLD MICROCAVITY HOLLOW CATHODE

2.3.1 Main features

In the cold MCHC, samples are excited at currents of 10–200 mA. In order to ensure efficient cooling (mainly with water) the cathodes are generally made of iron, aluminium, magnesium, copper and other metals. In the cold MCHC cathode, samples are transferred to the plasma by cathode sputtering. The analytical advantages inherent in the cold MCHC, as compared with the hot one, are as follows: (i) better precision and accuracy of results; (ii) more favourable excitation conditions as compared with the porous graphite hot MCHC (mainly, preliminary degassing of the cathode is not necessary, the cathode walls can be cooled more efficiently, and liquid samples are not adsorbed onto the cathode walls); (iii) reduced thermal effects and therefore improved precision; (iv) narrow and very bright spectral lines; (v) possibility of recovering samples.

2.3.2 Working parameters

The cold MCHC consists of a cylindrical side-wall and a bottom. The two parts are held together within a threaded-joint brass casing (Fig. 2.8). This design permits the cathode to be used many times simply by cleaning the cylindrical wall and fitting a new bottom. Suitable tooling is necessary for cutting bottoms from metal foils. A plate (e.g. of 'Plexiglas'), having a recess 2 mm in diameter and 1.5 mm deep is also needed, together with a rod of the same material with one end rounded to conform with the shape of the recess. The recessed plate and the rod are used to shape the bottom. The cavity thus formed can take small amounts of solution which are simply poured in. Investigations have shown that the cylindrical part gradually undergoes some deformation due to axially asymmetrical sputtering of material, particularly at the outlet. This limits the useful

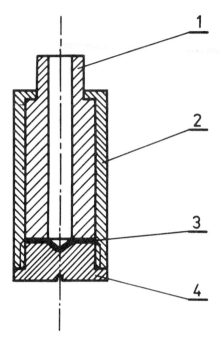

Fig. 2.8 – Encased two-part cold microcavity hollow cathode: 1, cylindrical part of microcavity hollow cathode; 2, cylindrical part of cathode casing; 3, bottom of microcavity hollow cathode; 4, bottom part of cathode casing.

life-span of the cathodes, depending on the materials used. The selection of a suitable cathode material is therefore of particular importance. The following properties are necessary: (i) a spectrum with few spectral lines and a negligible background; (ii) good thermal conductivity and high melting point; (iii) low susceptibility to cathode sputtering; (iv) chemical resistance; (v) good machinability; (vi) lack of toxicity; (vii) high purity and ease of purification; and (viii) cheapness.

It is difficult to find a material which meets all these requirements and therefore a compromise must be made on an ad hoc basis. Table 2.3 shows data for some suitable materials. Copper and aluminium seem to be the most suitable (along with gold and silver, but these are too expensive). Graphite would be appropriate, but because of its poor thermal conductivity cannot be used. It is better to use aluminium rather than copper cathodes, because of the significantly lower cathode sputtering and continuous spectrum. MCHCs made of materials with a high degree of cathode sputtering are less advantageous, since the sputtered cathode material deposits on the sample during excitation.

According to the empirical formula (2.1), any reduction in the cathode diameter results in an increase in intensity of the spectral lines. This is confirmed in Fig. 2.9, which shows the results obtained with an aluminium MCHC of 2 or 1.5 mm bore, and 15 mm depth. Results similar to those for the 1.5 mm cavity

Table 2.3 — Properties of various materials which can be used for making MCHCs.

element	Be	Al	Fe	Cu	Nb	Pd	Ag	Pt	Au	C	Ni
number of spectral lines 200–1000 nm range)	92	425	4757	913	3303	908	347	806	333	183	1176
high purity attainable	−	+	+	+	−	−	++	−	+	+	+
chemical resistance	−	−	−	+−	−	+	+	++	++	++	+−
machinability	−	+−	+	+	+	+	+	+	+	++	+
cathode sputtering (μmole/min)	−	9	12.5	33.1	11.3	31	44.4	29.9	34.5	9	15
melting point ($^\circ$C)	1280	660	1539	1083	2500	1552	962	1769	1064	3550	1453
thermal conductivity (cal. cm.$^{-1}$ sec.$^{-1}$ deg^{-1})	0.4	0.5	0.17	0.9	0.12	0.17	1.0	0.17	0.7	0.2	0.2
	*						**		**	***	

* toxic;   ** very expensive;   *** disturbed excitation

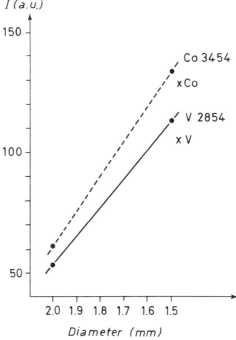

Fig. 2.9 — Effect of change in diameter of cold microcavity hollow cathode, and of reducing its diameter at the outlet, on intensity of spectral lines: x, values obtained for a 2-mm hollow cathode having a diameter of 1.5 mm at its outlet.

were obtained with a cathode having 2 mm bore for the first 10 mm of its length and 1.5 mm bore over the remaining 5 mm nearest the outlet. This form of MCHC is more convenient to use.

The depth of the cathode cavity must be selected empirically. The optimum depth depends on the cathode diameter, the conditions under which the analysis is performed, the nature of the sample, and the like. Usually, the depth is several times greater than the diameter, and its optimal value depends on the element to be determined. Therefore, the depth is normally the mean of a number of optimum values when several elements are to be determined. After prolonged glowing of the cold MCHC, serious changes in its internal geometry and also

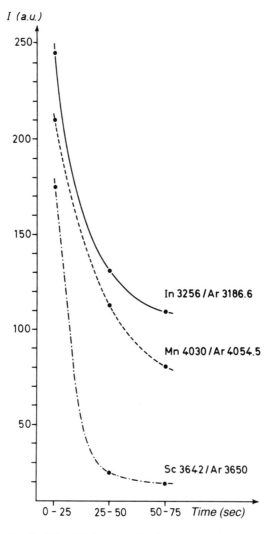

Fig. 2.10 – Graph of $I = f(t)$ for the cold microcavity hollow cathode. Weight of element being determined: 5 ng; a.u. = arbitrary units.

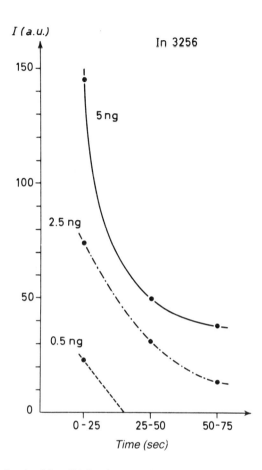

Fig. 2.11 – Graph of $I = f(t)$ for the cold microcavity hollow cathode. Weight of indium being determined: 5. 2.5 and 0.5 ng; a.u. = arbitrary units.

substantial losses of cathode material will take place [17]. The maximum intensity of the spectral lines of elements determined by the cold MCHC is usually reached within the first 25 sec of glowing [9] (see Figs. 2.10 and 2.11). It is therefore pointless to record the spectrum after this time. It is thought that factors such as high current, sample volatility and cathode sputtering of electrode material are responsible for this behaviour of the cold MCHC. The preglow time, obviously, is not taken into account, because of the minute quantities involved of the elements to be determined and the brief time of residence in the plasma. Deep cooling of the MCHC (e.g. with liquid nitrogen) results in a longer residence time of atoms in the plasma, but cooling with water only prevents melting of the cathode and does not significantly increase the residence time.

2.3.3 Analytical applications

The cold MCHC can give results that are comparable to those of other methods of equally high potential such as AAS or ICP. The advantages of the cold MCHC are that when used for simultaneous determination of a variety of elements at the ng/g level in samples weighing a few mg or μg in the presence of a matrix, or in pg amounts in its absence, the range of error will be 5-20%. Such results have been obtained by Fassmann et al. [22]. Drobyshev et al. [23] have determined 0.8 ng of Be in a 1-mg sample of Al-Mg alloy by using a cold MCHC of 2-mm bore. In our studies [9] we have determined the detection power for a 2-mm bore cold MCHC. In solutions without a matrix, the detectability is ca. 0.1 ng. For metals in 1-mg specimens it is about 100 ng/g. For excitation purposes, a glow discharge lamp [24, 25] and that patented by INR were used [26].

2.3.4 Future prospects

It has been shown that the detection power of the MCHC can be increased by further reduction in the hollow cathode diameter, use of pulsed discharges of a special type (with short high-power discharge pulses of msec duration), by correct selection of photoelectronic recording methods, by use of suitable argon-containing gaseous mixtures of high ionization potential, and by addition of suitable chemical compounds to the samples to be analysed.

REFERENCES

[1]   V. A. Novosielov and V. B. Znamenskii, *Spektroskop., Tr. Sib. Soveshch., 4th*, 1965, 273; *Chem. Abstr.*, 1971, **74**, 18994q.

[2]   V. Z. Krasil'shchik, *Prikl. Spektrosk., Proc. 16th Symposium (Moscow 1965)*, Izd. Nauka, Moscow, 1969, Vol. I, 1969.

[3]   J. Czakow, *New Trends in Atomic Spectrometric Analysis*, Ossolineum, Wroclaw, 1979, pp. 129-144.

[4]   J. Czakow, *Kém. Közlem.*, 1976, **45**, 159.

[5]   R. B. Djulgerova and D. Z. Zhechev, *Spectrosc. Lett.*, 1979, **12**, 615.

[6]   N. T. Kolev, *Spectral excitation sources for hollow cathode and their application in emission spectral analysis*. Ph.D. Dissertation, 1980, Univ. Plovdiv.

[7]   S. Tolansky, *High Resolution Spectroscopy*, Methuen, London, 1947.

[8]   G. Tölg, *Z. Anal. Chem.*, 1979, **294**, 1.

[9]   J. Czakow, in *Proceedings of the VI Polish Spectroanalytical Conference, Bialowieza*, 1981, p. 32.

[10]   J. Czakow, *Problemy Agrofizyki*, 1974, **12**, 83.

[11]   G. A. Pevtsov and V. Z. Krasil'schchik, *Zh. Prikl. Spectrosk.*, 1968, **9**, 504.

[12]   A. N. Shteinberg, Ph.D. Dissertation, 1963, Moscow.

[13]   Zil'bershtein, Kh.I., *The Spectrochemical Analysis of Pure Substances*, Hilger, Bristol, 1977.

[14]   A. I. Drobyshev, A. G. Zhiglinskii and Yu.I. Turkin, *Zh. Prikl. Spektrosk.*, 1973, **19**, 620.

[15]   N. Kolev, J. Patsheva and Chr. Koleva, *Plovdivsky Univ. Fizyka*, 1975, **3**, 63.

[16]   J. Czakow, *Chem. Anal. (Warsaw)*, 1973, **18**, 891-895.

[17] J. Czakow, in *Proceedings of the Symposium on the Analysis of Mineral Raw Materials Using Optical Methods,* Smolenice, 1973, Czechoslovakia.

[18] J. Swietoslawska and S. Held, *Chem. Anal. (Warsaw),* 1958, **3**, 515.

[19] J. Czakow and J. Glinski, in *Proc. Euroanalysis II,* Budapest, 1975, 84.

[20] V. L. Sabatovskaya, I. A. Kuzovlev and I. G. Yudelevich, *Zh. Prikl. Spektrosk.,* 1977, **26**, 207.

[21] H. Falk, E. Hoffmann and Ch. Lüdke, *Spectrochim. Acta,* 1981, **36B**, 767.

[22] P. Fassmann, P. Tschöpel and G. Tölg, in *Proc. Symposium Microchemical Techniques,* Davos, 1977.

[23] A. I. Drobyshev, S. M. Nemets and Yu. I. Turkin, *Zh. Prikl. Spektrosk.,* 1979, **30**, 329.

[24] K. Boboli, J. Czakow, J. Fijałkowski, J. Gałązka, B. Kucharzewski, K. Molenda and B. Strzyżewska, *Basic Problems of Atomic Spectral Analysis,* WNT, Warsaw, 1972.

[25] J. Czakow, W. Hammer and J. Otrebski, *Polish Pat.* 101146 (30 Dec. 1978) and 112682 (27 Feb. 1982); *GDR Pat.* 126571 (27 July 1977); *Hungarian Pat.* 171913 (19 March 1980).

[26] W. Grimm, *Spectrochim. Acta,* 1968, **23B**, 443.

3

The pulsed hollow-cathode discharge – new spectroanalytical possibilities

R. B. Djulgerova

3.1 INTRODUCTION

The main qualities of the hollow-cathode discharge (HCD) which distinguish it from other spectral sources are the simultaneous stable emission of intense and narrow spectral lines of the atoms of the cathode material, of the sample contained therein, and of the carrier gas, including atomic and ionic lines with high excitation potentials. The intensities and the width of the spectral lines emitted depend on the way the substance enters the plasma and on the excitation of its atoms. The substance enters the HCD plasma as a result of cathodic sputtering and thermal evaporation and remains in it for various periods of time, depending on the rate of diffusion. The main excitation processes are believed to result from direct collisions of electrons with atoms. The various attempts to improve this source aim at a better correlation of the processes of entrance and excitation in the HCD plasma. One of these is considered here, namely the application of a pulsed system.

Generally, in a pulsed system, energy is supplied to the HCD in pulses [1] of different duration (t), amplitude (a) and frequency of repetition (f). At the same time, a constant current component (i_o) runs through the discharge, usually weaker than or of the same magnitude as the average pulse current (i_p). The main spectroscopic effects of a pulsed supply on an HCD are a significant (by up to two orders of magnitude) increase of intensity (I) of the emitted spectral lines of the cathode material or the sample, with maintenance or reduction of width ($\Delta\nu$), a sharp decrease in noise, and a considerable increase in signal-to-background ratio. As a consequence, the reproducibility of results, the sensitivity and the detection limit of analyses are greatly improved.

Numerous investigations have shown that these factors hold both for elements which enter the plasma with difficulty, and those which enter with ease. The reason in the first case is the considerably increased rate of cathode sputtering, in comparision to that in the non-pulsed mode, because the voltage and discharge current are increased in the HCD in a pulse of high amplitude [2,3]. By change in the parameters of the pulsed supply, the intensity of the average pulse current can be changed, thus exerting an influence on the rate of thermal evaporation. By control of the speed of entry into the plasma in this way, the optimal concentration of atoms of elements which differ in properties can be obtained, and the influence of self-absorption on I and $\Delta\nu$ of the spectral lines prevented. On the other hand, by varying the concentration, the electron energy distribution, the temporal electron distribution and the electric-discharge characteristics, the pulsed supply increases the probability of recombination processes, step-like transitions, etc., in the excitation of the atoms.

The most popular application of the hollow-cathode spectral source is as a source of monochromatic emission in atomic-absorption spectroscopy (AAS) and atomic-fluorescence spectroscopy (AFS).

However, this source is also very useful for solving important spectroscopic problems in atomic-emission spectroscopic analysis (AES). Because there are differences in the mode of application of the pulsed supply, AAS and AES will be considered separately. Moreover, we will restrict ourselves to use of the pulsed HCD only when the glow discharge does not become an arc and is at lower current densities than in laser media systems [4].

3.2 APPLICATION OF THE PULSED HCD IN AAS AND AFS ANALYSES

3.2.1 Pulsed hollow-cathode lamps as sources of monochromatic emission

At present, hollow-cathode lamps (HCLs) are the most widely used source of monochromatic emission for AAS and AFS. When adapted for use with a pulsed supply, they are usually fed by orthogonal pulses with parameters that lead to i_p values in the mA range; a small direct current i_o of similar magnitude also runs through the discharge. Very useful information on pulsed HCLs is given in [5].

The first experimental study [1] outlined the spectroscopic possibilities of applying a pulsed supply to the HCD, with use of a simple scheme in which the voltage supply was switched off at definite intervals. Other schemes have been described for varying the pulse-supply parameters over wide ranges [6–11], for automation and connection with computers [12–14], and for operating in different pulsed modes (glow, arc, high-frequency) [15].

The most important spectroscopic effect when a pulsed supply is applied to the HCL is the increase (by up to two orders of magnitude) of the intensity I of the resonance lines of the cathode material, compared with their intensity in the non-pulsed system (I_o) [1, 6, 16–23]. The ratio I/I_o was found to have values of 50–800 for Ca, Co, Cu, Pb, Mg and Mn [6]. For the elements Ag, Al, Co, Cr, Mo, Ni, Pd, Si, Mn, Sr, Ca and Rb, I is greater than I_o by up to two orders of magnitude [16]. For these elements the expression $I = bi^n$ can be derived, where b and n are constants typical of a given combination of element and gas. This function changes its character when the influences of self-absorption and diffusion begin to increase [24]. To make the best use of the pulsed supply, synchronous detection is recommended (as it is with other modes of power supply).

In this case, however, its usefulness can readily be understood. A 20-fold increase in the spectral line intensity for Al, Ba and Ca has been reported [17]; short pulses with high amplitude gave greater intensity than long pulses with smaller amplitude. Pulses with orthogonal and triangle forms were found to have an analogous spectroscopic effect. Intermittent operation at constant voltage has been applied for multielement AFS [19]; the short pulses obtained are grouped in "packets", with a pause between each packet. A ratio $I/I_o = 10\text{-}250$ was obtained for the spectral lines of 18 elements by individual selection of suitable pulse parameters for each element.

It is well known that for AES and AFS the main requirement is sufficient intensity of the analytical lines, whereas for AAS it is also necessary that the lines are narrow [25-27]. However, attention has been drawn to the fact that the pulse status influences $\Delta \nu$ [6]. For this reason the profiles and widths of the spectral lines emitted from a pulsed HCL were studied in detail and compared with those ($\Delta \nu_o$) obtained in the non-pulsed mode [10, 16, 17, 20, 28, 29]. It was found that usually $\Delta \nu$ was $\leqslant \Delta \nu_o$, and that extension of the spectral lines and deformation of their profiles at some pulse-parameter values was due to intensified self-absorption and diffusion. In some cases, the diffusion changed to rapid ejection of atoms from the hollow cathode, as a result of thermal expansion of the gas as its temperature T increased rapidly at the start of the pulse.

Usually, investigation of the dependence of both I and $\Delta \nu$ for the spectral lines of interest on the pulse parameters, when these are varied over sufficiently wide ranges, results in optimal values being found. These ensure the maximum value of I/I_o at $\Delta \nu \leqslant \Delta \nu_o$, and also better stability of the discharge. For example, the spectral effect of applying a pulsed supply to an HCD has been investigated for Cu, Fe, Zn and Al [21–23]. As can be seen from Fig. 3.1, the ratio I/I_o depends on all the three pulse parameters (a, t, f) and reaches a maximum value in a narrow range of pulse-parameter variations. The functions $\Delta \nu = \Phi(a, t, f)$ and $I_{max}/I_{min} = \Phi(a, t, f)$ for the chosen resonance line are investigated and compared with those for the non-pulsed mode, $\Delta \nu_o = \Phi(i_o)$ and $I_{max}/I_{min} = \Phi(i)$. These comparisons are made at equal values of the mean discharge current in the two modes. The ratio of the intensities, I_{max}/I_{min}, of the two hyperfine components of the Cu(I) 324.7-nm spectral line gives a qualitative measure of the change in the self-absorption in the discharge [30]. The observed relationships show that at high a, t and f values, the role of self-absorption increases. This could be caused by the influence of some of the following factors: (a) residual atoms in the discharge volume from previous pulses (at high f values); (b) excessive numbers of new atoms entering in consecutive pulses (at high a values); (c) increased atomization due to increased T in the discharge (at large t values); or by a combination of all three factors. The experimental results for I/I_o, and I_{max}/I_{min} show that at the optimal values of the pulse parameters

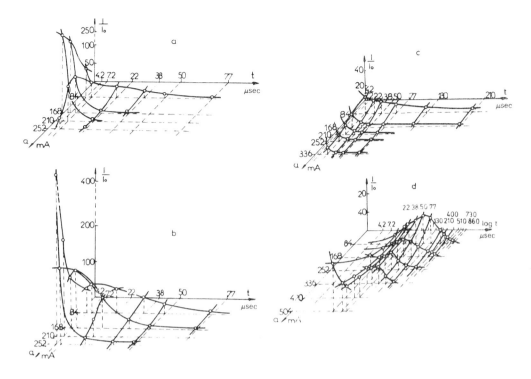

Fig. 3.1 – Variation of I/I_0 for the Cu(I) 324.7 nm line with t and a of pulses with frequencies of (a) 4.5 kHz; (b) 2.2 kHz; (c) 0.6 kHz; (d) 0.3 kHz. (Reprinted from [21] by permission of the Bulgarian Academy of Sciences).

(t = 4-7 μsec, a = 0.2-0.25 A, $f \approx$ 1 kHz) for the Cu(I) 324.7 nm resonance-line, the intensity is increased by up to 80 times, and $\Delta\nu$ is no greater than in the non-pulsed system. The values depend on many factors in the discharge, and even if a good theoretical model existed, the prediction of optimal values would be very difficult. However, the experimentally determined dependences for a given element may prove a useful starting point in determination of the optimal values of the pulse parameters for elements that are similar with respect to, for example, sputtering rates, vapour pressure, or diffusion rate.

The influence of the tendency of spectral lines towards self-absorption, and of the kind of working gas on the extent of the effect of using a pulsed supply has been investigated [23,31] (see Table 3.1). It is easy to conclude that the increase in the i_0 values makes the discharge more inert, i.e. decreases sensitivity of the discharge and its spectral features to changes in the pulse parameters, but sometimes this method is used to increase further the intensity of inert-gas spectral lines is said to be affected very little by the pulsed supply [6]. This has been shown by investigation of the Ne(I) 603 nm line [8] and by the values of $I/I_0 = \Phi(a)$ [31] presented in Table 3.1 for numerous Ne, Ar and He spectral lines with different characteristics.

Table 3.1 – The variation of I/I_0 with a for spectral lines of differing characteristics (excitation energy E, multiplicity of ionization, energy at maximum of optical excitation function, E_{max}, etc.) of the inert gases He, Ne, Ar. (Reprinted from [31] by permission of the Bulgarian Academy of Sciences).

Gas	Line and λ (nm)	E(eV)	E_{max}(eV)	a(mA) (at $t = 7.2\ \mu sec, f = 4.5$ kHz) 60	120	240
	I 388.9	23.00	28	1.3	1.6	1.6
	I 396.5	23.73	100–120	0.6	0.7	0.7
	I 438.8	24.04	40	1.2	1.8	1.8
He	I 447.2	23.73	25–30	1.0	1.2	1.3
	II 468.6	51.00	170–190	1.0	0.9	0.9
	I 471.3	23.58	27	1.2	1.5	1.5
	I 501.6	23.08	100–110	0.7	0.8	0.8
	II 296.7	38.19		1.4	1.2	1.3
	I 341.7	20.29	47	1.0	1.2	1.1
	II 342.8	35.12		0.9	0.8	1.0
	I 344.7	20.21	55–60	0.7	0.8	0.9
	I 352.0	20.37	50–51	0.8	0.9	0.9
Ne	I 359.3	20.29	46	1.1	1.2	1.5
	I 363.3	20.26	80–90	1.0	1.1	1.3
	II 371.3	31.11		0.7	0.7	0.8
	I 478.9	21.14	31	1.0	1.1	1.2
	I 482.7	21.14	100–110	0.9	0.9	1.0
	I 483.7	20.91	30	1.0	1.0	0.9
	I 503.7	21.01	30	1.0	0.8	0.9
	I 394.9	14.68	21–27	1.0	0.9	0.9
Ar	I 426.6	14.53	24	1.2	1.3	1.5
	II 438.5	23.57	21–27	0.7	0.8	0.8

The use of a pulsed supply has a highly beneficial effect on another very important characteristic of the HCD – its stability (both short- and long-term) [19]. The reduced noise-level and the increase in absorption signal for AAS measurements of chromium have been pointed out [16]. The particular advantage of applying a pulsed supply in the investigation of weak analytical signals (comparable to or smaller than the dark current level) is seen in Fig. 3.2 [8]. By theoretical and experimental estimation of the signal-to-noise ratio, the favourable effect of a pulsed supply in the AFS of Cu and Ca has been shown [32]. A detailed investigation of the pulsed HCL has been made [33–36]. A special apparatus was devised (which gave a relative error of < 0.1%, and zero-line drift of ⩽ 0.001%/min) to increase the measurement accuracy [34].

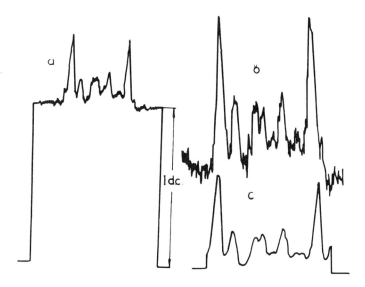

Fig. 3.2 — Recordings of the hyperfine structure of the Cu(I) 578.2 nm line: (a) non-pulsed discharge, HCD current 8.5 mA; (b) same source conditions, but with compensation of the constant component of the dark current; (c) pulsed mode (pulse current 0.2 A, pulse width 8 μsec, frequency 3200 Hz). (Reprinted from [87] by permission of the copyright holders).

Very low emission drift has been obtained for different types of lamps, depending on the construction and on the element investigated (see Table 3.2) [35]. The emission drift (σ) is evaluated from the formula

$$\sigma = \frac{I^{\text{begin}} - I^{\text{end}}}{I^{\text{begin}} \times t_{\text{meas}}} \times 100\%/\text{min}$$

where I^{begin} and I^{end} are the intensities of the measured spectral line at the beginning and end of the run and t_{meas} is the duration of the run (60 min from the end of the initial heating of the lamp). Use of a pulsed supply also changes the initial heating time needed [36]. Detailed investigations of the new LT-2 series of lamps, suitable for pulsed operation, showed that the initial heating time, 30 min for non-pulsed measurements, was decreased to 10 min when pulsed supply was used, and the emission drift was then only 0.05–0.08%/min. It can therefore be said that with pulsed supply, the measuring equipment can be utilized more effectively, and the life of the HCL is prolonged. It has been proposed that not only should records be kept of the running time of the HCL (so that its life expectancy is not exceeded) but its emission stability should also be monitored. It is recommended that a lamp should not be used for longer than is recommended by the maker or if the emission drift exceeds 0.2%/min. It is generally considered that, in spite of the increased cathode sputtering caused by high-amplitude pulses, the lifetime of the pulsed HCL is longer than that of the

Table 3.2 — Optimum values for the pulsed supply at pulse current $i_p = 100$ mA; (Reprinted from [35] by kind permission of the copyright holders).

Type of lamp	t (μsec)	$k*$	Emission drift (%/min)
LSP-1			
Ag	200	20	0.007
Pb	400	20	0.009
Cu	400	15–20	0.007
Zn	400	20–25	0.004
Zr	200–400	15–20	0.004
Mn	50–100	20–30	0.004
Fe	50–400	15–30	0.004
Cr	50–400	10–15	0.005
TSPK			
Ni	150, 400	10, 15	0.023–0.038
Au(31)	400–500	10, 15	0.013
Au(180)	500 (150)	10–20(30)	0.01 (0.005)
Ti(67)	500, 200	10, 15	0.02–0.03
Ti(68)	200, 500	15, 10	0.021–0.034

*$k=tf$.

non-pulsed type because the lamps work for a shorter time and at lower average current. The improvement of the spectral and electrical characteristics of pulsed lamps leads to an improvement in the quality of the AAS and AFS analyses performed. Moreover, as pointed out initially [6], under optimal conditions, not only is the spectral line intensity increased for Cu(I) 324.7 nm, but also the detection limit (0.015 ppm) and sensitivity (0.055 ppm/1% abs) are improved for copper determination. Improved detection limits in the AFS of various elements (see Table 3.3) have been found [37]; the detection limit is reported to be lower by a factor of 8–16 than for the non-pulsed system, by a factor of 7–70 than that for AAS with a pulsed HCL, for Ag, Cu, Co, Fe and Ni [38]. For Mo, Co, Ni, Cu, Mn, Fe, Ag, Zn, Ca and K [39], the dependence of the concentration sensitivity of AAS on the pulse parameters is different not only for each element but also for determination of the same element with different HCLs. As a rule, use of a pulsed supply increases the spectral line intensity, permitting photoelectric measurement with lower noise, and consequently an improved detection limit. This result is particularly useful for high-temperature atomizers, because they have a high intrinsic emission intensity, and also in determination of elements for which the appropriate HCIs do not emit intense resonance lines [40]. A considerable increase in the sensitivity of AAS of many elements is obtained by the use of a pulsed supply [14, 41, 42]. Still greater improvement is

Table 3.3 — Fluorescence detection limits. (Reprinted from [37] by permission of the copyright holders).

Lamp†	Line (nm)	Peak current (nA)	Detection limit (μg/ml)
W#45459	Zn 213.9	250	0.04
W#36042	Mg 285.2	450	0.02
W#36042	Mg 285.2	50	0.30
		250	0.07
PE#29405	Fe 248.3	250	10.00
		450	3.20
W#45456	Co 240.7	50	16.20
		350	1.10
W#23174	Co 240.7	50	9.30
		450	0.70
W#36024	Cu 324.7	50	4.00
		450	0.39

† W, Westinghouse; PE, Perkin-Elmer.

achieved by also applying a radio-frequency discharge (150 MHz) to the pulsed HCL [43]: the intensity of the Cd spectral line is then 5 times that for the normal pulsed mode and about 150 times that for the non-pulsed mode, and the signal-to-noise ratio is also improved. The full potential of these radio frequency-coupled pulsed lamps has not yet been achieved*. However, any progress in this field will clearly lead to an improvement in the quality of AAS and AFS analysis. The analytical and spectral characteristics with atomic–magneto-optical rotational spectroscopy (Faraday's atomic effect) have been studied for Sb, Bi, Ag, Cu and Pb by using a pulsed HCL [44, 45]. The influence of the magnetic field on I (Fig. 3.3) and $\Delta\nu$ of the analytical lines emitted from the HCD (pulsed and non-pulsed) was studied. The pulsed HCD gave detection limits lower by a factor of 10 for Sb, Bi, Ag and Cu (Table 3.4) [45]. In the determination of traces of lead in tree leaves, human blood and volcanic ash by using an HCL in the pulsed mode, a detection limit of 5×10^{-11} g was achieved.

3.2.2 Other applications of the pulsed HCD in AAS

Pulsed HCLs can be useful for dealing with background absorption in AAS. One of the methods for background correction is based on the fact that the resonance lines increase and decrease in intensity during the pulse time more quickly than the ion lines do [46]. By using a monochromator with a large slit

---

* See Chapter 5.

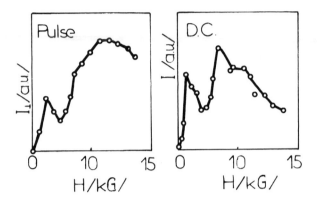

Fig. 3.3 — Dependence of transmitted intensity of the Cu(I) 324.7 nm line emitted from the lamp in d.c. and pulsed modes, on the magnetic field strength. Pulsed mode; pulse rate = 300/sec, peak current = 200 mA: d.c. mode; d.c. current = 10 mA. The mass of Cu introduced is 1.2 ng. (Reprinted from [45] by permission of the copyright holders, Pergamon Press Ltd., Oxford).

Table 3.4 — Detection limits. (Reprinted from [45] by permission of the copyright holders, Pergamon Press Ltd., Oxford)

Element	Atomic temperature (°C)	Wavelength (nm)	d.c. mode		pulse mode				
			i (mA)	D.L. (pg)	H (kG)	i_p (mA)	P.R. (Hz)	P.W. (μsec)	D.L. (pg)
Sb	2000	231.1	20	N.D.	5.0	200	300	400	500
Bi	2000	306.8	15	500	3.5	200	1000	150	50
		223.1	15	N.D.	10.0	200	1000	150	500
Ag	1800	328.1*	15	20	6.0	200	300	300	2
		328.3*							
Cu	1800	324.8	20	30	2.5	300	300	530	3

i: d.c. discharge current of the hollow cathode lamp.
D.L.: detection limit ($S/N=2$).
H.: magnetic field strength.
i_p: peak discharge current of the hollow-cathode lamp.
P.R.: rate of the discharge-current pulses (frequency f).
P.W.: width of the discharge-current pulses (duration t).
N.D.: not detectable.

*The lines are not separated, because of the wide band-pass of the monochromator.

(so that the resonance line of the element and some nearby ion lines pass through) it is possible to select time intervals (at the beginning of the pulse) during which the resonance line reaches maximum intensity, while the ion line is still absent from the spectrum; at the end of the pulse the opposite happens.

Thus, by using a pulsed supply for an HCL and a detector with temporal resolution, the absorption due to the analytical line and that due to the ion line close to it can both be determined. Thus the pulsed HCL replaces two sources working consecutively (Fig. 3.4). This method is useful for the AAS of Fe, Mg and Cd; suitable ion lines and the optimal values of the pulse parameters for various elements have been listed [46]. It is seen from the curves for Ni determination, in Fig. 3.5, that there is better linearity; the signal-to-noise ratio also improves when a dual-wavelength AAS spectrophotometer with a pulsed HCD is used.

Another procedure having the same purpose measures the absorption of the analytical line by use of two HCLs with different absorption coefficients. [47]. An alternative is to use a single lamp supplied with two consecutive but different current pulses which produce different widths of the analytical line [48]. A suitable ratio of the two absorption signals (from 1.5 to 4, depending on the element) is obtained by choosing the parameters of the consecutive pulses, and the background absorption can thus be recorded automatically without having to use another source [49]. By analysis of the dependence of spectral-line intensity and discharge voltage on the pulse amplitude, a criterion can be developed for selecting pulse parameters which do not reduce the life-span of the pulsed HCL.

A modified HCL with selective modulation [50] is used in non-dispersive AAS spectrophotometers [51, 52]. The basic characteristics of this lamp are a hollow cathode operating with direct current, and in front of it a second hollow cathode operating in pulsed mode, with a joint anode located co-axially between

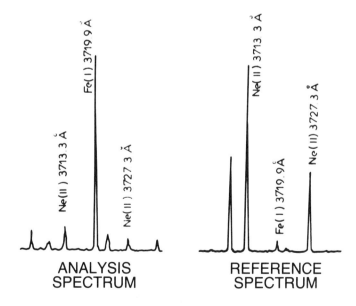

Fig. 3.4 – Reference and analysis emission spectra in the 370-nm region for an Fe–Ni–Cu HCL operated in pulsed dual-wavelength mode. (Reprinted from [46] by permission of the copyright holders).

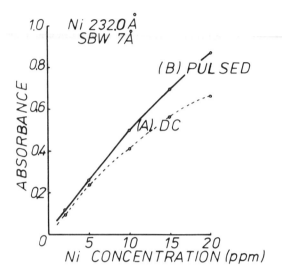

Fig. 3.5 – Calibration curves for Ni, with a monochromator spectral band width of 0.7 nm, an Fe–Ni–Cu hollow cathode lamp, with (A) d.c. operation and (B) pulsed operation. (Reprinted from [46] by permission of the copyright holders).

them. The pulsed supply of the second cathode causes, as a result of cathode sputtering, a cloud of neutral atoms in the ground state, pulsing with the frequency of the supply. The resonance lines emitted from the first cathode are selectively absorbed by the atoms from the second cathode, and the signal thus modulated is recorded at the output of a synchronous detector having the same modulating frequency. In this way, an efficient separation of the useful signal from the background is achieved, this being a precondition for increasing the signal-to-noise ratio (for Fe and Ni AAS by a factor of 200–500), extending the linearity range of the calibration curves and improving the sensitivity of the analysis.

In recent years, resonance detectors (RD) have also been developed. These form the basis of a simplified AAS spectrophotometer, that can out-perform ordinary spectrophotometers with dispersing elements [53-56]. The resonance detector consists of a discharge tube with a hollow cathode which is entered by the emitted monochromatic light from an HCL or a tunable laser after passage through the atomization cell; the analytical signal is the fluorescence radiation from this discharge tube. It can be seen from a detailed study of the space–time characteristics of a pulsed RD [55, 56] that this fluorescence signal can be increased by one order of magnitude by replacing the direct current with a pulsed supply, because between the pulses the signal becomes stronger than the discharge emission itself.

In addition to its use as a source of monochromatic emission in AAS, the HCD is also used as an atomizer [57]. This allows more efficient atomization of samples that are difficult to sputter, and avoids a need for preliminary sample dissolution; also, narrower absorption lines are emitted because of the lower gas temperature and the low pressure of the working gas. These advantages are more pronounced when direct current is replaced by a pulsed supply. For example, significant improvement in reproducibility and increase in sensitivity can be achieved [58].

Pulsed hollow-cathode lamps have been used for time- and spatially-resolved AAS measurements, together with a tuning laser to atomize solid samples of Cu, Al and Pb alloys, steel and graphite [59] and for investigation of the absorption profile of the U(I) 591.5 nm spectral line [60].

3.3 APPLICATION OF THE PULSED HCD AS A SOURCE FOR AES

3.3.1 AES with a pulsed discharge in an uncooled hollow cathode

The hollow-cathode discharge has established itself as an excellent source for AES of difficultly excitable elements, powdered samples, trace elements, ultra-high-purity substances, etc. Often the detection limit is better by several orders of magnitude than with other methods. Very useful information on the HCD as a source in AES is available in the literature [61-63].

When an HCD is used for AES, the main problem is to improve the reproducibility of the results. Lack of reproducibility is caused by discharge instability, ejection of sample particles from the cathode cavity, and transition to arcing. The various ways of overcoming these difficulties (e.g. placing the sample in tablet form at the bottom of the cathode; separating powdered samples from the excitation zone by thin carbon cathode discs or other such barriers; inserting a piece of graphite into the hollow of the cathode; dividing the entrance from the excitation zone of the sample with a possibility for independent control of both processes, etc.) have many shortcomings because of the complexity of their execution, and also contamination, prolonged analysis time, etc. The use of a pulsed supply eliminates these difficulties and successfully solves the problems.

A simple supply* has been used for AES of mixtures of dry residues (from solutions) with graphite powder and semiconducting silicon [64-69] (Table 3.5). This allows the HCD to be operated in three supply modes: non-pulsed, pulsed and combined (non-pulsed + pulsed) with pulse parameters varying over a wide range ($a = 0.02\text{-}2A$, $t = 5\text{-}1000\,\mu\text{sec}$, $f = 0.02\text{-}10$ kHz).

The discharge stability is improved and the spectral line intensity increased as the supply is changed from non-pulsed to pulsed and then to the combined mode. The results are most clear for spectral lines with high excitation potential. At the same time, the intensity of the background increases but to a much smaller extent than the intensity of the analytical lines. The molecular band intensity increases in the reverse order. The experimental results obtained in the pulsed and combined conditions can be explained by the increase in electron concentration, the enrichment of the plasma with fast electrons, and the increase in degree of ionization of the atoms, which causes the intensity to increase for spectral lines having low as well as high excitation potentials [65, 70]. The decrease in intensity for molecular bands and the increase in intensity for the

---

* See Chapter 6.

Table 3.5 – Detection limits for trace elements in various samples, using
combined, non-pulsed and pulsed modes of current supply to the discharge tube.
(Reprinted from [69] by permission of the copyright holders).

Substance analysed	Element line and λ (nm) (excitation energy, eV)	Detection limits (g)		
		non-pulsed discharge	pulsed discharge	combined discharge
Dry	Ag (I)328.0 (3.78)	4×10^{-11}	–	4×10^{-12}
residues of	In (I)325.6 (4.08)	3×10^{-10}	–	5×10^{-11}
salt solutions	Ga (I)294.4 (4.31)	3×10^{-10}	–	5×10^{-11}
	P (II)525.4 (16.38)	1×10^{-6}	–	2×10^{-8}
	La(II) 412.0 (3.32)	8×10^{-7}	–	1×10^{-8}
	Gd(II)365.6 (3.53)	6×10^{-8}	6×10^{-9}	4×10^{-9}
	Yb(II)398.8 (3.10)	4×10^{-9}	1×10^{-9}	6×10^{-10}
	Br(II)481.7 (14.22)	1×10^{-7}	–	1×10^{-8}
	Ag (I)328.0 (3.78)	3×10^{-10}	–	3×10^{-11}
Carbon	In (I)325.6 (4.08)	2×10^{-9}	–	3×10^{-10}
powder	Ga (I)294.4 (4.31)	2×10^{-9}	–	5×10^{-10}
	Br (II)481.7 (14.22)	2.5×10^{-7}	1×10^{-7}	7.5×10^{-8}
Si	Cl (II)476.7 (19.69)	5×10^{-7}	–	7.5×10^{-8}

continuous background is due to the increase in the degree of dissociation of
the molecules, and confirms the role of recombination processes in spectrum
excitation. Comparison of the voltage/current characteristics of the discharge
on transition from non-pulsed to pulsed to combined supply shows that the
linearity improves. This indicates an improvement in discharge stability and,
therefore, in the reproducibility of the results when the combined mode is used
[65]. The results given in Table 3.1 show that use of pulsed and combined HCD
supplies lowers the detection limit of by 1-2 orders of magnitude.

In a typical case of use of HCD for AES of gases, improved reproducibility
and sensitivity is achieved by using a pulsed supply. This is demonstrated in the
determination of small quantities of He in air [71].

An interesting application of a pulsed supply is outlined in a study [72], in
which the characteristics of a double hollow cathode (Fig. 3.6), consisting of a
non-pulsed cathode-evaporator and a pulsed cathode-exciter (with t up to
$60 \mu sec, a = 0.5$-10 A, $f = 0.02$-1 kHz), were studied. Varying the f values varies
the average pulse current and therefore changes the manner of atomization of
traces of Cd, Zn, Bi and Pb, this being at $f = 0.02$-0.1 kHz mainly by cathode
sputtering and by thermal evaporation at $f = 0.6$-1 kHz. In pulsed conditions,
the intensity of the spectral lines of all trace elements increases, that of the lines
with high excitation potential increasing most (e.g. I for the Fe atomic lines
increases 3-5 times and I for the ion lines 12-15 times).

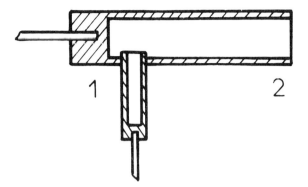

Fig. 3.6 – Double hollow cathode: 1: cathode-evaporator; 2: cathode-exciter.

A useful peculiarity of the pulsed HCD is the previously mentioned weaker dependence of the rate of thermal evaporation on gas presuure. The reason for this is believed to be the higher energy of the bombarding ions, owing to the higher voltage during the pulse. The pulsed supply changes the radial distribution of the spectral-line intensities, shifting their maximum from the axis to the cathode walls because of the change in electron-energy distribution. The differences between oscillograms showing the noble-gas line intensity and the current pulse imply changes in the processes of excitation, and redistribution of the current density over the cathode surface. Because of the increased intensity of the analytical lines and the improved stability of the HCD with this design, the quality of analysis for easily volatile traces and readily excited elements is improved. For example, in the analysis of ZrO_2, the detection limit for determination of Cd is 3 pg, and of Zn, Pb and Bi, 5 μg; the relative standard deviation for trace concentrations of $1 \times 10^{-4}\%$ is $< 5\%$.

3.3.2 AES with a pulsed discharge in a cooled hollow cathode

Cooling the HCD with liquid nitrogen is one of the oldest ways of improving its characteristics. Because of the slower entry of a cathode substance into the discharge volume and the reduced rate of diffusion of the atoms, the discharge stability improves markedly and the intensity of the emitted spectral lines increases as their width is reduced.

The influence of the temperature of the hollow-cathode walls has been investigated [73]. Comparison of the values of the I/I_0 ratio for the Cu(I) 324.7-nm spectral line emitted from an uncooled and a liquid-nitrogen cooled hollow cathode (see Table 3.6), shows that this ratio decreases more in the latter, as the current is increased. This decrease, resulting from the pulsed supply, can be used to eliminate thermal evaporation of the cathode material.

The cooled hollow-cathode discharge (CHCD) proves to be more favourable for comparative theoretical and experimental investigations. For instance, for a CHCD [74], a suitable theoretical model [75] has been used to calculate the concentrations of copper atoms in the non-pulsed (n_0) and pulsed (n_p) systems

Table 3.6 – The variation of I/I_0 with a for the spectral line Cu(I) 324.7 nm emitted from (1) the uncooled and (2) the liquid-nitrogen cooled hollow-cathode discharge. (Reprinted from [73] by permission of the copyright holders, Pergamon Press Ltd., Oxford).

a(mA)	30	60	90	120	180	240
1	50.0	85.0	62.5	44.7	15.5	4.1
2	39.0	43.4	17.6	2.9	1.2	1.1

and these were compared with the experimentally measured absolute values of these concentration [73]. The measurements were made in a discharge tube with a hollow cathode, as shown in Fig. 3.7. A probe, at the plasma potential, was placed along the cathode axis. The sputtered copper atoms condensed on it and

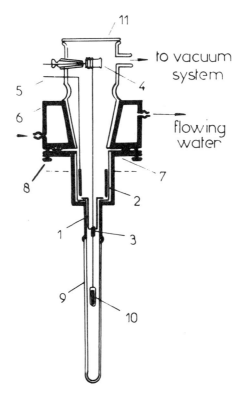

Fig. 3.7 – Diagram of the hollow-cathode discharge tube: 1, cathode; 2, anode; 3, isolated glass capillary; 4, coil; 5, anode supply; 6, copper vessel with running water for heating the glass slit of the discharge tube; 7, pressure ring; 8, tightening screws; 9, glass tube; 10, weight; 11, quartz window. (Reprinted from [73] by permission of the copyright holders, Pergamon Press Ltd., Oxford).

their mass M was measured by spectral analysis. The atom concentration n near the probe was then given by

$$n = \frac{2M N_A}{m_A t\, v\pi l\alpha r},$$

where M is the mass of copper atoms sputtered during time t, N_A is Avogadro's number, m_A is the atomic height of copper, V is the mean square velocity of the thermal movement of the atoms, α is the sputtering coefficient, and r and l are respectively the radius and length of the probe. Good correlation was obtained between the theoretically calculated and experimentally observed concentrations of copper atoms in the non-pulsed and pulsed states, and in both cases n_p was $<$ n_o. However, the effect of pulsed supply on the process of entrance of analyte atoms into the plasma is not itself sufficient to explain the results obtained. Various changes in the excitation processes should also be taken into account. Such changes have been reported [76–79] for an HCD operated under conditions similar to the pulsed condition considered here. The change in intensity of the spectral lines during pulsing and in the period between pulses is explained by the complicated change in the function expressing the electron-energy distribution, the concentration of electrons, and the electric-field intensity in the discharge in the pulsed state. Whereas at the beginning of the pulse, the excitation occurs mainly by direct collisions with electrons, at the end of the pulse the probability of excitation by different recombination processes and by state transitions increases. These results can be used to explain the different experimentally obtained spectroscopic effects accompanying the use of a pulsed supply.

We can therefore say then that the application of a pulsed supply to the CHCD extends the analytical possibilities of this spectral source even further. Thus, for example, the replacement of a non-pulsed supply with a pulse leads to improved detection power for traces of Be, Ti and Mn in KCl and CaSO$_4$: for Be the detection limit is 2 ng, for Ti and Mn, 0.02 μg and the relative standard deviation of the results is 7–12% [80].

The hollow-cathode discharge cooled with liquid nitrogen and with a pulsed supply appears to be a very suitable source for direct AES of non-conducting and poorly conducting samples [80–82]. With such samples (unlike metals) it is necessary to run the discharge beforehand for a prolonged time until it stabilizes and the spectrum appears [63]. This disadvantage can be overcome by preliminary metallization of the powdered dielectric samples, by addition of conducting substances. However, theoretical and experimental investigations of the ion bombardment of untreated dielectric samples at the bottom of the hollow cathode show that use of a pulsed supply allows direct sputtering of the sample. After the current pulse, the dielectric loses its polarization; the positive-ion charge from its surface spreads partially over the cathode in the pauses between the pulses and is partially compensated by the electron current existing in the plasma afterglow. For this reason, the spectra of dielectric samples appear immediately the pulsed-supply discharge is lit, and they are quite stable. In this case a mean-square error of 0.20 is obtained for log I of the Ba, Sc and Ni lines, and 0.05 for an Fe line. The high stability of the pulsed CHCD has made it suitable for determination of the stoichiometry of, for instance, single crystal samples of $BaSc_x Fe_{12-x} O_{19}$. An improvement of this method makes it suitable for determination of x for Sc in the range 0.06–0.92 with a mean-square error of 0.05–0.08.

We know that the substance enters the CHCD as a result of cathode sputtering of the surface cathode layer of the inserted sample, usually to a depth of several nm. This is the basis for use of CHCD for layer-by-layer analysis with high depth resolution (0.1–0.2 μm), in contrast to laser microspectral analysis which is suitable for layer analysis at low depth resolution [83].

In comparison with the Grimm discharge often used for this purpose, the CHCD is more suitable because of its good stability and reproducibility of results [84]. A pulsed CHCD has been used for direct layer-by-layer atomization of a semiconductor [85]. The sample, in disc form, is put at the bottom of the hollow cathode (Fig. 3.8). Preliminary investigations show that the layers undergo plane-parallel sputtering only when the ratio $D:d = 1.5$ (D = diameter of the hollow cathode, d = sample diameter). Interesting element-distribution profiles can be obtained, e.g. from layer-by-layer analyses of a monocrystalline layer of $Y_3Fe_5O_{12}$ on monocrystalline $Gd_3Ga_5O_{12}$ as substrate.

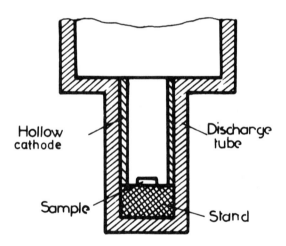

Fig. 3.8 — Hollow cathode with sample at the cavity bottom.

A series of works [7,8,86–94] on spatial and temporal resolution of the heating and excitation processes in the CHCD is of particular interest in connection with the analytical possibilities of the pulsed supply. An extensive theoretical and experimental investigation of gas formation temperature (T_{gas}) and estimation of thermal balance in the CHCD, has been made [86]. Attention was paid to the fact that the regions of excitation and heating of the gas are spatially separated: the heating occurs in the region of the dark cathode space

(DCS) where the electric field energy is transferred to the neutral atoms in collisions with noble gas ions, whereas the excitation takes place in the region of negative glow (NG), mainly by direct collisions with electrons. Moreover, the increased width of the non-resonance spectral lines emitted from the HCD is chiefly due to the Doppler effect. These facts suggest that a pulsed HCD should be used for temporal separation of the excitation–heating processes. If the emission is recorded over a time interval during which excitation takes place but at low gas temperature, the spectral lines emitted will be both intense and narrow. Solution of the non-steady-state thermal conductivity equation [8, 87] yields data for the time-distribution of heat transfer from the cathode surface to the cathode axis, and values of the pulse parameters at which the values of T_{gas} in the centre and at the cathode walls still differ only slightly. The experimental check made by determining T_{gas} by measurement of the redistribution of the hyperfine components of the Cu(I) 578.2 nm line confirms the results obtained theoretically. For example, for a copper CHCD with diameter 7 mm and length 18 mm, at $t = 10 \, \mu sec, f = 3 \, kHz, a = 0.2 \, A$, T_{gas} along the cathode axis exceeds T_{gas} at the walls by only 100°C. The intensity of the line is 5–6 times that for the direct-current discharge at the same T_{gas}, and the signal-to-noise ratio is increased 50-fold. The separation of the heating and excitation processes favourably influences the recording of the Cu(I) 578.2 nm spectral line, as shown in Fig. 3.2 (p. 57).

Although the main cause of the increased width of non-resonance lines emitted from the HCD is the Doppler effect, the broadening of resonance lines results from self-absorption. Based on the fact that the regions of entry and excitation of atoms in the HCD plasma are spatially separated (the analyte atoms enter from the cathode walls but are excited in the negative glow) a theoretical estimation has been made of the optimal pulse parameter values [88]. A separation can also be achieved that will ensure an optimal concentration (not high enough to cause self-absorption) of the atoms in the discharge. The experimental measurement of the Cu(I) 578.2 nm spectral line intensity shows good agreement of the calculated and the experimentally obtained optimal values ($t = 6 \, \mu sec, f = 1 \, kHz, a = 0.2 \, A, i = 2 \, mA$), confirming the concept of temporal separation of the entry and excitation processes, and restricting broadening of the spectral lines by self-absorption [7].

According to the diffusion model developed for describing atom movement in the CHCD [7, 88], the plasma is enriched with atoms of one or other of the elements (differing in their masses and gas-kinetic cross-sections), by applying a pulsed supply [89, 90]. It is clear from qualitative considerations that, since atoms with small mass numbers and gas-kinetic cross-sections will diffuse more quickly from the hollow-cathode walls to the centre, the spectral lines emitted from light elements will be intensified by sufficiently short pulses. Conversely, the heavier atoms will remain for a longer time in the centre of the source after application of the pulse. The effect is more evident for heavier noble gases and for atoms with larger gas-kinetic cross-sections. An experimental confirmation is obtained with Bi (atomic weight 209.0) containing 0.05% Cu (atomic weight 63.5) excited in a pulsed CHCD. The spectral lines of Bi are very strong and those of Cu are quite weak in the non-pulsed mode, but in a pulsed state with $t = 10$ μsec, $a = 0.6$ A and a suitable f, the ratio I_{Cu}/I_{Bi} increases by two orders of magnitude. If this is applied to analysis for Be, V and Ti in calcium and sodium salts, the detection limit is decreased by 1–2 orders of magnitude relative to other methods, and is 5 ng, 0.05 μg and 3 ng for the three elements respectively [91, 92]; the detection limit for Be and Mg is improved and is $8 \times 10^{-5}\%$ [93]. There is a possibility of direct determination of Be in niobium oxide at $< 10^{-2}\%$ level and in europium oxide at $< 5 \times 10^{-4}\%$ by using a pulsed supply, thereby overcoming the problem of matrix spectral lines close to the analytical Be line [94]. The possibilities of this method for determination of Al in Cu–Zn alloys and of C and B in steel have also been described [95].

3.4 CONCLUSIONS

We hope we have shown that the use of a pulsed supply not only contributes to a more efficient solution of those spectroscopic problems for which this spectral source is recommended, but offers still wider scope. The method is simpler and gives more possibilities than some others. The high-frequency supply usually used gives improved results for a variety of elements. That is, the pulsed hollow-cathode discharge is one of the most useful and promising spectral sources in modern analytical practice.

Acknowledgements – Thanks are expressed to the authors and publishers who have given permission for the reproduction of figures and tables from the original literature: K. Kitagawa, M. Suzuki, N. Aoi, S. Tsuge (Japan) and Pergamon Press Ltd., Oxford, England; A. Zhiglinsky, N. Rudnevsky, D. Maksimov, K. Kureichik (USSR) and the Copyright Agency of the USSR; T. Araki, T. Uchida, S. Minamu (Japan) and the Society for Applied Spectroscopy; A. Datseff (Bulgaria), Editor-in-Chief of *Bulg. J. Phys.*, and also to D. Zhechev (Bulgaria) for supporting this work.

REFERENCES

[1] I. Roig and M. Becart, *Compt. Rend.*, 1952, **235**, 1625.

[2] M. Kaminsky, *Atomic and ionic collisions on the metal surface*, Mir, Moska, 1967.

[3] P. W. J. M. Boumans, *Anal. Chem.*, 1972, **44**, 1219.

[4] R. W. Falcone and K. D. Pedrotti, *Opt. Lett.* 1982, **7**, 74.

[5] G. F. Kirkbright and M. Sargent, *Atomic Absorption and Fluorescence Spectroscopy*, Academic Press, London, 1974.

[6] J. B. Dawson and D. J. Ellis, *Spectrochim. Acta,* 1967, **23A**, 565.

[7] B. M. Boshnyak, A. G. Zhiglinsky and I. P. Presnukhina, in *Proceedings of 7th Uralsk. Conf. Spectrosc.*, Sverdlovsk 1, 1971, p. 19.

[8] E. S. Dobrosavljević, A. G. Zhiglinsky and T. N. Khlopina. *Bull. B. Kidrič Inst. Nucl. Sciences, Phys.*, 1969, **19**, 1.

[9] K. P. Kureichik, *Zh. Prikl. Spectrosk.*, 1977, **27**, 1114.

[10] G. J. De Jong and E. H. Piepmeier, *Spectrochim. Acta,* 1974, **29B**, 159.

[11] A. I. Bezlepkin, A. S. Khomyak, V. V. Alexandrov, T. N. Voronina, and O. V. Mel'nikova, *Zh. Prikl. Spectrosk.* 1983, **39**, 367.

[12] E. Cordos and H. V. Malmstadt, *Anal. Chem.* 1972, **44**, 2277, 2407.

[13] E. R. Johnson, C. K. Mann and T. J. Vickers, *Appl. Spectrosc.* 1976, **30**, 415.

[14] T. Araki, T. Uchida and S. Minami, *Appl. Spectrosc.* 1977, **31**, 150.

[15] I. R. Gulakov, S. S. Katushonok and A. P. Klistenko, *Zh. Prikl. Spectrosk.* 1978, **28**, 334.

[16] D. A. Katskov, G. G. Lebedev and B. V. L'vov, *Zh. Prikl. Spectrosk.*, 1969, **10**, 215.

[17] H. Prugger, R. Grosskopf and R. Torge, *Spectrochim. Acta*, 1971, **26B**, 191.

[18] D. G. Mitchell and A. Johansson, *Spectrochim. Acta*, 1970, **25B**, 175.

[19] E. Cordos and H. V. Malmstadt, *Anal. Chem.*, 1973, **45**, 27.

[20] E. H. Piepmeier and L. de Galan, *Spectrochim. Acta*, 1975, **30B**, 211.

[21] R. Djulgerova, *Bulg. J. Phys.* 1977, **4**, 459.

[22] R. Djulgerova, *Spectrosc. Lett.* 1977, **10**, 727.

[23] R. Djulgerova, *Bulg. J. Phys.,* 1977, **4**, 569.

[24] J. Tilch, in *Proceedings of 8th ICPJG, Berlin, DDR,* 1977, **1**, 313.

[25] B. V. L'vov, *Atomic Absorption Spectral Analysis,* Nauka, Moskva, 1966.

[26] H. C. Wagenaar, I. Novotny and L. de Galan, *Spectrochim. Acta*, 1977, **29B**, 301.

[27] H. C. Wagenaar, and L. de Galan, *Spectrochim. Acta*, 1975, **30B**, 361.

[28] E. H. Piepmeir and L. de Galan, *Spectrochim. Acta*, 1975, **30B**, 263.

[29] S. Mohamad and A. Petkof, *J. Phys. Colloq. (France)*, 1979, **40**, 195.

[30] Yu. I. Turkin, *Opt. Spektrosk.*, 1957, **2**, 290.

[31] R. Djulgerova, *Bulg. J. Phys.,* 1980, **7**, 90.

[32] H. G. C. Human, *Spectrosc. Lett.,* 1973, **6**, 170, 719.

[33] K. P. Kureichik, *Zh. Prikl. Spektrosk.,* 1980, **32**, 614.

[34] K. P. Kureichik, I. R. Gulakov and A. M. Sarzevsky, *Zh. Prikl. Spectrosk.,* 1980, **33**, 184.

[35] K. P. Kureichik, *Zh. Prikl. Spektrosk.,* 1982, **36**, 907.

[36] K. P. Kureichik, S. A. Zolotoi, V. V. Alexandrov, T. N. Voronina, A. S. Khomyak and A. I. Bezlepkin, *Zh. Prikl. Spektrosk.,* 1983, **38**, 727.

[37] T. C. Wolf and T. J. Vickers, *Appl. Spectrosc.,* 1978, **32**, 265.

[38] E. E. Maizil and Yu. Z. Shnitman, *Zh. Prikl. Spektrosk.,* 1978, **29**, 759.

[39] A. G. Zhiglinsky, M. A. Kabanova and E. M. Sautina, *Trudy VNII Nauchpribora (USSR),* 1975, **4**, 31.

[40] M. A. Kabanova and E. M. Sautina, *Zh. Prikl. Spektrosk.,* 1977, **26**, 593.

[41] T. Araki, T. Uchida, and S. Minami, *J. Spectrosc. Soc. Japan,* 1977, **26**, 16.

[42] T. Araki, T. Uchida and S. Minami, *J. Spectrosc. Soc. Japan,* 1977, **26**, 317.

[43] T. Araki, J. P. Walters and S. Minami, *Appl. Spectrosc.,* 1980, **34**, 33.

[44] K. Kitagawa, T. Nanya and S. Tsuge, *Spectrochim. Acta*, 1981, **36B**, 9.

[45] K. Kitagawa, M. Suzuki, N. Aoi and S. Tsuge, *Spectrochim. Acta*, 1981, **36**, 21.

[46] T. Araki, T. Uchida and S. Minami, *Appl. Spectrosc.,* 1977, **31**, 150.

[47] S. V. Baranov, B. D. Grachyov, I. A. Zemskova and E. M. Rukin, *Zh. Prikl. Spektrosk.,* 1983, **39**, 917.

[48] S. V. Baranov, G. L. Zhuravlev, I. A. Zemskova and G. I. Satarina, *Atomic absorption analyser,* Inventor's certificate No 700787 (USSR), 1979. *Bull. Invent.,* 44.

[49] S. V. Baranov, I. A. Zemskova and G. I. Satarina, *Spectral method for determination of substance concentration,* Inventor's certificate No 711441 (USSR), 1980. *Bull. Invent.,* 3.

[50] I. M. Veselnitskii, O. V. Mel'nikova and A. B. Fromberg, *Spectral gas discharge lamp,* Inventor's certificate No 395927 (USSR), 1973. *Bull. Invent.* 35.

[51] V. V. Alexandrov, A. I. Bezlepkin and A. S. Khomyak, *Spectrochim. Acta,* 1981, **36B**, 1163.

[52] A. I. Bezlepkin, A. S. Khomyak and V. V. Alexandrov, *Zavodsk. Lab.,* 1981, **47**, 29.

[53] J. V. Sullivan and A. Walsh, *Appl. Opt.,* 1968, **7**, 1271.

[54] E. F. Palermo and S. R. Crouch, *Anal. Chem.,* 1973, **45**, 1594.

[55] V. S. Burakov, P. A. Naumenkov, S. V. Nechaev and N. V. Tarasenko, *Zh. Prikl. Spektrosk.,* 1982, **36**, 199.

[56] V. S. Burakov, P. A. Naumenkov and N. V. Tarasenko, *Zh. Prikl. Spektrosk.,* 1983, **38**, 709.

[57] H. Massmann, *Spectrochim. Acta,* 1970, **25B**, 393.

[58] A. I. Drobyshev, A. M. Rish and Y. I. Turkin, *Vest. Leningrad. Univ. Ser. Fiz. Khim.,* 1983, **3**, 107.

[59] R. M. Manabe and E. H. Piepmeier, *Anal. Chem.,* 1979, **51**, 2066.

[60] B. Le Blanc, M. Carller, Y. Demers and J. M. Gaghé, *Appl. Opt.,* 1980, **19**, 463.

[61] G. H. Morrison, *Trace Analysis Phys. Methods,* Interscience Publ., Ithaca, New York, 1965.

[62] Kh. I. Zil'bershtein, *Spectral Analysis of Pure Materials,* Khimija, Leningrad, 1971.

[63] S. Tolansky, *High Resolution Spectroscopy,* Methuen, London, 1947.

[64] N. K. Rudnevsky, D. E. Maksimov, N. G. Pichugin and R. H. Hasjanov, *Zh. Prikl. Spektrosk.,* 1974, **20**, 707.

[65] N. K. Rudnevsky, N. G. Pichugin and D. E. Maksimov, *Zh. Prikl. Spektrosk.,* 1973, **19**, 5.

[66] N. K. Rudnevsky, N. G. Pichugin and D. E. Maksimov, *Zh. Prikl. Spektrosk.,* 1976, **25**, 921.

[67] N. K. Rudnevsky, N. G. Pichugin, D. E. Maksimov and E. E. Kachan, *Production and analysis of highly pure materials,* Nauka, Moskva, 1978, p. 215.

[68] N. G. Pichugin, N. K. Rudnevsky and D. E. Maksimov, *Zh. Analit. Khim.* 1977, **32**, 12.

[69] D. E. Maksimov and N. K. Rudnevsky, *Zh. Prikl. Spektrosk.,* 1983, **39**, 5.

[70] J. F. Kielkopf, *Spectrochim. Acta,* 1971, **26B**, 371.

[71] V. I. Gladushchak and E. Ya. Shreider, *Zavodsk. Lab.* 1964, **30**, 47.

[72] Y. B. Atnashev and V. N. Muzgin, *Zh. Prikl. Spektrosk.,* 1974, **21**, 414.

[73] R. Djulgerova, D. Zhechev and N. Krasnobaeva, *Spectrochim. Acta,* 1980, **35B**, 521.

[74] R. B. Djulgerova, *Dissertation,* Bulg. Acad. Sci., Sofia 1980.

[75] B. M. Boshnyak, A. G. Zhiglinsky, G. G. Kund and T. N. Khlopina, *Opt. Spektrosk.,* 1972, **33**, 1032.

[76] F. V. Kravchenko and V. F. Papakin, *Zh. Tekh. Fiz.,* 1973, **43**, 2057.

[77] F. V. Kravchenko, V. S. Mihailevski and V. F. Papakin, *Zh. Tekh. Fiz.,* 1973, **43**, 2173.

[78] P. A. Pogorely and A. M. Shukhtin, *Optk. Spektrosk.,* 1975, **38**, 244.

[79] Yu. M. Kagan, V. M. Milenin and N. A. Timofeev, in *Proceedings of 8th ICPIG, Berlin, DDR,* 1977, **1**, 229.

[80] A. I. Drobyshev and Yu. I. Turkin, *Zh. Prikl. Spektrosk.,* 1975, **22**, 755.

[81] A. I. Drobyshev, Yu. I. Turkin and E. V. Gorchakova, *Zh. Prikl. Spektrosk.,* 1982, **36**, 903; A. I. Drobyshev and Yu. I. Turkin, *Zh. Prikl. Spectrosk.,* 1982, **37**, 158.

[82] A. I. Drobyshev, Yu. I. Turkin, N. M. Jakimova and I. V. Ogurtzova, in *Proceedings of 19th Congress Spectrosc., Tomsk, USSR,* 1983, **5**, 55.

[83] Kh. I. Zilbershtein, *Zavodsk. Lab.,* 1980, **12**, 1095.

[84] S. Caroli and P., Delle Femmine, *Spectrosc. Lett.,* 1978, **11**, 299; S. Caroli and O. Senofonte, *Can. J. Spectrosc.,* 1980, **25**, 73.

[85] A. I. Drobyshev and Yu. I. Turkin, *Spectrochim. Acta,* 1981, **36B**, 1153.

[86] A. G. Zhiglinsky and T. N. Khlopina, *Zh. Prikl. Spektrosk.,* 1968, **8**, 562.

[87] B. M. Boshnyak, E. S. Dobrosavljević, A. G. Zhiglinsky and T. N. Khlopina, *Zh. Prikl. Spektrosk.,* 1969, **10**, 554.

[88] B. M. Boshnyak, A. G. Zhiglinsky, I. P. Presnukhina and T. N. Khlopina, *Advances in Atomic Absorption Spectroscopy,* Izd. LDNTP, Leningrad, USSR, 1969, p. 23.

[89] A. I. Drobyshev, A. G. Zhiglinsky and Yu. I. Turkin, *Zh. Prikl. Spektrosk.,* 1973, **19**, 620.

[90] A. I. Drobyshev, *Study of the possibilities for the application of a pulsed light source with cooled hollow cathode in emission spectral analysis,* Dissertation, Leningrad University, USSR, 1977.

[91] O. A. Grigor'eva, A. I. Drobyshev, A. G. Zhiglinsky, N. P. Zaretskaya and Y. I. Turkin, *Some problems of modern analytical chemistry,* Leningrad University, USSR, 1977, pp. 2, 5.

[92] O. A. Grigoryeva, A. I. Drobyshev, N. N. Zaretskaya, A. G. Zhiglinsky and Yu. I. Turkin, in *Proceedings of 18th CSI,* Grenoble, 1975. p. 223.

[93] A. I. Drobyshev, S. M. Nemets and Yu. I. Turkin, *Zh. Prikl. Spektrosk.,* 1979, **30**, 329.

[94] A. I. Drobyshev and Yu. I. Turkin, *Physico-chemical methods for analysis,* Gorky, USSR, 1978, pp. 3, 66.

[95] R. Djulgerova, D. Zhechev, S. Valkanov and M. Mihailov, in *Proceedings of 2nd Nat. Conf. Physics-Industry,* Kazanlak, Bulgaria, 1977, **2**, 646.

4

Hollow-cathode discharge within a graphite furnace: furnace atomic non-thermal excitation spectrometry (FANES)

H. Falk

4.1 INTRODUCTION

Since the discovery of the hollow-cathode effect in 1914 by Paschen [1] there have been many publications dealing with the electrical, plasma and spectroscopic characteristics of this special gas discharge. These papers include experimental works as well as attempts to give a theoretical description of the hollow-cathode discharge (HCD). Most of the experimental and theoretical work done on HCD up to 1969 have been reviewed in the monograph by Moskalev [2]. In 1981 Pillow [3] gave a summary of the state of knowledge of the different features of HCD. It is not the aim of this chapter to review all the material on HCD published up to now, but to draw conclusions on those features of HCD which are essential for its use as a spectroscopic radiation source. These features are:

geometrical, pressure and electrical characteristics;

plasma parameters, such as electron and ion densities, energy and spatial distributions of electrons and ions;

gas temperature and line profiles emitted by HCD;

release of atomic species from the surface and their residence inside the hollow cathode;

excitation mechanisms for carrier gases and other species.

4.2 GEOMETRICAL PRESSURE AND ELECTRICAL CHARACTERISTICS OF HCD

4.2.1 Usual glow-discharges

The HCD is a special case of a low-pressure glow discharge. Such a discharge can be observed between two electrodes inside an insulating evacuated envelope at a pressure of 0.05–5 kPa, when a d.c. or low-frequency a.c. voltage of several hundred volts is applied. The term glow discharge is applied to a self-sustained current through the gas diode, which is connected with a steady glow occupying most of the discharge tube. When the lateral dimensions of the discharge tube are much less than the length of the tube, then most of the tube appears to be filled with a glow of uniform light intensity. Near to the electrodes, however, there are regions where the light intensity is not uniform. If the distance between cathode and anode is decreased, then the more or less uniform glow starting near to the anode ('the positive column') will increasingly disappear, but the features near to the cathode continue almost unchanged. The most intense part of the glow discharge is the 'negative glow' which is situated over a certain distance from the cathode, called the 'cathode dark space'. The existence of the negative glow is essential for sustaining the glow discharge, because the discharge will be extinguished when the cathode–anode distance approaches the length of the cathode dark space. In the following we will deal with glow discharges where the anode–cathode distance is such that the negative glow can be formed, but the positive column is suppressed. That is the situation we find in an HCD.

There is a general behaviour of the cathode region of glow discharges which should be discussed in more detail. Because glow discharges are operated with cold cathodes, the electrons necessary to sustain the discharge current are not formed by thermionic emission but by interactions between the gas discharge and cathode surface. Such indirect processes, usually called secondary emission, consist of ejection of electrons from the cathode by energetic particles such as ions, accelerated atoms and metastable atoms, or photons.

The most important part of a glow discharge is the cathode region, consisting mainly of the cathode dark space and the negative glow. Most of the voltage applied to the discharge tube drops within the cathode dark space, and this voltage drop is called the 'cathode fall'. In other words, there is a high electric field between the cathode surface and the border of the negative glow.

When a double cathode is used instead of a single flat cathode, at high pressure two separate negative glows are present. If the pressure is decreased, a joint glow belonging to both cathodes is formed. This process is connected with a considerable increase of the discharge current, the voltage remaining constant. This 'hollow-cathode effect' has been observed to give a current increase of up to 900-fold [4]. A further current enhancement will take place if the double cathode is replaced by a hollow cylinder.

Typical voltage–current characteristics of the HCD are shown in Figs. 4.1 and 4.2. The region where the discharge voltage is almost independent of the current is called the 'normal glow discharge', and further current increase is only possible at higher voltage, leading to the 'abnormal discharge'.

There are various approaches to quantitative description of the hollow-cathode effect, but the whole phenomenon is rather complex because a large number of processes contribute to the discharge current in the cathode region. Furthermore, various geometrical configurations, cathode materials and carrier gases are used. Therefore, a general quantitative theory of the HCD cannot be

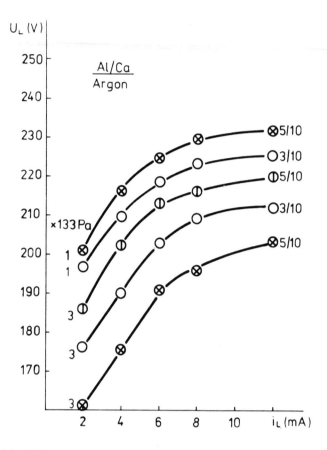

Fig. 4.1 – Voltage–current characteristics of various argon-filled hollow-cathode lamps [15]. Cathode material, pressure and geometry are given in the figures. At the right-hand end of each curve the cathode diameter/cathode length are given (in mm), and the pressure is given at the left-hand end. By permission of Humbold-University Berlin, and with acknowledgements to the author.

expected, but the validity of the theoretical picture can be tested for actual cases. It is evident that in the steady-state of the discharge, for every electron released from the cathode a certain number of ions, fast neutral atoms, metastable atoms and photons must fall onto the cathode. On the other hand, only a fraction of all the energetic species formed by an electron released from the cathode will reach the cathode again; the rest is lost in maintaining the discharge. With the hollow cathode, the energetic species produced in the cathode dark space and negative glow have a much reduced chance of getting anywhere except to the cathode, and the electron-producing efficiency is much greater than that of a plane cathode. Practically all authors agree with this explanation of the hollow-cathode effect.

Whereas the ions formed in the cathode dark space will reach the cathode whether it is plane or hollow, there are differences for ions and photons formed

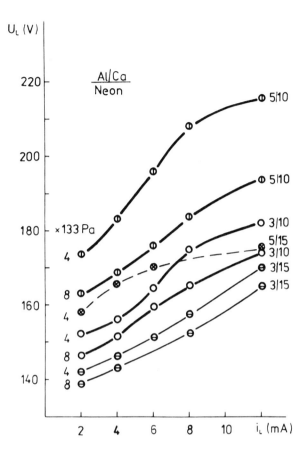

Fig. 4.2 – Voltage–current characteristics for various helium-filled hollow-cathode lamps [15]. By permission of Humboldt-University Berlin, and with acknowledgements to the author.

in the negative glow. The likelihood for a photon from the glow to get to the cathode is about 0.3 for a plane cathode and about 0.8 for a hollow cathode [5]. The chance that an ion of the negative glow will diffuse into the cathode dark space is much larger for hollow than for plane cathodes. The energetic electrons entering the negative glow give their energy to the smaller volume of the glow inside the hollow cathode and, consequently, the ion density is higher than in a glow in front of a plane cathode. Additionally, most of the surface of the negative glow is surrounded by the hollow cathode whereas a plane cathode has a much smaller contact area with the glow border.

The peculiarity of the HCD that the negative glow is restricted to the cavity of the hollow cathode has several interesting consequences. Some of the electrons accelerated across the dark space are fast enough to penetrate the negative glow and enter the opposite dark space, where they suffer a reversal of direction, re-entering the glow at approximately their previous speed. Therefore, a number of electrons make double or multiple passages within the cavity, producing, as compared with a plane cathode discharge, a greatly increased number-density of ions and photons. The quantitative effect of this process depends partly on the cathode geometry, but mainly on the gas pressure and the nature of the carrier gas. As a result, the relative contributions of the secondary electron emission of the cathode, caused by impinging photons, can vary greatly with the carrier gas and the cathode material. The quantum efficiency of the photoelectron emission γ_p of different cathode materials and different wavelengths (Table 4.1) shows that for resonance photons of the inert gases the value of γ_p is not a linear function of the photon energy. In other words, the relative contribution of photoelectron emission to the hollow-cathode effect will increase from N_2 through Ar and Ne to He [5]. Little and von Engel [6] estimated the photo-electron emission to be the main reason for the hollow-cathode effect. For an HCD in He, with a nickel cathode, Falk [5] calculated from experimental data that the contribution of photoelectron emission was 90%. This contribution can be decreased to 70% by adding chlorine to the carrier gas, which results in a higher cathode fall of 400 V. This effect could be attributed to surface coverage of the nickel cathode, since the original cathode fall of 200 V can be re-established by flushing the discharge with pure helium after a long period of burning. Obviously, there are chemical reactions of the nickel surface with the chlorine, to give products which can be removed by the sputtering action of the helium ions to restore a clean nickel surface.

Table 4.1 — Photoelectric yield as a function of wavelength and cathode material [57].

Line notation	Wavelength (nm)	Photon energy (eV)	Photoelectric yield (%)			
			Ni	Cu	Ta	W
He $1s^3$ ^1S-$2'p^0$	58.43	21.22	10	9	11	14
Ne $2p^6$ ^1S-$3s'[1/2]^0$	73.59	16.85	12	12	17	14
Ar $3p^6$ ^1S-$4s'[1/2]^0$	104.82	11.83	6	10	10	10
Kr $4p^6$ ^1S-$5s$ $[1/2]^0$	123.58	10.03	2	4	2	3
Xe $5p^6$ ^1S-$7s'[1/2]^0$	129.56	9.57	2	2	1	1

The sensitivity of HCD parameters to cathode surface effects through the quantum efficiency for photoelectron emission is very important for application of the HCD as an atomic emission source. Whereas for metals such as copper, nickel and molybdenum the maximum quantum efficiency of the photoeffect γ_p is of the order of 10% in the wavelength range 30–120 nm, γ_p drops to 10^{-3}% and lower for wavelengths longer than 160 nm [7]. It is well known that a very thin alkali-metal coverage can increase γ_p of a metal in the UV–visible range by several orders of magnitude [8]. Consequently, introducing a sample into the hollow cathode will also affect the voltage–current characteristics by a change in γ_p and eventually in secondary emission by particle impact. In this case the excitation conditions in an HCD are continuously changing as a function of sample concentration.

4.2.2 Peculiarities of FANES

When a tubular graphite furnace is used as the cathode of an HCD [9] as shown in Fig. 4.3, the influence of the cathode temperature has to be considered. In Furnace Atomic Non-thermal Excitation Spectrometry (FANES) a thermal volatilization process is taking place while a glow discharge plasma is sustained within the furnace tube. The HCD deviates from local thermodynamic equilibrium (LTE) because of the great difference between the temperatures of the electrons and carrier-gas atoms in the glow. To get a high rate of volatilization of a sample placed on the inner surface of the graphite tube, the temperature of the latter is increased rapidly, at up to 2000 K/sec. For temperatures higher than about 2000 K the thermionic emission from graphite becomes remarkably high [10].

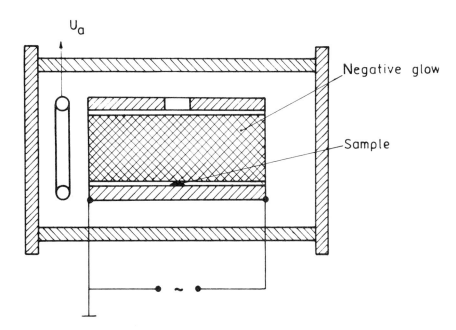

Fig. 4.3 – Schematic diagram of the FANES source [9]. By permission of the publishers, Pergamon Press Ltd., and with acknowledgement to the authors.

Consequently, in the FANES system the character of the voltage–current characteristic is changed when the cathode temperature exceeds 2000 K, because of the contribution of thermionic emission besides the secondary emission of electrons from the cathode surface. The threshold of thermionic emission leads to a remarkable drop of the discharge voltage at a given discharge current. An example of this behaviour of the FANES system is given in Fig. 4.4.

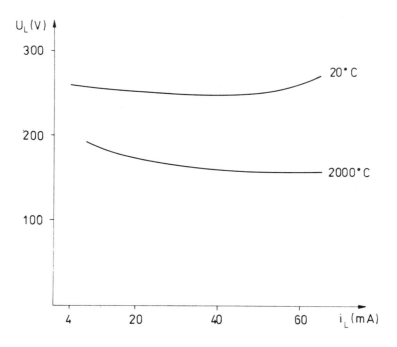

Fig. 4.4 – Discharge voltage of a FANES source as a function of discharge current. Carrier gas: Ar, 2.50 kPa. Parameter: cathode temperature.

4.3 PLASMA PARAMETERS OF HOLLOW-CATHODE DISCHARGES

4.3.1 Mechanism of plasma formation in HCD

The region of the cathode dark space has the function of an 'electron gun'. Since the negative glow represents an equipotential plasma the only energy source to maintain the negative glow is provided by the electrons coming from the negative dark space. With regard to the total ionization cross-section of rare gases [11] the contribution of secondary electrons formed in the dark space is negligible for He but of the same order as the primary electron current for Ar (see Table 4.2). By the same argument it is evident that a considerable fraction of the primary electrons is able to penetrate the negative glow and to reach the opposite dark space, when He is used as a carrier gas. Consequently, this mechanism, which leads to a decrease of the positive space charge, can contribute to the hollow-cathode effect [12] only for He as the carrier gas.

The motion of positive ions within the cathode dark space is governed by charge-transfer collisions. The cross-section for charge transfer is very large when the ionization energies of the colliding particles are not very different [13].

Table 4.2 – Average path length l_T of electrons accelerated in the dark space, before loss of their energy by collisions with the carrier gas of an HCD.

Carrier gas	P (Pa)	V_c (V)	E_i (eV)	δ_T (10^{-17} cm^2)	l_T (mm)
He	600	300	24.58	3.6	26.0
Ne	600	180	21.56	8.1	8.0
Ar	600	200	15.76	30.0	3.3

P = pressure, V_c = cathode fall, E_i = ionization energy, δ_T = total ionization cross-section [11].

Therefore, the energy of carrier-gas ions corresponds to the potential difference between particles involved in the charge-transfer collisions, whereas foreign gas ions gain the full cathode fall potential, but the current density is much lower.

Besides the secondary emission created by energetic particles hitting the cathode surface, the photoelectric emission is important in the HCD. This contribution varies for different carrier gases [5, 14] and has been estimated to be more than 70% of the total electron emission in He.

The influence of fast neutral atoms and metastable atoms on the electron emission of the cathode can be neglected when the cathode surface is fully covered by the discharge [14].

From the fact that the mean free path of primary electrons accelerated by the cathode fall potential is comparable to or only slightly smaller than the cathode diameter, it can be realized that the negative glow is far from being in local thermodynamic equilibrium.

4.3.2 Gas temperature in HCD

The translational temperature of discharge species can be determined by measurements of the Doppler-broadened line profile. If the influence of self-absorption broadening can be neglected, then the half-intensity width of an emission or absorption spectral line under low-pressure conditions is given by

$$\Delta \nu_D = \frac{2\sqrt{(2R\ln2)}}{c} \nu_0 \sqrt{\frac{T}{M}} \tag{4.1}$$

where R = gas constant (8.314 J. mole^{-1} K^{-1}), c = speed of light (2.998 × 10^8 m/sec), ν_0 = central frequency of a spectral line (sec^{-1}), T = translational temperature (K), M = molecular weight of the gas. For a number of hollow-cathode lamps with different cathode geometries and operated in the current range 2.5–30 mA, Kowollik [15] measured the half-widths of various spectral lines of the carrier gas Ne and of sputtered cathode material. Within the experimental accuracy the temperatures of the gas and metal atoms were the same.

With a maximum deviation of ±60 K he found a linear relationship between gas temperature T_G (K) and discharge current I (mA):

$$T_G = (27.8 \pm 0.94)I + (516 \pm 14.7) \tag{4.2}$$

for cathode diameter and length 3 and 10 mm respectively, and

$$T_G = (14.2 + 0.86)I + (393 \pm 13.5) \tag{4.3}$$

for cathode diameter and length 5 and 10 mm. Figure 4.5 shows Kowollik's experimental results [15] for the dependence of the gas temperature on the discharge current. It is necessary to notice here that the cathodes of the lamps used by Kowollik had no water cooling provided, so the temperature increase found when the discharge current was increased was to a certain extent due to heating up of the cathode cylinder. The gas temperatures in an HCD determined by Kowollik [15] agree satisfactorily with the results of other authors [16, 17].

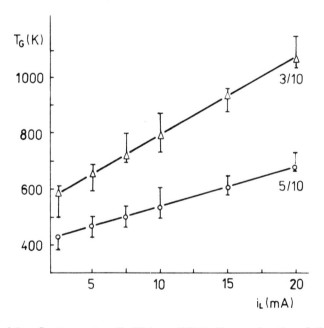

Fig. 4.5 — Gas temperature T_G(K) in an HCD in Ne, as a function of discharge current [15]. The cathodes had no water cooling. At the right-hand end of each curve the cathode diameter/cathode length (in mm) are given. By permission of Humboldt-University Berlin, and with acknowledgements to the author.

Gas-temperature measurements at higher discharge currents have been made by Falk [18], using non-resonance lines of Ca. Because of the water cooling of the cathode the temperature increase with discharge current, as shown in Fig. 4.6, can be attributed to heating up of the gas, the cathode temperature being constant.

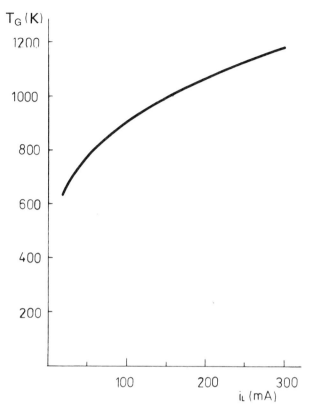

Fig. 4.6 – Gas temperature $T_G(K)$ in an HCD in He, as a function of discharge current. Cathode diameter 5 mm, length 40 mm, water-cooled [18]. By permission of the publishers, Pergamon Press Ltd.

The gas-temperature measurements have shown that even at high currents the temperature difference between gas and cathode does not exceed 900 K. This fact and the dependence of the line half-width on the square root of the gas temperature [see Eq. (4.1)] is the reason why the lines emitted by the HCD are generally narrow. Only if the hollow cathode is allowed to reach a high temperature or the spectral lines are influenced by self-absorption or diffusion of resonance radiation, is considerable line-broadening observed [18].

In a FANES-system where the cathode can reach a temperature of up to 3200 K the line-widths are up to three times those in the case of the usual water-cooled cathodes. At the heating rates applied in FANES, deviations of the gas temperature from that of the wall can be neglected [19]. Therefore the line-width of a FANES-source can be calculated by using Eq. (4.1) and the known wall-temperature, as long as self-absorption of the line under study is negligible.

4.3.3 Electron number density and energy distribution

Both the electron number density and energy distribution have been determined

by using probes and electrostatic analysers. All experimenters have found considerable deviations of the energy distribution from the Maxwellian. This basic
result can be applied to all modifications of HCD. Borodin *et al.* [20, 21] used
probes introduced into the plasma to study energy distributions in HCD for the
energy range up to 25 eV, and electrostatic analysers for the energy range from
30 eV up to the total cathode fall potential [22]. From the measurements
published by Borodin *et al.* [20-22] the following normalized expression for the
electron energy distribution has been calculated [23]

$$f^*(E_e) = \left[\int_0^{E_e} f(E'_e)\, dE'_e \right] \bigg/ \left[\int_0^\infty f(E'_e)\, dE'_e \right] \tag{4.4}$$

The result for He is shown in Table 4.3. Most of the glow electrons have
energies lower than 20 eV. From 20 eV up to the total cathode fall potential of
300 eV the electron distribution function is practically constant. For the total
electron number density Borodin *et al.* [20-22] found $n_e = 6 \times 10^{11}/cm^3$ at a
discharge current $I = 50$ mA. This result corresponds reasonably to the findings
of Büger and Fink [24] who reported $n_e = 10^{13}/cm^3$ at $I = 1$ A. Unfortunately,
there are no accurate measurements of the electron energy distribution in the
range 20-40 eV. The probe signal is too low and the electrostatic analyser is
noisy for energies lower than 40 eV. This range would be of considerable interest
for He as carrier gas because of the fact that the threshold for ionization and
excitation of He is situated there. Howorka and Pahl [25] studied the electron
number-density and energy distribution of HCD in Ar for $I = 5$-20 mA. They
used the probe method and were not able to analyse the high-energy part of the
energy distribution. In the pressure range from 11 to 60 Pa they found two
groups of electrons with nearly Maxwellian distributions: a fast group at 3 eV
and a slow group at 0.5 eV. The number-densities of these groups were found to
be 2-20 $\times 10^8$ and 2-20 $\times 10^9$ per cm^3 for the fast and slow electrons, respectively, in the current range 5-20 mA. Büger and Fink [24] also gave results for
the electron distribution measured for an HCD in the high-current range for two
different electron groups having temperatures corresponding to 0.4 and 8 eV,

Table 4.3 — Normalized electron energy distribution for an HCD in He for
various pressures P and discharge currents (I), from the results of Borodin *et al.*
[20-22].

Parameter		Electron energy (eV)			
P (Pa)	I (mA)	5	10	20	300
400	30	0.37	0.62	0.71	1
400	60	0.47	0.61	0.67	1
260	60	0.35	0.54	0.62	1

respectively. The number-density of the fast group was lower by a factor of ≈ 50 than that of the slow group. The results discussed here did not account for the high-energy tail of the electron distribution. In this case it is possible to replace the measured distribution by two Maxwellian functions with satisfactory accuracy, but such a procedure is not applicable for adequate description of the high-energy range from 20 eV up to the full potential of the cathode fall. Therefore, such approximations of the real electron distribution must be used with care, especially when excitation and ionization of ions or atoms with high excitation potentials are involved.

It is well known from spectroscopic applications of the HCD that there is an optimal pressure range for an HCD, in which the intensity is maximal. Borodin and Kagan [20] studied the pressure-dependence of the high-energy tail (19–26 eV) of the electron energy distribution. The results of their measurements are shown in Fig. 4.7. There indeed exists a certain pressure within the working

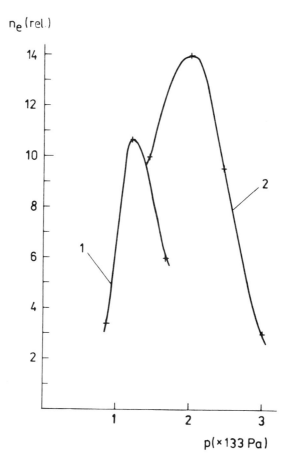

Fig. 4.7 – Relative number of fast electrons (19–26 eV) as a function of gas pressure [20]. Carrier gas He, discharge current 20 mA, cathode diameter 20 mm (1) and 10 mm (2), cathode length 100 mm (1) and 50 mm (2), respectively.

range of the HCD where the fraction of fast electrons is maximal. This maximum reflects the fact that pressure changes have a strong influence on the electron energy distribution. For the atomic triplet levels the excitation rate, as a function of the energy of the exciting electrons, shows a narrow maximum, whereas for the singlet levels the maximum is very broad. Hence the gas pressure at which the excitation efficiency for a given level is optimal differs according to the nature of the atomic energy level. The radial distribution of the electron number-density is strongly dependent on the carrier-gas pressure [25]. With rising gas pressure a central maximum is converted into two peaks near to the cathode dark space and a minimum in the centre. This observation corresponds satisfactorily to the values of the average path length of electrons accelerated in the dark space, as given in Table 4.3.

4.3.4 Ion number-density

Different authors have measured the field distribution within the glow plasma [21, 25] and found that the field strength there amounts to 0.1–4 V/cm. Under these circumstances it is not surprising that the ion number-density [26] was found to be equal to the electron number-density and its radial distribution. Therefore, it is generally accepted that the negative glow plasma has nearly neutral and equipotential character where the space charge is essentially zero. As a consequence the motion of the charge carrier within the plasma is determined by ambipolar diffusion.

4.3.5 Concentration of metastable atoms

In the literature on HCD we find many hints on the importance of metastable rare-gas atoms for the excitation of other species in the glow plasma. Such excitation mechanisms are very well known from the He–Ne laser system where the energy of metastable He atoms is transferred to Ne levels by collisions of the second kind.

Borodin and Kagan [22] determined the concentration of metastable He atoms at the 2^3S_1 level by a re-absorption method. The results are given in Table 4.4. It is interesting to notice that the number-density of metastable He mostly reaches a maximum or saturation at 60 mA, which corresponds here to a relatively low current density (~ 4 mA/cm^2). For the same system, besides the concentration of metastable He Borodin and Kagan [22] determined the electron number-density and energy distribution in the plasma. With the help of these data they were able to calculate the population of different He levels, taking into account excitation by electron collision. They found reasonable agreement between the calculated population and the concentration of excited atoms determined from absorption measurements, which supported the validity of the theoretical framework.

The measurement of the number-density of He* (2^3S) is sufficient to estimate the concentration of metastable He atoms. That is because the cross-section of the reaction

$$He^* (2^1S) + e^- \rightarrow He^* (2^3S) + (e^- + 0.78 \text{ eV}) \tag{4.5}$$

Table 4.4 – Measured number-density (cm^{-3}) of He (2^3S_1) metastable atoms in an HCD with He carrier gas [22].

ϕ (mm)	Cathode length (mm)	P (Pa)	Discharge current (mA)		
			15 mA	30 mA	60 mA
10	50	260	1.1×10^{12}	3.5×10^{12}	7×10^{12}
10	50	400	3×10^{12}	5×10^{12}	6×10^{12}
10	50	780	3×10^{12}	3×10^{12}	4×10^{12}
20	100	67	3.6×10^{11}	3.6×10^{11}	2×10^{11}
20	100	133	3×10^{11}	4×10^{11}	3×10^{11}
20	100	266	4×10^{11}	6×10^{11}	6×10^{11}

is very high for slow electrons. When the electron energy corresponds to 300 K then the cross-section for the reaction in Eq. (4.5) amounts to 3×10^{-14} cm^2 [39]. The glow plasma contains a considerable portion of slow electrons, with the result that the lifetime of He*(2^1S) is very short and He* (2^1S) formed within the glow plasma will be quickly converted into He* (2^3S).

The observed saturation of He* (2^3S) at relatively low discharge current density can be explained as due to the increasing rate of deactivation processes at higher electron densities. The same dependence on discharge current is to be expected for any foreign gas atoms which are excited by collisions of the second kind with metastable carrier-gas atoms. This point will be re-examined later on when the excitation processes within the HCD are discussed.

4.4 SPUTTERING, VAPORIZATION AND NUMBER-DENSITY OF CATHODE MATERIAL IN HCD

4.4.1 Cathode sputtering

When fast ions or atoms hit a solid surface physical sputtering takes place, i.e. there is ejection of atoms from the target surface as a result of transfer of momentum from the incident particles to the target atoms. The sputtering rate, defined as the average number of atoms sputtered per incident particle, depends on the material of the surface as well as on the nature of the particle and its kinetic energy. As discussed in Section 4.3.1 the motion of positive ions in their own gas within the dark space under the influence of the strong electric field is determined by the process of charge transfer. Therefore, the ion energy is less than the charge on the electron times the cathode fall V_c and amounts to about 20-100 eV, depending on the pressure and carrier gas. The ion energy is approximately inversely proportional to the gas pressure [27]. As a function of the gas-target combination there is a characteristic threshold for the ion energy, at which the sputtering yield starts to increase linearly with ion energy up to 100 eV or multiples thereof, where it levels off [28-30]. As a rule, the sputtering yield grows with the mass of the incident particle and is maximum when the masses of the incident particle and target atoms are equal. An HCD in pure He gives the least sputtering; in this case impurities in the carrier gas probably make a higher contribution than He* to the sputtering, because foreign gas ions have a higher mass as well as higher kinetic energy than He^+ (see Section 4.3.1).

The energy of sputtered atoms is of the order of several eV, for the energy range of incident ions which is relevant for the HCD [29]. When the emission of sputtered atoms is observed very near to the cathode surface, the high kinetic energy of these atoms influences their line widths. Hannaford and Lowe [31] found an abnormal broadening of boron emission lines in a glow discharge, which could be explained by the high initial energy of sputtered boron atoms.

The direction taken by sputtered atoms is grouped around that of the specular reflection, referred to the direction of the incident ion. Additionally, when crystalline target surfaces are used, there are certain directions of preferred sputtering, correlated with the crystal axis [29]. The incidence of ions in an HCD is roughly normal to the macroscopic surface of the cathode, but the maximum sputtering yield occurs at incident angles (to the normal) of 40-80° [32]. That is one reason why the sputtering rate is not uniform across a poly-crystalline target surface, a characteristic etching pattern (depending on the microcrystalline surface structure) being formed [33]. It is very important for application of the HCD that any coverage of the cathode surface, e.g. the dry residue of any sample, has a striking influence on the sputtering rate in the area where it is present. This affects the whole discharge mechanism, and results in relatively poor reproducibility of quantitative analyses with the HCD, typically 10-30% relative standard derivation (rsd) [33]. In the HCD the result of the sputtering process is not only determined by the interaction between the cathode surface and incident ions but also by redeposition of the sputtered material under the influence of diffusion within the carrier gas. Hence at elevated target temperatures the sputtering yield is generally increased [32] but the diffusion and redeposition processes of the sputtered material are also modified. Because of the complexity of the whole process it seems to be more informative to study the relationship between discharge parameters and atomic density of the target material within the plasma.

4.4.2 Thermal vaporization in HCD

Besides sputtering, thermal vaporization can also be applied to bring the cathode material itself, or a sample deposited on it, into the plasma of the HCD. The easiest way to do this is to use the electric power dissipated at the cathode, to heat it up. In such hot cathodes no provision for cooling is made and the discharge current density must be > 200 mA to get a sufficiently high final temperature [34, 35]. A relatively low electric power of roughly 100 W allows only low heating rates, of the order of 50 K/sec at low temperatures, and substantially lower at above 1000°C. Besides the limited heating rate, which causes long and flat peaks of the sample vapour density within the cathode in the hot hollow cathode, the processes of excitation and vaporization of the sample are also affected by the discharge current. Consequently, the experimenter is forced to find compromise conditions acceptable for both vaporization and excitation.

Another approach to achieve a high rate of vaporization of sample material to be excited in an HCD is Furnace Atomic Non-thermal Excitation Spectrometry (FANES) introduced by Falk *et al.* [19, 36-38]. In FANES a tubular graphite furnace incorporated into a discharge vessel is used as the hollow cathode. The tube is heated by electric power supply with a maximum of 5 kW, which allows heating rates of up to 2000 K/sec. In contrast to other HCD constructions, in FANES a sample can be vaporized almost instantaneously, allowing a very high density of sample vapour. With this system a maximum temperature of 3000°C can be reached. Hot hollow cathodes cannot achieve a temperature above 2000°C.

A cross-section of the FANES source is given in Fig. 4.8. To restrict the glow discharge to the graphite tube the inner metal parts of the vacuum vessel are coated with insulating material (PTFE), which for the sake of simplicity is not shown in Fig. 4.8. The operating parameters are summarized in Table 4.5. As a result of the high heating rate available in the FANES system the time needed to volatilize a sample from the hollow-cathode surface is only 0.2-1 sec [19]. This means the flow-rate of the sample material is of the order of

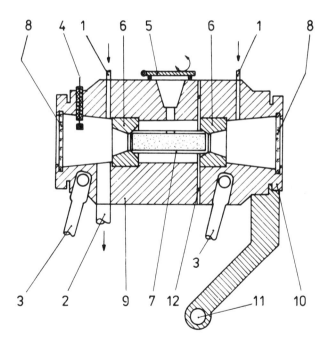

Fig. 4.8 – Cross-section of the FANES source: (1) carrier-gas port, (2) pump port, (3) electric connector to heating transformer, (4) anode, (5) removable lid for sample injection, (6) graphite electrode, (7) graphite furnace and hollow cathode, (8) window, (9) water-cooled vacuum vessel, (10) water-cooled part of the vacuum vessel and rotation arm for changing the graphite tube, (11) pivot, (12) gasket.

Table 4.5 – Operational parameters of the FANES source

atomizer = hollow cathode	graphite tube, length 28 mm, bore 5.8 mm
rest gas pressure	< 1 mPa
carrier gas	He or Ar, 100–500 Pa
discharge voltage	400–600 V
discharge current	20–30 mA
sample volume	5–50 μl (hand-pipetting)
atomizer voltage	0–10 V
atomizer current	0–500 A
atomization temperature	800–3000°C
heating rate	$\leqslant 2000$°C/sec
signal duration	0.3–1 sec
spectrometer resolution	$1–2 \times 10^4$
time constant, detection system	$\leqslant 0.1$ sec

1 mg/sec, assuming that the dry residue from 50 μl of a 10-g/l. solution is evaporated. On the other hand the sputtering rate dm_s/dt is given by

$$dm_s/dt = i_{c+}\eta_s m_A/e \tag{4.6}$$

where m_s = mass sputtered in time t, i_{c+} = total ion-current at the cathode, η_s = sputtering yield, m_A = atomic mass, e = charge on the electron. At a discharge current of 20 mA, the order of magnitude of dm_s/dt is thus 1 μg/sec, assuming η_s = 0.2 atoms/ion [32]. This estimate shows that in FANES the contribution of cathode sputtering is negligible compared to thermal vaporization when the atomizer tube is heated at high rates. In a hot HCD the thermal vaporization rate is orders of magnitude lower than in FANES and becomes comparable to the sputtering rate.

There is another aspect of the evaporation in FANES which is of considerable practical interest. The sputtering process acts in the same manner on all the constituents of a sample on the hollow-cathode surface, after steady-state conditions have been established. Consequently, the release rates of a matrix and an analyte correspond roughly to their abundance in the sample. In contrast, the heating regime in FANES can usually be chosen so that the matrix and analyte are evaporated at different times. This procedure allows the influence of matrix constitutents on the excitation conditions in the FANES plasma to be considerably suppressed.

Because of the thermal nature of the volatilization process in FANES, the conditions are very similar to those in graphite-furnace atomic-absorption spectrometry (GFAAS), but the boiling points are several hundred K lower in FANES than in GFAAS, since the atomization is done at low pressure. Nevertheless, with FANES (just as with GFAAS) only samples which are volatile at the maximum available cathode temperature can be handled, whereas the sputtering process is applicable to all conducting materials independent of their boiling points.

4.4.3 Number-density of cathode material in HCD

The number-density of atoms released by sputtering from the hollow cathode surface, n_c, reaches a steady state after a build-up time of the order of 20 μsec when a d.c. voltage is applied to the HCD tube [18]. Investigations of the pulsed HCD have shown that the concentration of sputtered atoms decays with a time constant of $\tau_d \sim 50$ μsec when the discharge current is switched off [18]. If the discharge current is interrupted at $t = 0$, then n_c follows the relationship

$$n_c(t) = n_c(0) \exp[-t/\tau_d] \tag{4.7}$$

The total number of atoms (N_s) within a hollow cathode of volume V_h, as a function of time, can be described by

$$dN_s/dt = -V_h \, dn_c/dt \tag{4.8}$$

The sputtering rate is

$$dN_s/dt = \eta_s S_c I_{c+}/e \tag{4.9}$$

where η_s = sputtering yield, S_c = inner surface area of the hollow cathode and I_{c+} = ion-current density of the cathode. In a steady state the loss of sputtered atoms by diffusion out of the hollow-cathode volume is compensated by the sputtering rate and therefore the total sputtering rate can be expressed in terms of the steady-state atomic number-density $n_{c(ss)}$

$$dN_s/dt = \frac{\pi r^2 h_c}{\tau_d} n_{c(ss)} \tag{4.10}$$

or of the mass sputtered per second

$$dm_s/dt = \frac{\pi r^2 h_c m_A}{\tau_d} n_{c(ss)} \tag{4.11}$$

assuming that the hollow cathode is an open-ended cylinder of radius r and length h_c, and where m_A is the atomic mass. Using Eqs. (4.9) and (4.10) we find for the sputtering yield

$$\eta_s = \frac{er n_{c(ss)}}{2 \tau_d I_{c+}} \tag{4.12}$$

From Eqs. (4.10) and (4.11) the sputtering rate of the cathode material of an HCD can be evaluated by determining the steady-state density of the species under study and its decay time constant. This can be done by measuring the atomic-absorption signal of the species in a pulsed HCD with a d.c.-operated line-source as background light-source. An evaluation of the sputtering yield needs additional information on the discharge mechanism because the ion-current density at the cathode is not directly measurable.

Despite the relatively low expense of measuring the density of sputtered atoms inside the HCD by atomic-absorption only a few such investigations are reported in the literature. Using Eq. (4.11) and an order-of-magnitude estimate of $\tau_d = 20$ μsec, and with the help of the known density measured by Kowollik [15], which will be discussed below, we find $dm_s/dt \sim 0.1$ μg/sec. This rough estimate of the sputtering rate refers to the following experimental conditions: discharge current 10 mA; argon gas pressure 400 Pa; cathode diameter 5 mm; cathode length 10 mm; cathode material Mg or Al.

Zhiglinsky et al. [40] determined the concentration of sputtered atoms in an HCD by inserting a thin wire into the plasma, keeping the probe at plasma potential and exposing it to the discharge for about 100 sec. The amount of metal deposited on the probe was then determined by spectrochemical analysis. It was found that in a copper hollow cathode (diameter 8 mm, length 15 mm), there was a linear relationship between Cu number-density and discharge current. At 10 mA and 100 Pa argon pressure the Cu number-density was $2 \times 10^{11}/cm^3$. At a distance of 20 mm from the cathode the atom concentration was $5 \times 10^9/cm^3$.

Persson et al. [41,42] determined the Cu concentration within a copper slot hollow cathode (6×2 mm^2) by atomic absorption. For Ne as carrier gas at a pressure of 1–2.7 kPa they observed a linear relationship between discharge current and Cu number-density at current density higher than about 30 mA/cm^2. At a current density of 310 mA/cm^2 the density of neutral copper atoms was $4 \times 10^{13}/cm^3$. At such high current densities the metal atom density is of the order of 0.1% of the carrier gas density. In this case the sputtering action of the metal ions should already play a role. The sputtering yield of the metal ions is expected to be much higher than that of the carrier gas ions since the metal ions can gain more energy in the dark space due to the fact that they are practically not subject to charge-transfer collisions (see Section 4.3.1).

A comprehensive study on the density of sputtered atoms in HCD was made by Kowollik [15]. He applied a modified version of the absorption method introduced by Ladenburg and Reiche [43]. In his experiments the radiation of the HCD itself was used for the absorption measurement, by reflecting the emitted radiation back through the open-ended hollow cathode. The emission signal of the HCD with and without the mirror allows evaluation of the absorbance if the line profile is known. Kowollik [15] investigated a variety of cathode dimensions and materials, with Ne and Ar as carrier gases in the low current regime which is usually applied to sources for atomic-absorption spectrometry. The cathodes consisted of pure Mg or an Al–Ca alloy containing 18% Ca. Examples of the results obtained by Kowollik are shown in Figs. 4.9 and 4.10 and give the same pattern as that for all the other cases investigated. The general feature of all density plots is their linearity with respect to discharge current. At constant pressure the atom density is higher for smaller cathode diamters. For a given cathode geometry the density increases when the pressure is decreased. Usually, there is no significant dependence on the kind of carrier gas. The only exception is for calcium where the densities at comparable conditions are higher in Ne than in Ar. The linearity of atom density and discharge current shows that the sputtering rate is proportional to the total current density. This is not a trivial result, since the sputtering rate depends on both the ion-current density and the ion energy at the cathode surface. Consequently, the conclusion can be drawn that the ratio of the ion-current and total current densities at the cathode and the ion energy are not substantially changed over the current range investigated. The increase of the atom density at lower pressure is in agreement with theoretical expectation since both the cathode fall and the mean free path of ions between charge-transfer collisions are higher when the pressure is decreased. As a result the ion velocity will rise and so will the sputtering yield.

Summarizing, it can be stated that the experimental results on the density of sputtered atoms in the HCD plasma are in qualitative agreement with theory. A quantitative description could be given if more experimental parameters were known. In Kowollik's measurements, these parameters would mainly be the decay time constant of the atom density, and the dark-space length.

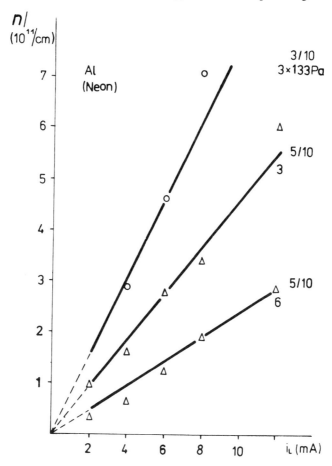

Fig. 4.9 – Density of sputtered Al atoms in an HCD in Ne, as a function of discharge current [15]. Diameter/length of the open-ended cathodes given in mm. By permission of Humboldt-University Berlin, and with acknowledgements to the author.

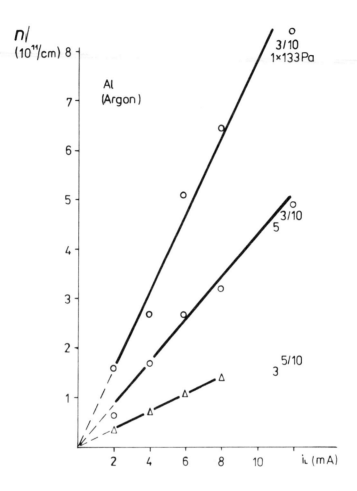

Fig. 4.10 – Density of sputtered Al atoms in an HCD in Ar, as a function of discharge current [15]. Diameter/length of the open-ended cathodes given in mm [15]. By permission of Humboldt-University Berlin, and with acknowledgements to the author.

To determine the atomic density of an analyte present in a FANES system during atomization, absorption measurements have been made [44]. In Figs. 4.11 and 4.12, absorption signals at atmospheric and low pressure as well as FANES-emission signals for Cd and Cr, obtained with the same system, are shown. From these measurements the maximum atomic densities present in the atomizer-tube hollow cathode have been calculated, and are listed in Table 4.6. Calculating the number of atoms present in the tube at peak maximum for atmospheric and low pressure as a fraction of the number which have been introduced, we find 7.7 and 0.21% respectively for Cd and 3.6 and 0.36% respectively for Cr. In other words, the peak atomic density when the low pressure system is used instead of an atomizer at atmospheric pressure is lower by a factor of 36 for Cd and 10 for Cr.

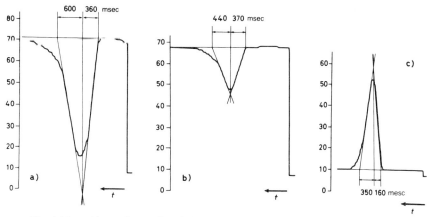

Fig. 4.11 – Absorption and emission signals of Cd (at 228.8 nm) in a FANES-system. Heating rate: 800 K/sec. (a) AAS at atmospheric pressure (Ar), 0.2 ng Cd; (b) AAS at 200 Pa He, 1 ng Cd; (c) AES at 200 Pa He, 1 ng Cd, i = 20 mA.

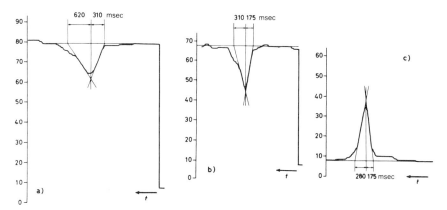

Fig. 4.12 – Absorption and emission signals of Cr (at 357.9 nm) in a FANES-system. Heating rate: 1500 K/sec. (a) AAS at atmospheric pressure (Ar), 0.2 ng Cr; (b) AAS at 200 Pa He, 2.5 ng Cr; (c) AES at 200 Pa He, 1 ng Cr, i = 20 mA.

Table 4.6 – Maximum atomic density in a FANES-system as calculated from absorption measurements (see Figs. 4.11 and 4.12).

Element	Atmospheric pressure (Ar)			Low pressure (200 Pa Ar)		
	n_{peak} measured $\times 10^{11}/cm^3$	N_{peak} $\times 10^{11}$	N_{peak} introduced $\times 10^{11}$	n_{peak} measured $\times 10^{11}/cm^3$	N_{peak} $\times 10^{11}$	N_{peak} introduced $\times 10^{11}$
Cd	1.5	0.84	10	0.2	0.11	53
Cr	1.5	0.84	23	1.9	1.1	290

n_{peak} = atomic density at peak absorbance
N_{peak} = number of atoms within the absorption volume

It is interesting that there are significant differences in the peak shapes for the volatile element Cd and the refractory element Cr. Whereas the rise times of the absorption peaks for Cd at atmospheric and low pressure are identical, Cr is evaporated much faster at low pressure. Consequently, the Cr peak is drastically shortened by reducing the pressure, with a corresponding increase of the peak height at the expense of area of the integrated signal. The difference in behaviour of Cd and Cr with respect to the pressure in the atomizer can be explained by the fact that the decrease in boiling point with decrease in pressure is practically not important for Cd, since the heating rate is high at volatilization anyway, but is of great influence for the non-volatile element Cr. A large decrease in the boiling point of Cr is equivalent to a greatly increased heating rate in the temperature interval of volatilization.

Finally for the atomic density in a FANES system it has been found that:

(a) the contribution of cathode sputtering to the density of the sample vapour is negligible compared to thermal sample volatilization;

(b) reducing the carrier gas pressure from atmospheric to low pressure (several hundred Pa) leads to a decrease of the peak atomic density by more than an order of magnitude;

(c) at reduced pressure in the FANES system the atomization temperatures are several hundred kelvins lower than those for GFAAS at atmospheric pressure.

4.5 EXCITATION MECHANISM IN HCD

4.5.1 Excitation of carrier gas species

As in the preceding sections, we restrict ourselves to the HCD in rare gases.

As explained in Section 4.3 the energy to form and to sustain the hollow-cathode plasma is delivered by the dark space, acting as an 'electron gun'. These energetic electrons lose their energy mainly by inelastic collisions with atoms of the carrier gas, which are thus excited and ionized. In Section 4.3.3 it was stated that the highest electron number-density measured in an HCD plasma is $\sim 10^{13}/cm^3$, which means that this is also the upper limit for the ion number-density. The carrier gas number-density in an HCD is roughly proportional to the discharge current. The close interdependence of the spatial distribution of radiation intensity of carrier-gas lines and of electron density in the negative glow has been shown by the measurements made by Hofmeister and Kagan [45] and Howorka and Pahl [25]. Their observations also support the results on the energy distribution of the glow electrons, which has its maximum at the border of the glow at high gas pressures. In this area the population of the levels with high excitation potential is maximal.

The main processes in the hollow-cathode plasma which populate the levels of the carrier-gas atoms and ions are direct electron collision and recombination:

$$A + e^- \rightarrow A^+ + 2e^- \tag{4.13}$$

$$A^+ + e^- + X \rightarrow A^* + X \tag{4.14}$$

where A stands for the carrier-gas atom and X is any third partner such as an electron or atom. Besides these processes there are many other possibilities for excitation and de-excitation for carrier-gas species in the plasma. There is no doubt that the resonance photons of carrier-gas atoms and ions play a role in the HCD, as shown by Falk and Lucht [46] by measurements of the afterglow in He and Ar. The absorption cross-section for the resonance transitions is high enough in an HCD to make the plasma optically thick at the resonance wavelengths. As a result the resonance photons are trapped within the plasma for a time of the order of 1 μsec [46]. In other words, the effective lifetime of an excited reson-ance level is more than a hundred times that for other lines where the plasma is optically thin. This longer lifetime of the resonance levels of the carrier gas causes a higher density of these levels compared to other rare-gas levels. In this respect the resonance levels are similar to the metastable levels of the rare-gas atoms. Whereas the rate of the inverse process to that in Eq. (4.13), which means a radiationless deactivation, can usually be neglected, that is not the case for resonance and metastable levels of the rare gases. Additionally, these levels can also be subject to further excitation to a higher level by electron collision.

The dependence of the intensity emitted by HCD on the discharge current is of special interest because it is decisive for the excitation processes involved. The total intensity emitted from the volume element dV for direct electron excitation can be written as

$$\mathrm{d}\,S_{\mathrm{Le}} = h\,\nu_0\,n_{\mathrm{e}}\,n\int_0^\infty Q_{\mathrm{a}}(E_{\mathrm{e}})\,v_{\mathrm{e}}(E_{\mathrm{e}})\,\mathrm{f}(E_{\mathrm{e}})\,\mathrm{d}E_{\mathrm{e}}\,\mathrm{d}V \qquad (4.15)$$

where n is the number-density of ground-level atoms, $Q_{\mathrm{a}}(E_{\mathrm{e}})$ is the excitation cross-section (m^2), and $v_{\mathrm{e}}(E_{\mathrm{e}})$ is the electron velocity. As discussed in Section 4.3.5 the concentration of metastable atoms in an HCD is of the order of $10^{13}/\mathrm{cm}^3$ at maximum. From absorption measurements we know [22,47] that the number-density of other excited levels is lower than that of the metastable levels. Compared to the atom concentration of 10^{16}–$10^{17}/\mathrm{cm}^3$ in the ground level, the concentration of excited levels can be neglected and the factor n in Eq. (4.15) is practically constant. For direct electron excitation we find from Eq. (4.15) that there is proportionality between line intensity and electron density in the plasma when the electron energy distribution is not changed substantially. The contribution to the line intensity by electron excitation collisions starting from excited levels can be neglected because of the much lower number-density of the excited levels, for which the excitation cross-section is smaller than that of the corresponding transition starting from the ground level.

As discussed in [46] the line intensity for recombination radiation in the quasi-neutral plasma has the form

$$\mathrm{d}S_{\mathrm{Lr}} = A_{\mathrm{r}}\,\alpha\,n_{\mathrm{e}}^2\,\mathrm{d}V \qquad (4.16)$$

where A_{r} is a constant. The recombination coefficient α is constant when the two-body or three-body recombination with a neutral carrier-gas atom as the third body is the dominating process. Then we can write

$$dS_{Lr}(2) = A_r(2)n_e^2 dV \qquad (4.17)$$

but for three-body recombination with an electron or an ion as the third body, α is proportional to n_e and in this case we find

$$dS_{Lr}(3) = A_r(3) n_e^3 dV \qquad (4.18)$$

$A_r(2)$ and $A_r(3)$ are constants depending on the kind of carrier-gas atoms, the excitation level involved and the electron energy distribution function. The electron density in a hollow-cathode plasma is proportional to the discharge current for a given carrier-gas pressure as long as the cathode fall voltage is not essentially changed (see Section 4.3.3). The dependence of the intensity on discharge current to be expected for emission lines of carrier-gas ions is the same as that for atom lines, when ionization and excitation of the atom are accomplished by a single electron collision. If formation and excitation of ions is a two-step process, then a quadratic dependence on the discharge current can be expected. The same is true for other two-step processes such as electron-collision excitation of excited atoms.

Summarizing, we can state for the relationships to be expected for the discharge current I and line intensity:

direct electron-collision excitation:

$$dS_{Le} \sim I \qquad (4.19)$$

two-body recombination, three-body with neutral carrier-gas atom, two-step ionization and excitation:

$$dS_{Lr}(2) \sim I^2 \qquad (4.20)$$

three-body recombination:

$$dS_{Lr}(3) I^3 \qquad (4.21)$$

For a comparison of theory with experimental results for the current–intensity dependence in the HCD it is necessary to make sure that the plasma is optically thin at the lines under study. Kowollik [15] checked this condition in his measurements of line intensities emitted by the HCD. Figures 4.13–4.16 show some examples for carrier-gas lines of Ne and Ar. It was found that log–log plots were linear for both the ionic and atomic lines of the carrier gas. By statistical evaluation of his measurements Kowollik [15] found that

$$S_L = C_L I^k \qquad (4.22)$$

where S_L is the intensity, C_L a constant and $k = 0.93 \pm 0.16$ for atomic lines and 1.20 ± 0.10 for ionic lines.

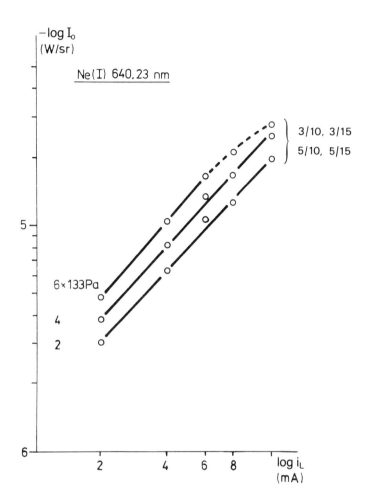

Fig. 4.13 — Absolute intensity of Ne(I) (640.23 nm) as a function of discharge current [15]. Diameter/length of the open-ended cathodes given in mm. By permission of Humboldt-University Berlin, and with acknowledgements to the author.

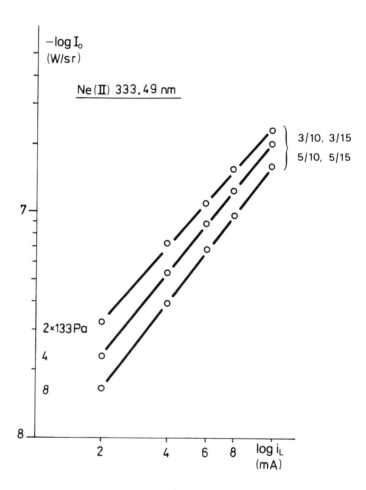

Fig. 4.14 — Absolute intensity of Ne(II) (33.49 nm) as a function of discharge current [15]. Diameter/length of the open-ended cathodes given in mm. By permission of Humboldt-University Berlin, and with acknowledgements to the authors.

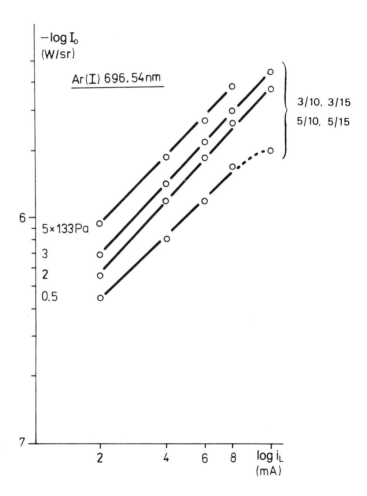

Fig. 4.15 – Absolute intensity of Ar(I) (696.54 nm) as a function of discharge current [15]. Diameter/length of the open-ended cathodes given in mm. By permission of Humboldt-University Berlin, and with acknowledgements to the authors.

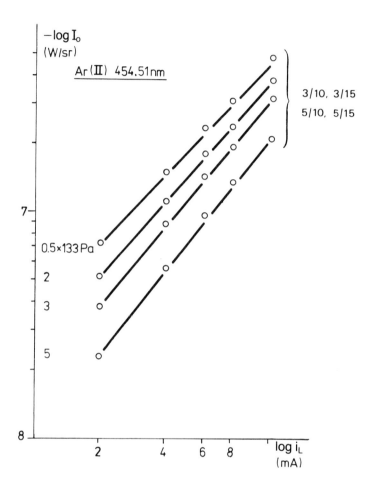

Fig. 4.16 – Absolute intensity of Ar(II) (454.51 nm) as a function of discharge current [15]. Diameter/length of the open-ended cathodes given in mm. By permission of Humboldt-University Berlin, and with acknowledgements to the authors.

From these results, which are in agreement with others [48], the conclusion can be drawn that atomic lines of the carrier gas are excited by direct electron collision. The same process is also mainly responsible for ionic excitation. Additionally, there is a small contribution from multistep excitation for ions.

Figures 4.13–4.16 show the striking difference in the behaviour of atomic and ionic lines of the carrier gas. For atomic lines the intensity increases with rising pressure, but it decreases for ionic lines. This effect can be explained by the shift of the electron energy distribution towards lower energies when the gas pressure is increased. As a result the number-density of ions will be decreased. This behaviour of an HCD (that ionic lines are enhanced at lower carrier-gas pressure) was already known from early experiments with the HCD [12].

4.5.2 Excitation of Foreign Species in the HCD

Knowledge of the mechanisms involved in the excitation of foreign species, such as sputtered cathode material or other additives to the carrier gas, is very important for analytical application of the HCD. When the spectra of foreign gas atoms and ions present in the plasma of an HCD are analysed, well-defined upper limits are found [5]. The agreement of those values with characteristic levels of the carrier gas can be seen from Table 4.7. There is another generalization about the spectra of foreign species in the HCD, namely, that the proportion of ionic lines to atomic lines increases from Ar through Ne to He [5]. These findings on excitation and ionization of foreign species in the HCD can be interpreted satisfactorily in the framework of the electron energy distribution discussed in Section 4.3.3.

The excitation processes for carrier-gas atoms, such as single-step or two-step electron collisions or ionic recombination are also possible for foreign species. However, when the foreign species are sputtered atoms, then their number-density is proportional to the discharge current (see Section 4.4.3). Consequently, from Eq. (4.15) a single-step collision excitation of sputtered atoms is connected with a quadratic dependence of the intensity on the discharge current. For other foreign species, such as gaseous impurities of the carrier gas, single-step electron excitation causes a linear relationship between line intensity and current. Foreign species can undergo some other elementary processes besides the excitation processes discussed above for the carrier gas. An

Table 4.7 – Characteristic energy limits for excitation in hollow-cathode discharges [5].

Carrier gas	Foreign-gas atoms excitation limit (eV)	Carrier-gas atoms		
		resonance level	metastable level (eV)	ionization energy
Ar	≈12	11.62 ($4s$ $[3/2]^\circ$)	11.83 ($4s'$ $[1/2]^\circ$)	15.76
Ne	≈17	16.67 ($3s$ $[3/2]^\circ$)	16.85 ($3s'$ $[1/2]^\circ$)	21.56
He	≈21	21.22 (2^1P_1)	19.77 (2^3S_1)	24.58
			20.55 (2^1S_0)	

additional source of excitation energy for foreign species is the inner energy of carrier-gas species. Species with concentrations high enough to make a measurable contribution to the excitation of foreign species are carrier-gas ions, metastable atoms and atoms at resonance levels.

The result of an inelastic collision of a carrier-gas ion with a foreign atom can be a charge transfer in which the difference between the ionization energies of the partners is converted into excitation energy of the newly formed ion:

$$A^+ + B \rightarrow A + (B^+)^* \qquad (4.23)$$

where A and B stand for the carrier-gas atom and the foreign atom, respectively. Similarly, the following process can occur in the HCD plasma:

$$A^* + B \rightarrow A + B^* \qquad (4.24)$$

where A^* can be a metastable atom or an atom at a resonance level.

Excitation by collisions of the second kind as described by Eqs. (4.23) and (4.24) has a resonance character, which means that the difference between the inner energies of the particles involved must be a minimum in order to give a large cross-section for the process. This energy resonance is very narrow; detuning by just a few tenths of an eV makes the cross-section negligible [49, 50]. Consequently, the reactions corresponding to Eqs. (4.23) and (4.24) can be responsible for the excitation of only a very few levels of the foreign species in the hollow-cathode plasma. One example has been discussed by Falk and Lucht [46] in connection with time-resolved measurements. There, for the excitation of Ne (I) (60.0 nm), collisions of the second kind with He^* (2^1S) are very likely, as suggested by the different decay time constant and higher intensity of that line compared those for neighbouring Ne-lines. In a study of the Cl (II) spectrum excited in an HCD with He as carrier gas, Falk [5] found no influence of metastable atoms but a well-defined upper limit for the excitation energy at 21.06 eV.

A further excitation process based on collisions of the second kind is the Penning effect. Here, excited carrier-gas atoms ionize foreign species and the rest of the energy is spent for excitation of the ion, according to the scheme

$$A^* + B \rightarrow A + (B^+)^* + e^- \qquad (4.25)$$

In this case we do not have such a sharp resonance behaviour as in the preceding collision mechanisms, since the free electron is able to carry arbitrary portions of kinetic energy. Nevertheless, the Penning effect is most efficient, when the kinetic energy of the free electron is low. So far, data in this field are scarce. Quantitative figures on the contribution of the Penning effect to ionization and excitation in the HCD are not yet possible.

The theoretical dependence on the discharge current for the different excitation processes, together with the energy ranges available, are shown in Table 4.8, from which we can see that the general function which accounts for

Table 4.8 — Various excitation processes for foreign species in an HCD, their expected current-intensity dependence and energy range: U_i is the ionization energy (eV) of the foreign species, U_1 is the excitation energy of the first excited level.

Excitation process	Emission intensity proportional to	Energy range (eV)		
		He	Ne	Ar
single-step electron collisions with sputtered atoms	I^2	$\leqslant 21$	$\leqslant 17$	$\leqslant 12$
two-step electron collisions with sputtered atoms	I^3	$\leqslant 21 + U_1$	$\leqslant 17 + U_1$	$\leqslant 12 + U_1$
single-step electron collisions with foreign ions (sputtered)	I^3	$\leqslant 21$	$\leqslant 17$	$\leqslant 12$
single-step electron collisions with foreign atoms (gaseous)	I	$\leqslant 21$	$\leqslant 17$	$\leqslant 12$
single-step electron collisions with foreign ions (gaseous)	I^2	$\leqslant 21$	$\leqslant 17$	$\leqslant 12$
2-body recombination of sputtered ions	I^3	$< U_i$	$< U_i$	$< U_i$
3-body recombination of sputtered ions with carrier-gas atom as third body	I^3	$< U_i$	$< U_i$	$< U_i$
3-body recombination of sputtered ions with electrons as third body	I^4	$< U_i$	$< U_i$	$< U_i$
collisions of the second kind, of sputtered atoms with metastable carrier-gas atoms	$\sim I^2$	19.8 ± 0.2	16.9 ± 0.2	11.8 ± 0.2
collisions of the second kind of sputtered atoms or with excited carrier gas atoms at resonance level	$\sim I^2$	$21,2 \pm 0.2$	16.7 ± 0.2	11.6 ± 0.2
Penning effect with sputtered atoms	I^2	$19.8 \pm U_i \pm 1$	$16.9 \pm U_i \pm 1$	$11.8 \pm U_i \pm 1$

all processes involved in the population of a given level of a foreign species is of the form

$$S_L = \sum_{i=1} C_{Li} I^i \tag{4.26}$$

The set of coefficients C_{Li} is different for the various species present in the HCD. The maximum value of i can be up to five for multistep processes. It is worth mentioning here that simple functions for S_L, where only one or two of the C_{Li} values will not be zero, can be expected only for a narrow range of the discharge current. If the current range exceeds one order of magnitude, then the situation becomes more complicated because of substantial changes in cathode fall voltage and dark space length with the result that the electron energy distribution is altered. In addition, at higher electron number-densities the reverse processes such as radiationless deactivation must be taken into account. However, occurrence of a linear log-log current-intensity plot suggests that some of the processes listed in Table 4.8 are predominant.

When the current-intensity relationship is investigated, the assumption that the plasma is optically thin has to be tested. Self-absorption of resonance lines can be observed for metal atom concentrations above $10^{10}/cm^3$, which can easily be reached in an HCD. Absolute intensities of metal resonance lines emitted by an HCD in Ne or Ar as carrier gas have been measured by Kowollik [15]. He measured the self-absorption and corrected for its effect on the intensity. The metal atoms studied were generated by cathode sputtering. Some of Kowollik's results [15] are shown in Figs. 4.17–4.22. He evaluated the current–intensity plots for 150 metal resonance lines at various pressures and cathode geometries, and in all cases found exponential functions of the type in Eq. (4.22) with an average k value of 2.91 ± 0.31. The standard deviation of k could be decreased by using the means for two carrier-gas pressure ranges: $k = 2.55 \pm 0.19$, ($\leqslant 260$ Pa); $k = 3.03 \pm 0.25$ (> 260 Pa).

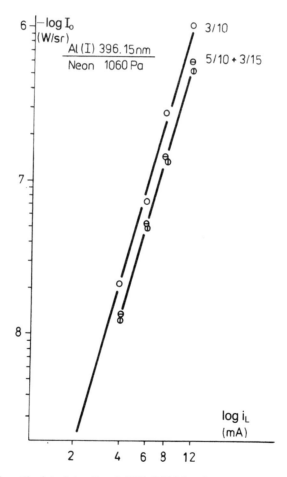

Fig. 4.17 – Absolute intensity of Al(I) (396.15 nm) as a function of discharge current [15]. Diameter/length of the open-ended cathodes given in mm. By permission of Humboldt-University Berlin, and with acknowledgements to the authors.

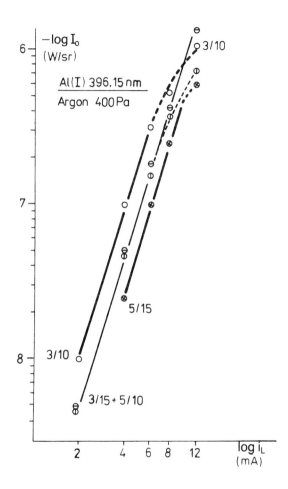

Fig. 4.18 – Absolute intensity of Al(I) (396.15 nm) as a function of discharge current [15]. Diameter/length of the open-ended cathodes given in mm. By permission of Humboldt-University Berlin, and with acknowledgements to the author.

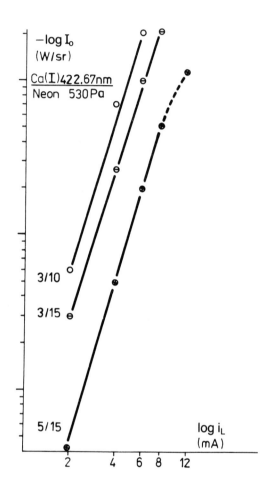

Fig. 4.19 – Absolute intensity of Ca(I) (422.67 nm) as a function of discharge
[15]. Diameter/length of the open-ended cathodes given in mm. By permission of
Humboldt-University Berlin, and with acknowledgements to the author.

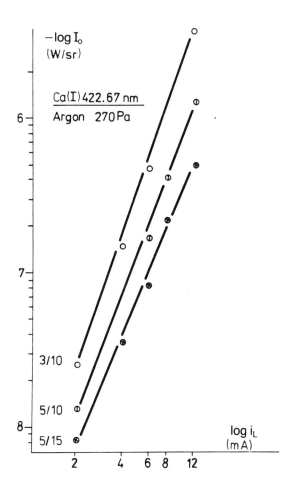

Fig. 4.20 — Absolute intensity of Ca(I) (422.67 nm) as a function of discharge current [15]. Diameter/length of the open-ended cathodes given in mm. By permission of Humboldt-University Berlin, and with acknowledgements to the author.

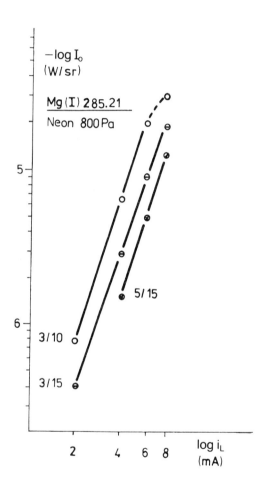

Fig. 4.21 — Absolute intensity of Mg(I) (285.21 nm) as a function of discharge current [15]. Diameter/length of the open-ended cathodes given in mm. By permission of Humboldt-University Berlin, and with acknowledgement to the author.

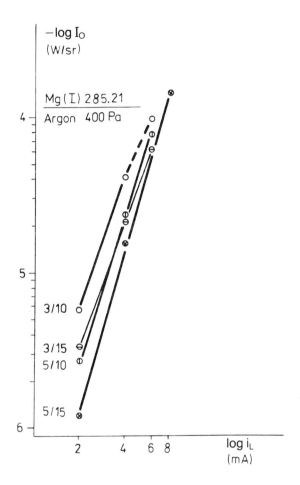

Fig. 4.22 — Absolute intensity of Mg(I) (285.21 nm) as a function of discharge current [15]. Diameter/length of the open-ended cathodes given in mm. By permission of Humboldt-University Berlin, and with acknowledgement to the author.

Comparing these findings by Kowollik [15] with Table 4.8 we see that the three-body recombination with a carrier-gas atom as the third body is dominant. Two-body recombination can be excluded because of its much lower cross-section [51]. A two-step electron excitation of sputtered atoms is impossible in this case of metal resonance lines, so the situation is clear for higher pressure and relatively low current density. In several cases the curves in Figs. 4.17–4.22 show a downward trend at the end of the current range investigated. This, and the lower k-values at low gas pressure suggest a remarkable contribution by single-step electron excitation in those cases. Collisions of the second kind can generally be excluded here because of the lack of resonance energy.

It is worth discussing here the different k values for metal resonance lines published by various authors [52–54]. Moehring and Kowollik found for the resonance lines of Ca($I = 5$-15 mA) and Mg ($I = 2.5$-7.5 mA) $k = 1$-3.0 and $k = 1.3$-3.4, respectively, by measurements of relative intensities [54]. The different findings of Kowollik [15] when he made absolute measurements, taking into account the self-absorption, show that relative intensity measurements without knowledge of absorption effects can be misleading.

On the basis of absolute intensity measurements and a known atomic density in an HCD, the relative population of the excited levels can be calculated. For an HCD at a discharge current of 50 mA the ratio of the population of metal resonance levels to that of the ground level has been estimated by Falk [23] to be 10^{-5}-10^{-4}. For metal resonance lines this is usually the upper limit for the relative population when the cathode material consists of the metal under study. In this case a further current increase would cause severe self-absorption, and the sputtering would rise. Consequently, the relative population of the resonance level of a foreign atom can be increased only when the sputtering process is inhibited or when another source of atomization is applied, e.g. thermal atomization as in the FANES-system (see Section 4.4.2). In the latter, atomization and excitation are independent of each other and at higher currents of the order of 100 mA the relative population of resonance levels of foreign atoms is expected to be one order of magnitude higher than in an ordinary metal hollow cathode.

As discussed in Section 4.4.2 the main process in generating the sample vapour in a FANES-system is thermal volatilization. Consequently, the density of the evaporated sample material is independent of the discharge current. For a given heating regime the lines emitted by the sample material should have the same dependence as those of gaseous foreign species on the discharge current I. Corresponding to Table 4.8, the intensity of atomic resonance lines of the sample is expected to be proportional to I, and that of the ionic resonance lines to I^2. For higher-lying levels higher powers of I can occur, depending on the contribution of multi-step excitation. The situation can be modified when the sample is volatilized in molecular form. In this case the influence of the plasma on the degree of dissociation of the sample molecules has to be considered. When this process of dissociation in the HCD is dominant then the same current-intensity dependence as for sputtered metal atoms has to be expected. This effect has not yet been reported in the literature, because of the lack of systematic investigation in this direction.

Summarizing, the following conclusions can be drawn on the excitation of foreign species in the HCD:

for atomic resonance lines the three-body recombination with a carrier-gas atom as the third body is predominant;

besides this recombination, the direct electron collisional excitation is of importance;

for the FANES-system no difference between excitation of the sample vapour and other foreign (gaseous) components is to be expected;

collisions of the second kind with metastable or resonance-state atoms of the carrier gas can only be important for a few levels in fair energy resonance.

4.5.3 Linear range of emission from the HCD

Methods of atomic-emission spectrochemical analysis (AES) are characterized by a wide dynamic range of up to more than five orders of magnitude of analyte concentration. The dynamic range of AAS amounts at most to three orders of magnitude. The upper limit of the dynamic range for an emission source is reached when self-absorption or diffusion of resonance radiation becomes important [18]. Therefore, the bending of the calibration curve at its upper end is to be expected for both AES and AAS at roughly the same absorbance for the atomic line under study. In other words, when the same atomizer is used for AAS and AES, the upper end of the dynamic range is reached for both at the same analyte concentration. Corresponding to the results of the preceding section the atomic density in FANES is more than one order of magnitude lower than that in a similar GFAAS-system working at atmospheric pressure. Consequently, the dynamic range of FANES should be extended by the same factor. Figure 4.23 shows an example of such behaviour. The calibration graph for the FANES signal of Ag (at 328.1 nm) is linear over more than one order of magnitude more than that for GFAAS.

As can be seen from Fig. 4.23 the lower end of the calibration graph is also superior to that of GFAAS. This fact is connected with the different physical reasons for the background noise in FANES and GFAAS [37]. Another example of the large dynamic range of FANES is given in Fig. 4.24, where the calibration graph for Na is shown.

For a FANES source we can state that the dynamic range is typically 5-6 orders of magnitude, and as a rule the FANES system is superior to a corresponding GFAAS system at atmospheric pressure at lower as well as at higher concentrations.

4.5.4 Noise figures of HCD

In a paper by Falk [23] a comparison was made of different excitation sources for AES. It was found that in thermal excitation sources, such as an arc, as well as in non-thermal ones, such as an HCD, the average population of the excited levels is of the order of 0.01% of the total. On the other hand, the background emission from an HCD plasma is much lower than that from a thermal plasma at

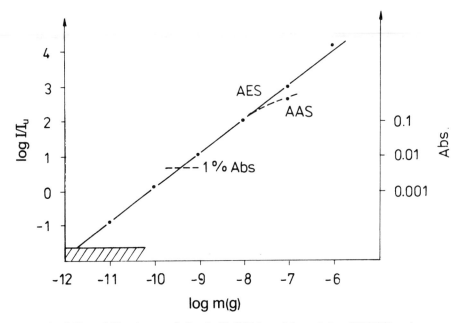

Fig. 4.23 – Calibration graph for Ag(I) (328.1 nm) in emission (FANES) and absorption (atmospheric pressure) with the FANES instrument [37]. Carrier gas Ar, sample volume 10 μl (AgNO$_3$, aqueous). By permission of the publishers, Pergamon Press Ltd. and with acknowledgement to the authors.

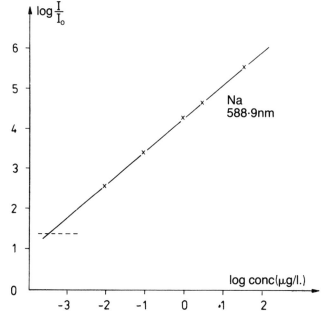

Fig. 4.24 – Calibration graph for Na(I) (588.9 nm) with the FANES system [19]. Carrier gas Ar, sample volume 20 μl (aqueous). By permission of the publishers, Pergamon Press Ltd. and with acknowledgement to the authors.

atmospheric pressure. The reason for this situation is the quadratic dependence of both the free-free and the free-bound continua on the electron density. As a result, in contrast to arc and spark where these continua make the main contribution to the source background, the continuous emission from HCD is negligible.

The general features of the background emission from the HCD has been confirmed by a study of the noise characteristics of a FANES source [55]. Indeed, the main noise component of FANES was found to consist of molecular bands generated by the excitation of impurities present in the plasma gas. As a consequence, this background noise could not be suppressed effectively by using a high-resolution echelle spectrometer with wavelength modulation, owing to the complex structured background spectrum of the FANES source. That structured background could be decreased by using a tighter vacuum system and purer carrier gas.

To estimate the analytical capability of an emission source the signal to noise ratio at a given analyte concentration is important. The corresponding figure of merit of the source is the detection limit. To get a unified representation of the detection limits for various elements, the following expression can be used:

$$C_g = \Phi M/f \qquad (4.27)$$

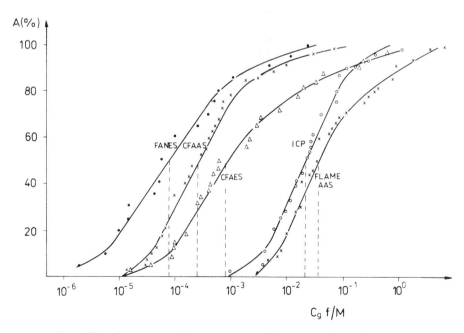

Fig. 4.25 — Percentage of the abundance of the reduced limit of detection for various techniques of optical atomic spectroscopy [19]. The centres of gravity of the distributions are given by broken perpendicular lines. By permission of the permission of the publishers, Pergamon Press Ltd. and with acknowledgement to the authors.

where C_g = concentration at the limit of detection, M = relative atomic mass, f = oscillator strength of the transition used and Φ = characteristic factor depending upon the method under study. Φ should obey a statistical (Gaussian) distribution for various elements, instruments and experimenters. Integrating the distribution as a function of Φ or, in other words, plotting the percentage A of a number of elements for which Φ is larger or equal to a given value, results in an S-shaped curve. The value of Φ corresponding to $A = 50\%$ represents the centre of gravity of the distribution and, consequently, is characteristic for this method. Such a representation of the abundance as a function of the reduced detection limit Φ is shown in Fig. 4.25 for various analytical methods [19]. From this comparison the superiority of the FANES method to AES in terms of multi-element capability is clearly seen.

4.6 CONCLUDING REMARKS

The situation in the theoretical description of the HCD is characterized by a very broad variety of parameters such as kind of carrier gas, pressure, current density, cathode material, dimensions and time regime on the one hand, and incomplete knowledge of the basic parameters for the plasma itself on the other hand. As a result there are only qualitative or semiquantitative theoretical approaches to the HCD. The applies also to the FANES system, where additional complications are introduced at higher cathode temperatures because of the contribution of thermal electron emission. The most important requirement for progress is a knowledge of the measurable parameters of an HCD, which should be determined during practical development of the various spectroscopical applications. These parameters are the current–voltage and current–intensity characteristics for different pressures, and the dark-space length. Additionally, it is desirable to extend the upper limit of the electron density measurements since the existing results are restricted to very low current densities. The same is true for the electron energy distribution. Of course, the probe technique is not applicable at higher currents, but in any case the results of probe measurements suffer from a more or less severe disturbance of the plasma under study. Methods of plasma diagnostics which have no influence on the subject to be investigated, e.g. optical field strength measurements within the dark space, as recently reported by Kawakita *et al.* [56], can be helpful. On the basis of such information on the HCD, substantial progress in its theoretical understanding can be expected, which should result in further improvements in practical application.

REFERENCES

[1] F. Paschen, *Ann. Phys.*, 1916, **50**, 901.
[2] B. I. Moskalev, *Hollow Cathode Discharge*, Energiya, Moscow, 1969.
[3] M. E. Pillow, *Spectrochim. Acta*, 1981, **36B**, 821.
[4] A. Güntherschulze, *Z. Techn. Phys.*, 1930, **11**, 49.
[5] H. Falk, *Ann. Phys.*, 1965, **16**, 160.
[6] P. F. Little and A. von Engel, *Proc. Roy. Soc. A*, 1954, **224**, 209.

[7] C. B. Childs, *J. Opt. Soc. Am.*, 1961, **51**, 583.

[8] V. K. Zworykin and E. G. Ramberg, *Photoelectricity and its Application*, Wiley, New York, 1949.

[9] H. Falk, E. Hoffmann and Ch. Lüdke, *Spectrochim. Acta*, 1981, **36B**, 767.

[10] M. von Ardenne, *Tabellen zur Angewandten Physik*, Vol. 1, p. 75, VEB Deutscher Verlag der Wissenschaften, Berlin, 1975.

[11] J. Fletcher and J. R. Cowling, *J. Phys. B*, 1973, **6**, L258.

[12] A. Lompe, R. Seeliger and E. Wolter, *Ann. Phys.*, 1939, **36**, 9.

[13] A. von Engel, *Ionized Gases*, Clarendon Press, Oxford, 1965.

[14] E. Badareu, I. Popescu and I. Iova, *Ann. Phys.*, 1960, **5**, 308.

[15] G. Kowollik, Thesis, *Investigations on emission and absorption in hollow cathode lamps for AAS at low discharge currents*, Humboldt-University, Berlin (1979).

[16] W. C. Kreye, *J. Opt. Soc. Am.*, 1974, **64**, 186.

[17] H. C. Wagenaar and L. de Galan, *Spectrochim. Acta*, 1973, **28B**, 157.

[18] H. Falk, *Prog. Anal. Atom. Spectrosc.*, 1982, **5**, 205.

[19] H. Falk, E. Hoffmann and Ch. Lüdke, *Spectrochim. Acta*, 1984, **39B**, 283.

[20] V. S. Borodin and Yu. M. Kagan, *Zh. Tekh. Fiz.*, 1966, **36**, 181.

[21] V. S. Borodin, Yu. M. Kagan and R. I. Lyagushchenko, *Zh. Tekh. Fiz.*, 1966, **36**, 1198.

[22] V. S. Borodin and Yu. M. Kagan, *Opt. Spektrosk.*, 1967, **23**, 200.

[23] H. Falk, *Spectrochim. Acta*, 1977, **32B**, 437.

[24] P. A. Büger and W. Fink, *Z. Phys.*, 1970, **236**, 314.

[25] F. Howorka and M. Pahl, *Z. Naturforsch.*, 1972, **27a**, 1425.

[26] F. Howorka, W. Lindinger and M. Pahl, *Int. J. Mass Spectrom. Ion Phys.*, 1973, **12**, 67.

[27] H. Falk, Thesis, *On the optical excitation in the HCD*, Humboldt-University, Berlin (1964).

[28] R. V. Stuart and G. K. Wehner, *J. Appl. Phys.*, 1962, **33**, 2345.

[29] R. V. Stuart and G. K. Wehner, *J. Appl. Phys.*, 1964, **35**, 1819.

[30] R. V. Stuart, G. K. Wehner and G. S. Anderson, *J. Appl. Phys.*, 1969, **40**, 803.

[31] P. Hannaford and R. M. Lowe, *J. Phys. B*, 1976, **9**, 2595.

[32] G. Carter and J. S. Colligon, *Ion Bombardment of Solids*, Heinemann, London, 1968.

[33] E. H. Daughtrey, P. E. Slevin and W. W. Harrison, *25th Pittsburgh Conf. Anal. Chem. Appl. Spectrosc.*, 1974.

[34] A. N. Shteinberg, *Zh. Prikl. Spektrosk.*, 1965, **2**, 385.

[35] N. K. Rudnevsky, D. E. Maksimov and V. V. Vysotskii, *Zh. Analit. Khim.*, 1967, **22**, 1051.

[36] H. Falk, E. Hoffmann, I. Jaeckel and Ch. Lüdke, *Spectrochim. Acta*, 1979, **34B**, 333.

[37] H. Falk, E. Hoffmann and Ch. Lüdke, *Spectrochim. Acta*, 1981, **36B**, 767.

[38] H. Falk, E. Hoffmann and Ch. Lüdke, *Z. Anal. Chem.*, 1981, **307**, 362.

[39] A. V. Phelps, *Phys. Rev.*, 1955, **99**, 1307.

[40] A. G. Zhiglinskii, G. G. Kund and I. P. Presnukhina, *Zh. Tekh. Fiz.*, 1976, **46**, 2218.

[41] F. J. De Hoog, J. R. McNeil, G. J. Collins and K. B. Persson, *J. Appl. Phys.*, 1977, **48**, 3701.

[42] B. E. Warner, K. B. Persson and G. J. Collins, *J. Appl. Phys.*, 1979, **50**, 5694.

[43] R. Ladenburg and F. Reiche, *Ann. Phys.*, 1913, **42**, 181.

[44] H. Falk, *9th Annual Meeting FACS, Philadelphia*, Paper No. 423, 1982.

[45] V. P. Gofmeister and Yu. M. Kagan, *Opt. Spektrosk.*, 1968, **25**, 337.

[46] H. Falk and H. Lucht, *J. Quant. Spectrosc. Radiat. Transfer*, 1976, **16**, 909.

[47] W. S. Borodin and Yu. M. Kagan, *Opt. Spektrosk.*, 1967, **23**, 3557.

[48] J. Tilch, Thesis, *Zur Bestimmung von absoluten und relativen Atomkonzentrationen durch atomare Absorption*, Humboldt-University, Berlin (1967).

[49] E. C. G. Stueckelberg, *Helv. Phys. Acta*, 1932, **5**, 370.

[50] H. S. W. Massey and E. H. S. Burhop, *Electronic and Ionic Impact Phenomena*, Clarendon Press, Oxford, 1952.

[51] W. L. Granowski, *Der Elektrische Strom im Gas*, Akademie-Verlag, Berlin, 1955.

[52] H. M. Crosswhite, G. H. Dieke and C. S. Legagneur *J. Opt. Soc. Am.*, 1955, **45**, 270.

[53] T. N. Khlopina, *Thesis*, LGU, Leningrad (1971).

[54] D. Moehring and G. Kowollik, *Konferenz Physik und Technik des Plasmas, Suhl*, Paper 1/147 (1972).

[55] H. Falk, E. Hoffmann, Ch. Lüdke, J. M. Ottaway and S. K. Giri, *Analyst*, 1983, **108**, 1459.

[56] K. Kawakita, T. Nakajima, Y. Adachi, S. Maeda and C. Hirose, *Opt. Commun.*, 1983, **48**, 121.

[57] R. B. Cairns and J. A. R. Samson, *J. Opt. Soc. Am.*, 1966, **56**, 1568.

5

The radiofrequency-boosted, pulsed hollow-cathode lamp

P. B. Farnsworth and J. P. Walters

5.1 INTRODUCTION

The direct-current hollow-cathode discharge, when operated at low currents, exhibits many of the characteristics of an ideal atomic line source. It produces a clean spectrum composed exclusively of lines from the cathode material and the buffer gas. The lines are narrow and there is no appreciable background. Unfortunately, these desirable characteristics are lost when the discharge current is increased. The atomic resonance lines become broadened by self-absorption, and in the extreme case can be completely self-reversed. This line-broadening with increased current has limited the use of d.c. hollow-cathode discharges to applications requiring relatively low line intensities. Early reports suggested that the use of pulsed current waveforms resulted in increased resonance-line intensity without degradation of the line profile [1–4]. Pulsed lamps did not produce the expected improvement in analytical performance, however [5, 6], for reasons that became apparent when their output was examined by DeJong and Piepmeier, using time-resolved interferometry [7]. They found that the resonance lines from pulsed copper and silver lamps were self-reversed, even when the lamps were operated with low duty cycles.

The RF-boosted, pulsed hollow-cathode lamp is one of several variations on the conventional hollow-cathode lamp that have been designed to overcome the limitations described above. Improved lamp output is obtained by use of a current pulse to sample the cathode material, followed by a short burst of radiofrequency energy to re-excite the vapour produced by the pulse. The current and RF burst injection-circuits were designed so that they could be used with sealed commercial hollow-cathode lamps. The lamp was first described by

Araki *et al.* [8], then later characterized in detail by Farnsworth and Walters [9]. This chapter includes a description of the lamp hardware, a detailed discussion of the lamp's excitation mechanisms, and an evaluation of the lamp's promise as an analytical light source.

5.2 LAMP DESIGN

The RF-boosted lamp consists of a sealed hollow-cathode lamp, a pulsed current source, a pulsed RF generator, a coupler for injecting the current and the RF into the lamp, and circuitry to control the duration and relative timing of the current pulse and RF burst. The current injection circuit, shown in Fig. 5.1, is composed of two independent sections. The resistor network on the right side of the figure controls a d.c. bias current, which is necessary to reduce turn-on jitter and rise time in the current pulse. Typically the lamp operates with the minimum bias current of 2 mA. The network on the left side of the figure controls the magnitude of the pulse current, with possible values ranging from 0 to 1.2 A. The duration and timing of the current pulse are controlled by an external TTL pulse.

The RF burst is supplied by a commercial pulsed RF generator, with burst duration and timing also controlled by an external pulse. The generator used in Walters's laboratories was a model PG1K manufactured by Applied Microwave Laboratories in Andover, MA, capable of operating at frequencies ranging from 150 MHz to 3 GHz. The operating frequency of 150 MHz was chosen to be sufficiently high to excite the cathode vapour efficiently yet low enough to allow the RF to be capacitively coupled to the lamp electrodes without any modification to the lamp itself.

The RF burst and the current pulse are coupled into the lamp through the circuit shown in Fig. 5.2. The coupling circuit consists of a low-pass filter through which the current pulse is passed to the electrodes, a high-pass filter through which the RF is passed, and impedance-matching capacitors which allow for efficient coupling of the RF energy to lamps with different electrode capacitances. The high- and low-pass filters provide mutual isolation between the RF and current supplies. The entire assembly is housed in a brass cylinder attached to the lamp socket.

Because the interelectrode capacitance differs from one lamp to the next, the coupling between the RF generator and the lamp must be optimized each time the lamp is changed. This can be done by maximizing the RF amplitude at the lamp base through adjustments to the impedance-matching capacitors. The amplitude is monitored with a fast oscilloscope.

5.3 INITIAL LAMP CHARACTERIZATION

The first experiments with the RF-boosted lamp were performed with a Westinghouse single-element hollow-cathode lamp, type WL-23041, which has a copper cathode and neon buffer gas. The experiments were designed with three objectives. The first was the determination of the residence time in the interelectrode

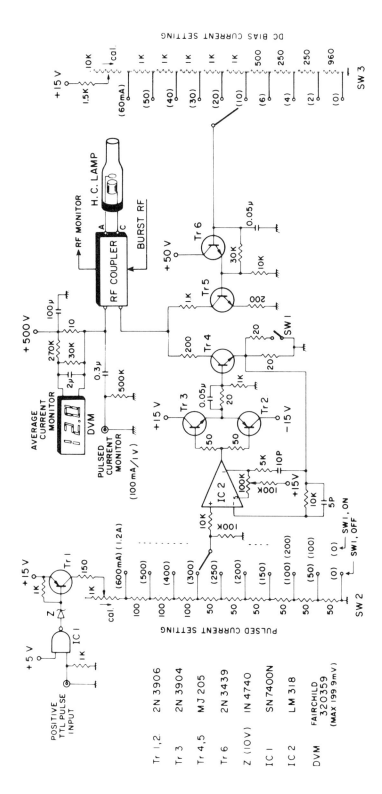

Fig. 5.1 – Current-pulse injection circuit for RF-boosted lamp [8]. (Reprinted by permission from T. Araki, J. P. Walters and S. Minami, *Appl. Spectrosc.*, 1980, **34**, 33. Copyright 1980, Society for Applied Spectroscopy).

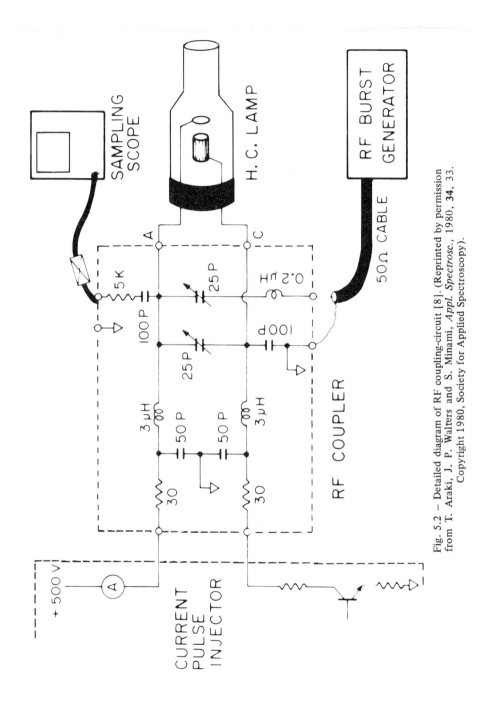

Fig. 5.2 – Detailed diagram of RF coupling-circuit [8]. (Reprinted by permission from T. Araki, J. P. Walters and S. Minami, *Appl. Spectrosc.*, 1980, **34**, 33. Copyright 1980, Society for Applied Spectroscopy).

region of the vapour produced by a current pulse, and of the location of the vapour during that period. The second was the measurement of the intensity enhancement relative to a d.c. hollow-cathode discharge produced by the RF burst. The third was the determination of the effect of the RF burst on line profiles.

The migration of cathode vapour was monitored indirectly by the measurement of the time-dependent intensity of a Cu (I) and a Cu(II) line as the lamp was operated in a double-pulse mode. The lines selected were the Cu(I) 324.75 nm line ($4s^2S_{\frac{1}{2}}-4p^2P_{\frac{3}{2}}$) and the Cu(II) 200.03 nm line ($4s^3D_3-4p^1F_3$). Pairs of 350-mA current pulses were applied to the lamp at a repetition rate of 1 kHz, and the line intensities and profiles were monitored as the pulse separation was varied. Figure 5.3 shows the time-dependent intensity of the two lines for a

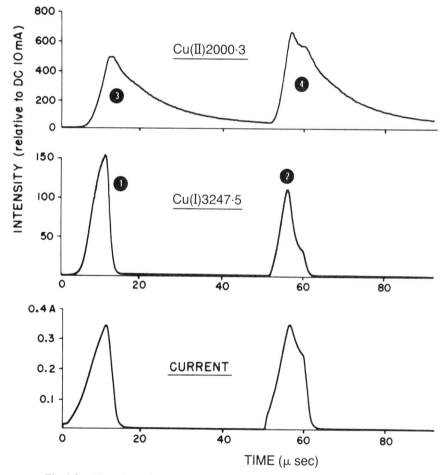

Fig. 5.3 – Time-dependent emission from the Cu(I) 324.8 nm and Cu(II) 200.0 nm lines with the hollow-cathode lamp operated in a double-pulse mode [8]. The current waveform is included for comparison. (Reprinted by permission from T. Araki, J. P. Walters and S. Minami, *Appl. Spectrosc.*, 1980, **34**, 33. Copyright 1980, Society for Applied Spectroscopy).

pulse separation of 50 μsec. For the neutral resonance line, the emission produced by the second pulse is lower in intensity than that produced by the first,
while the opposite is true of the emission from the ionic line. Line profiles
measured during the two current pulses, shown in Fig. 5.4, provide a ready
explanation for the observed intensity variations. The neutral resonance line
shows considerable self-absorption during the second pulse, indicating that
vapour from the first pulse remains in the emission path after 50 μsec. The ionic
emission is from a non-resonant transition and is not affected by self-absorption.

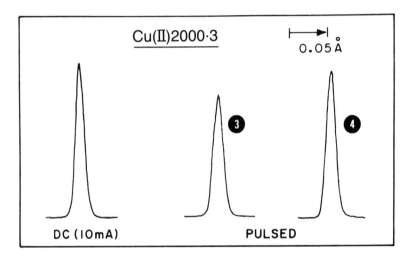

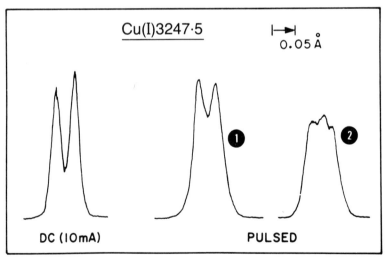

Fig. 5.4 — Line profiles corresponding to the pulsed emission shown in Fig. 5.3
together with the same line profiles from a d.c. lamp operated at 10 mA [8]. The
numbers refer to the Fig. 5.3 waveforms. (Reprinted by permission from T. Araki,
J. P. Walters and S. Minami, *Appl. Spectrosc.*, 1980, **34**, 33. Copyright 1980,
Society for Applied Spectroscopy).

Similar effects were observed with pulse separations of up to 400 μsec, suggesting that cathode vapour is present in the optical path for at least that long.

The double-pulse experiments indicated that the RF burst should be applied within 400 μsec of the current pulse. The optimum timing for the RF excitation was determined by applying a 400 V peak-to-peak voltage to the electrodes with delays from the current pulse ranging from 0 to 500 μsec. With a peak pulse-current of 350 mA the maximum RF-excited intensity was observed with a delay of 50 μsec.

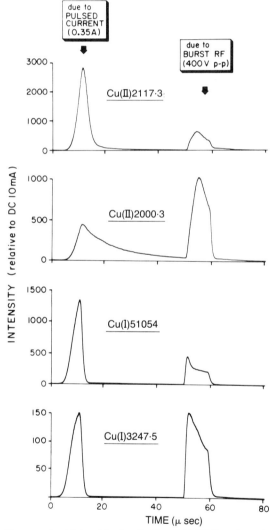

Fig. 5.5 – Time-resolved intensities for Cu(I) and Cu(II) lines from the RF-boosted lamp [8]. The current pulse had a peak amplitude of 350 mA and a duration of 10 μsec. The RF burst was applied 50 μsec after the start of the discharge, with a peak-to-peak amplitude of 400 V and a duration of 10 μsec. (Reprinted by permission from T. Araki, J. P. Walters and S. Minami, *Appl. Spectrosc.*, 1980, **34**, 33. Copyright 1980, Society for Applied Spectroscopy).

With the RF burst set to the optimum delay of 50 μsec, a series of measurements was made of the intensities of four lines chosen to be representative of different parts of the Cu(I) and Cu(II) term systems. In addition to the two lines mentioned above, the Cu(I) 510.54 nm ($m^2D_\frac{5}{2}-4p^2P_\frac{3}{2}$) and the Cu(II) 211.73 nm ($4p^3F_3-4d^3G_4$) lines were studied. The intensities of the four lines relative to those produced by a d.c. hollow-cathode discharge at 10 mA are shown in Fig. 5.5. The RF burst produces intensity enhancements ranging from 150-fold for the 324.75 nm line to over 1000-fold for the 200.03 nm line. With a pulse current of 350 mA and an RF delay of 50 μsec, the intensity during the RF burst exhibits a linear dependence on RF peak-to-peak voltage over the range from 100 to 700 V. Below 100 V there is a state-dependent threshold, below which there is no excitation by the RF. At above 700 V arcing occurs inside the lamp, between the electrode supports.

Increased line intensity is only useful if it is obtained without the sacrifice of two other desirable source properties, spatial uniformity and narrow lines. Figure 5.6 shows the spatial emission profiles of two lines with d.c., pulsed, and

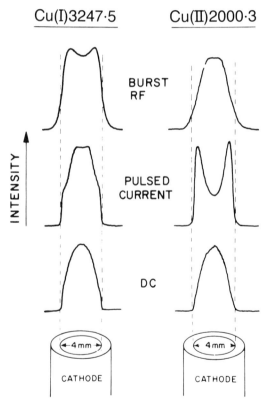

Fig. 5.6 – Spatial emission profiles of the Cu(I) 324.8 nm and Cu(II) 200.0 nm lines for d.c., pulsed, and RF excitation [8]. The d.c. lamp was operated at 10 mA. The pulsed and RF operating conditions were the same as for Fig. 5.5. (Reprinted by permission from T. Araki, J. P. Walters and S. Minami, *Appl. Spectrosc.*, 1980, **34**, 33. Copyright 1980, Society for Applied Spectroscopy).

RF excitation. While the intensity of the important neutral resonance line is fairly uniform across the cathode bore for both pulsed and RF excitation, the line profile is uniform only for the RF excitation, as illustrated in Fig. 5.7. These traces, recorded with an echelle monochromator, show that the resonance line is almost completely self-reversed near the edge of the cathode bore.

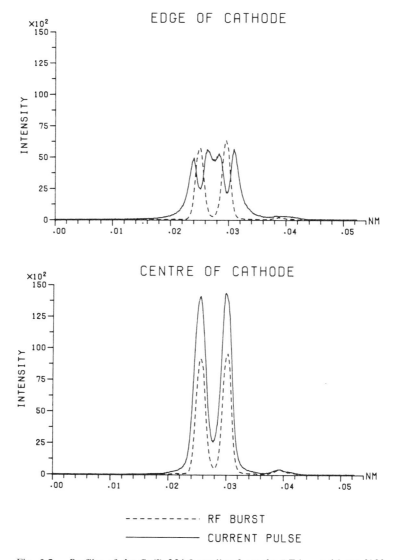

Fig. 5.7 – Profiles of the Cu(I) 324.8 nm line from the RF-boosted lamp [10]. The upper traces originate from a region 0.46 mm from the edge of the cathode and the lower traces from the centre of the cathode bore. The pulse current was 400 mA, the RF voltage 400 V peak-to-peak, and the RF delay 75 μsec. Both the current pulse and the RF burst had a duration of 10 μsec. (Reprinted with permission from P. B. Farnsworth and J. P. Walters, *Anal. Chem.,* 1982, **54**, 885. Copyright 1982 American Chemical Society.)

5.4 LAMP EXCITATION MECHANISMS

The initial efforts to characterize the RF-boosted lamp provided solid indication that it has potential as a light-source for atomic spectroscopy. However, they also raised a number of questions about the fundamental processes that control the lamp's behaviour. What, for example, is the predominant excitation mechanism by which the cathode material is excited in the discharge? Are the mechanisms during the current pulse and the RF burst the same? Why do some lines show a long afterglow while others do not? Why is the first ion spectrum so intense in the copper–neon lamp? These questions prompted a second, more detailed study of the lamp by Farnsworth and Walters [9], aimed primarily at characterizing the excitation mechanisms in the discharge, with the hope that the fundamental information provided by the study would point to means of further enhancing the lamp's desirable analytical properties.

5.4.1 Experimental conditions

This second set of experiments was designed to capitalize on the spatial, spectral, and temporal heterogeneity of the discharge. An instrumental system was constructed for use in the study that included an optical imaging system providing 50-μm spatial resolution, a computer-controlled boxcar integrator providing 1-μsec temporal resolution, and an echelle monochromator providing broad spectral coverage combined with spectral resolution of 0.0005 nm [10]. The instrument's controls over position, wavelength, and time were all independent so that it was possible to record intensity as a function of any one of the three variables, with the other two held constant. Several of these two-dimensional plots could be combined to generate three-dimensional surfaces showing intensity as a function of two of the variables.

The experiments were performed with Westinghouse copper hollow-cathode lamps with either neon or argon as the buffer gas. The lamps have 4 mm diameter bores and fill-gas pressures of 8 mmHg. Most of the effort was focused on the neon-filled lamp, since neon is the buffer gas most commonly used with copper cathodes. The argon-filled lamp was used for comparison. The discussion that follows refers to the neon-filled lamp unless otherwise noted.

The lamp operating conditions were similar to those used in the initial studies: the discharge was maintained with a bias current of 2 mA, the current pulses had a peak amplitude of 400 mA and a duration of 10 μsec, and the RF was applied in 10-μsec bursts with delays from the start of the current pulse ranging from 15 to 95 μsec and peak powers of approximately 10 W. All the data presented here were recorded with an RF delay of 75 μsec. The current pulse–RF burst sequence was triggered at a frequency of 1 kHz.

Emission data were collected for lines from the Cu(I), Cu(II), Ne(I), and Ne(II) spectra, selected to be representative of their respective term systems and to act as indicators of the effects of several possible excitation mechanisms. Figures 5.8 and 5.9 show the Cu(I) and Cu(II) transitions studied, on partial term diagrams of the two systems. The Cu(I) term system can be divided into two sections, one composed of a series of hydrogen-like doublets and the other composed of a series of doublets and quartets. The distribution of excited states

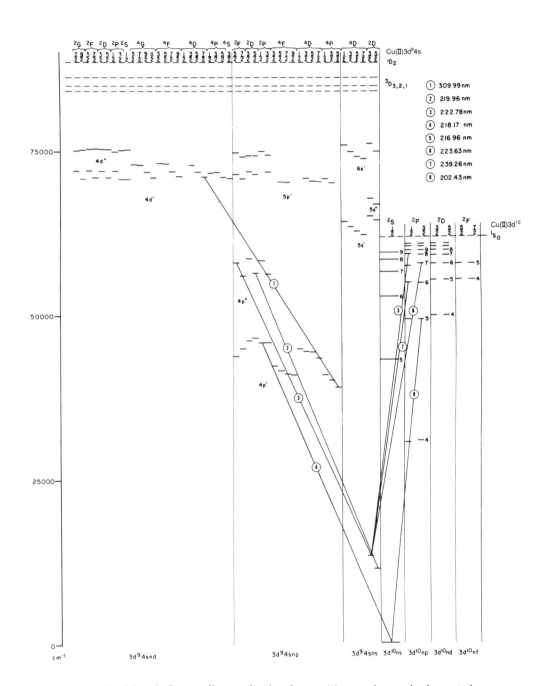

Fig. 5.8 – Cu(I) term diagram showing the transitions used to study the neutral atom emission [9]. (Represented by permission from *Spectrochim. Acta,* **37B**, P. B. Farnsworth and J. P. Walters, Excitation Processes in an RF-boosted, Pulsed Hollow Cathode Lamp, Copyright 1982, Pergamon Press, Ltd.)

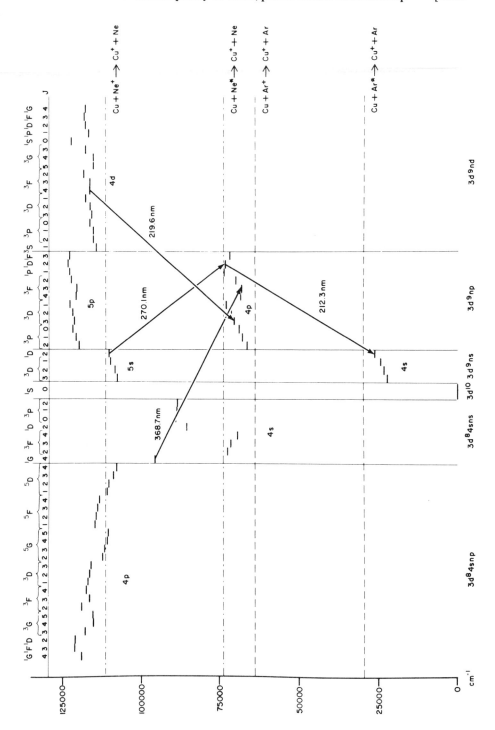

Fig. 5.9 – Cu(II) term diagram showing the transitions used to study the ionic emission [9]. (Reprinted by permission from *Spectrochim. Acta,* **37B**, P. B. Farnsworth and J. P. Walters, Excitation Processes in an RF-boosted, Pulsed Hollow Cathode Lamp, Copyright 1982, Pergamon Press, Ltd.)

in the two series was expected to show a strong dependence on the mechanism by which the states were populated. Lines from a wide range of energies were chosen to indicate the nature of that distribution. The lines in the Cu(II) system were chosen specifically to detect the effects of ion-production by charge exchange (Cu + Ne$^+$ → Cu$^+$ + Ne) and Penning ionization (Cu + Ne* → Cu$^+$ + Ne) collisions. The dashed lines in Fig. 5.9 show the energies that would be imparted to copper atoms by inelastic collisions of various buffer gas species with ground-state copper atoms.

Neon emission lines were included in the study because of the important role neon ions and metastable neon atoms play in the collisional excitation mechanisms mentioned above. The choice of neon lines was restricted by the fact that all the resonance lines for both the atom and the ion lie far into the vacuum ultraviolet. Both of the lines selected, Ne(I) 344.8 nm ($3s[3/2]_2$–$4p[3/2]_2$) and Ne(II) 329.8 nm ($3s^4P_{\frac{5}{2}}$–$3p^4D_{\frac{5}{2}}$), terminate in highly excited states. The Ne(I) $4p[3/2]_2$ state is metastable and can be involved in Penning ionization collisions.

5.4.2 Buffer gas excitation

Because the RF burst is injected into an environment created by the current pulse, it was essential that a study of excitation by the RF burst should also include examination of the excitation of cathode material by the current pulse. Figure 5.10 shows the time-dependent emission of lines from the four discharge species mentioned above during the 20 μsec after initiation of the current pulse. The current and voltage waveforms are included for comparison. The traces for Ne(I) and Ne(II), combined with the more detailed picture presented in Fig. 5.11, provide some interesting insights into the excitation of the buffer gas. Not surprisingly, the first emission observed after the initiation of the current pulse comes from neutral neon. The Ne(I) emission rises rapidly, then begins to decrease while the current is still increasing. On the falling edge of the current waveform, the Ne(I) emission rises again then decays slowly until it is interrupted by the RF burst. Following the RF burst, the afterglow is suppressed for several μsec until it begins to rise slowly at the end of the 100-μsec observation period. The Ne(II) emission follows the current waveform until near the mid-point of the falling edge. where there is a sharp emission spike. Unlike the neutral line, the ion line exhibits no detectable afterglow and shows only a small response to the RF.

The neon emission data suggest that during the rising portion of the current waveform, neon atoms undergo stepwise ionization by electron impact, with the metastable levels as intermediate states. The rapid population of these levels, followed by their depletion to form the ion, would account for the observed time-dependence of the Ne(I) emission. The intensity jumps observed in the Ne(I) and Ne(II) lines on the falling edge of the current waveform are similar to those observed in decaying argon arcs, resulting from differences in the decay lifetimes of the electron temperature and the electron density [11]. The long Ne(I) afterglow can be most readily explained as due to either radiative or collisional recombination of neon ions and electrons [12]. The lack of substantial Ne(II) emission during the RF burst suggests that the environment

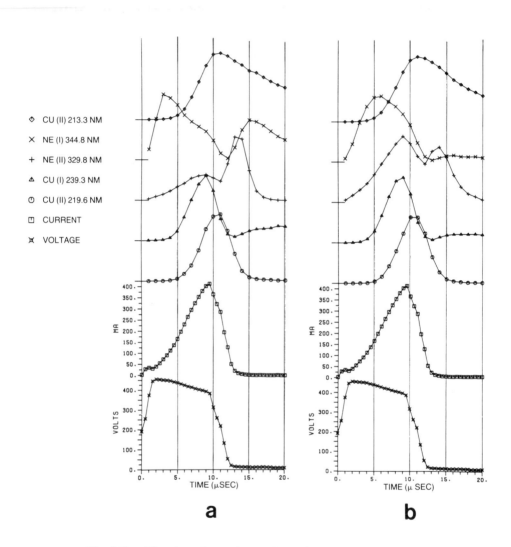

◇ CU (II) 213.3 NM

✕ NE (I) 344.8 NM

+ NE (II) 329.8 NM

△ CU (I) 239.3 NM

⊘ CU (II) 219.6 NM

▢ CURRENT

✖ VOLTAGE

Fig. 5.10 – Time-dependent emission of lines from four discharge species, compared with current and voltage waveforms: (a) centre of cathode bore, (b) 0.4 mm from cathode surface [9]. (Reprinted by permission from *Spectrochim. Acta,* **37B**, P. B. Farnsworth and J. P. Walters, Excitation Processes in an RF-boosted, Pulsed Hollow Cathode Lamp, Copyright 1982, Pergamon Press, Ltd.).

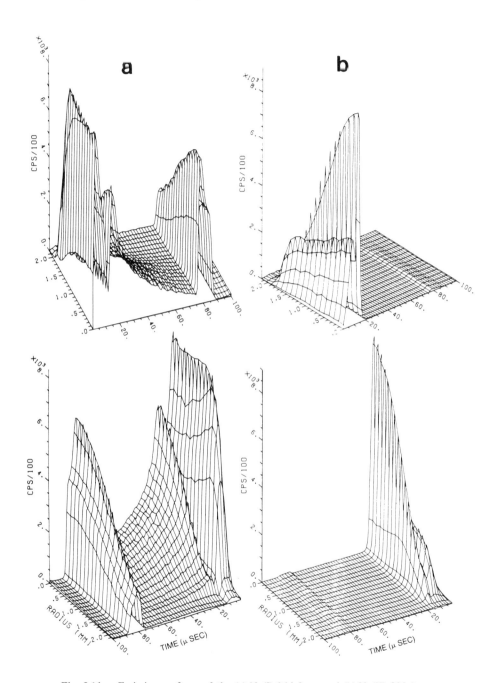

Fig. 5.11 − Emission surfaces of the (a) Ne(I) 344.8 nm and (b) Ne(II) 239.8 nm lines [9]. The emission surfaces in Figs. 5.11, 5.14, 5.15, 5.17 and 5.20 are presented in pairs, with two projections for each data set. For example, the upper left and lower left surfaces in this figure present the same data, viewed from different angles. (Reprinted by permission from *Spectrochim. Acta*, **37B**, P. B. Farnsworth and J. P. Walters, Excitation Processes in an RF-boosted, Pulsed Hollow Cathode Lamp, Copyright 1982, Pergamon Press, Ltd.)

created by the burst is less energetic than that produced by the current pulse. The suppressed afterglow following the RF burst can be accounted for by an increase in electron temperature during the burst [13]. Ion-electron recombination is inhibited until the electron temperature has dropped sufficiently to favour the process.

5.4.3 Excitation of Cu(II)

The emission data from the copper ion spectrum were examined for evidence of three excitation mechanisms: electron impact, charge exchange, and Penning ionization. There is strong evidence that charge-exchange reactions populate the upper levels of the laser transitions in Ne-Cu and He-Ne-Cu hollow-cathode lasers [14, 15]. It has also been suggested that electron impact excites many of the non-laser transitions in these lasers [16]. Excitation of the ion spectrum in conventional copper hollow-cathode discharges is reportedly the product of either Penning ionization or electron impact, depending on the magnitude of the current [17].

The time- and space-dependent emission intensities of three Cu(II) lines are shown in Fig. 5.12. The radial intensity profiles of the three lines are similar and are a reflection of the cylindrical cathode geometry. Cu(I) recombination data, to be discussed later, show that the cathode vapour requires 50-75 μsec to diffuse from the wall of the cylinder to the centre of the cathode bore. This means that the emission during the current pulse originates from a thin layer near the cathode surface. At the centre of the bore only a thin cross-section of the layer parallel to the end of the cylinder is viewed by the collection optics. At the edges of the bore, the layer parallel to the cylinder wall is viewed along its long dimension, resulting in increased intensity. By the time that the RF burst is applied the copper atoms sputtered by the current pulse have diffused to the centre of the cathode bore. The radial emission profiles during the RF burst are a reflection of the distribution of the copper atoms and ions, which has a maximum in the centre of the bore and decreases smoothly toward the edges.

In addition to the radial profiles, one feature that all the copper emission lines have in common is a delay of 4-5 μsec between the onset of the current pulse and the appearance of any significant emission intensity. This delay, best seen in Fig. 5.10, is a reflection of the time required for ionization of the neon, sputtering of the copper, and transport of the sputtered atoms to a region of excitation.

Other features of the temporal intensity profiles are strongly state-dependent, and point to the charge-exchange reaction,

$$Cu + Ne^+ = Cu^+(3d^9 5s) + Ne + \Delta E$$

as a major contributor to the production of excited copper ions. This conclusion is based on the following considerations.

1.   The energy defects, ΔE, for the reaction above are small (between +1250 and +3600 cm^{-1}). These values are well within the range of values over which charge-exchange reactions can be expected to have significant cross-sections [18].

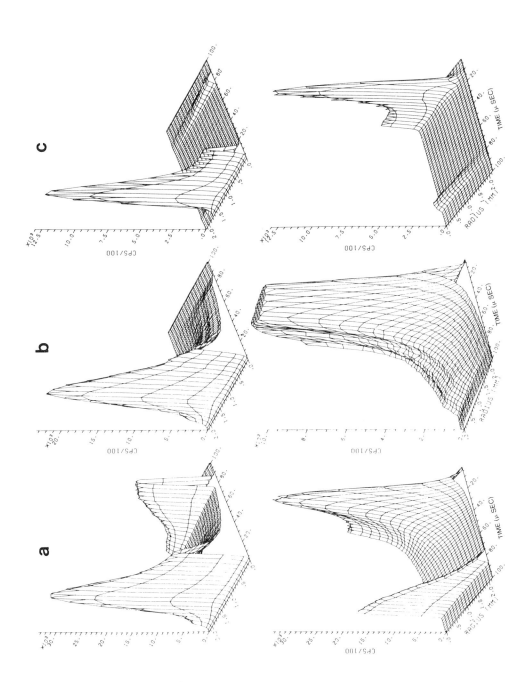

Fig. 5.12 – Emission surfaces of the Cu(II) (a) 212.3 nm, (b) 270.1 nm and (c) 219.6 nm lines [9]. (Reprinted by permission from *Spectrochim. Acta,* **37B**, P. B. Farnsworth and J. P. Walters, Excitation Processes in an RF-boosted, Pulsed Hollow Cathode Lamp, Copyright 1982, Pergamon Press, Ltd.)

2. The lines originating from the $3d^9 5s$ states are among the most intense in the Cu(II) spectrum when neon is the buffer gas. These same lines can barely be distinguished from the noise in an argon-filled lamp.

3. Only those states that could be populated either directly or indirectly by the charge-exchange reaction contribute to the afterglow that follows the current pulse. This is illustrated by comparison of plots 5.11a and 5.11b with plot 5.11c.

4. The afterglow from the $3d^9 5s$ states is quenched by the RF burst. RF heating of the electrons in the afterglow causes an increase in the ambipolar diffusion coefficients and accelerated loss of neon ions by collisions with the cathode walls [19].

In addition to accounting for the direct excitation of the Cu(II) $3d^9 5s$ levels, the charge-exchange reaction explains the afterglow observed from the $3d^9 4p$ levels. There are a number of strongly allowed transitions between these states, so that population of the $3d^9 5s$ states results indirectly in the population of the $3d^9 4p$ states by radiative cascade. This is illustrated by the Cu(II) 212.3 nm and 270.1 nm lines shown in plots 5.11a and 5.11b respectively. The lower state for the 270.1 nm transition is the upper state for the 212.3 nm transition. A comparison of the temporal profiles of the two lines in Fig. 5.13 shows that the afterglow regions are virtually identical.

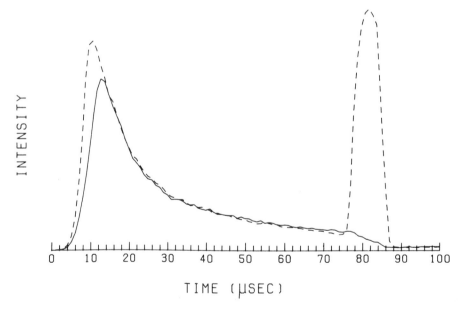

Fig. 5.13 – Comparison of the time-dependent emission of the Cu(II) 212.3 nm (dashed line) and Cu(II) 270.1 nm (solid line) lines [9]. The intensities have been scaled to match in the afterglow region to facilitate comparison. (Reprinted by permission from *Spectrochim. Acta,* **37B**, P. B. Farnsworth and J. P. Walters, Excitation Processes in an RF-boosted, Pulsed Hollow Cathode Lamp, Copyright 1982, Pergamon Press, Ltd.).

The differences between the profiles in Fig. 5.13 indicate that for the 212.3 nm line some mechanism other than charge exchange is active during the current pulse and the RF burst. Of the three mechanisms considered in the experiments, electron-impact excitation is most consistent with the data. Penning ionization can be eliminated because the excitation that cannot be attributed to charge exchange is neither buffer-gas- nor state-specific. Penning ionization of ground-state copper atoms could only populate ion states with energies of 72500 cm^{-1} or less in a neon buffer gas or 32200 cm^{-1} or less in an argon buffer gas. Figures 5.12c, 5.14, and 5.15 show that these restrictions do not apply to excitation during the current pulse and RF burst. Figure 5.14 shows the effect on the 212.3 nm line of changing the buffer gas from neon to argon. The observed emission is similar to what would be obtained by subtraction of the solid curve from the dashed curve in Fig. 5.13. Figures 5.12c and 5.15 show the emission characteristics of two lines from the neon-filled lamp that have excitation energies far in excess of the 72500 cm^{-1} mentioned above.

The possibility that Penning ionization produces ground-state ions must also be considered. Energy defects for Penning-ionization reactions can be quite large because the free electron produced by the collision can absorb the defect in the form of kinetic energy. Green and Webb [18] have suggested that the Penning-ionization reactions with the largest cross-sections may be those that produce

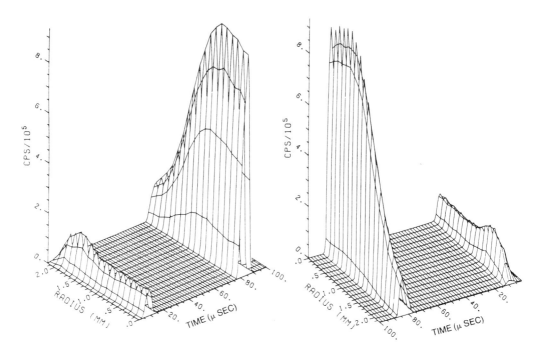

Fig. 5.14 – Emission surfaces of the Cu(II) 213.3 nm line in argon [9]. (Reprinted by permission from *Spectrochim. Acta,* **37B**, P. B. Farnsworth and J. P. Walters, Excitation Processes in an RF-boosted, Pulsed Hollow Cathode Lamp, Copyright 1982, Pergamon Press, Ltd.).

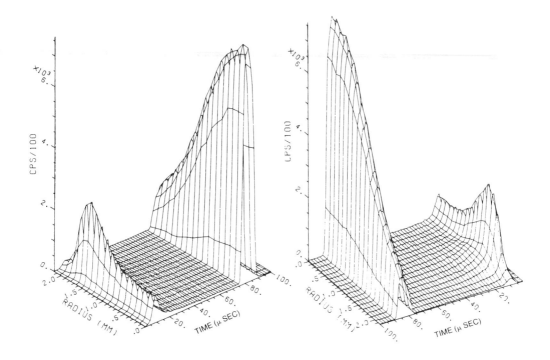

Fig. 5.15 – Emission surfaces of the Cu(II) 368.7 nm line [9]. (Reprinted by permission from *Spectrochim. Acta*, **37B**, P. B. Farnsworth and J. P. Walters, Excitation Processes in an RF-boosted, Pulsed Hollow Cathode Lamp, Copyright 1982, Pergamon Press, Ltd.).

ground-state ions, even though the energy defects may be "several eV". Evidence of an increase in the ground-state copper ion population caused by Penning ionization would not appear in the Cu(II) emission spectrum, but rather in the Cu(I) recombination afterglow.

5.4.4 Excitation of Cu(I)

Figures 5.16 and 5.17 show the emission characteristics of pairs of lines from the two halves of the Cu(I) term system. The lines in Fig. 5.16 are from the hydrogen-like series of doublets and the lines in Fig. 5.17 are from the two-electron series on the left side of the term diagram. The radial profiles during the current pulse and the RF burst are similar to those observed in the ion spectrum, with the exception that the U-shaped profiles characteristic of the current pulse are truncated to varying degrees near the edge of the cathode bore. This is due to self-absorption. When viewed parallel to the cathode axis, the layer of atoms near the cathode surface is optically thick for these transitions, all of which terminate either in the ground state or in low-lying metastable states. The same effect is apparent in the radial profile during the current pulse of the 324.8 nm resonance line shown in Fig. 5.6.

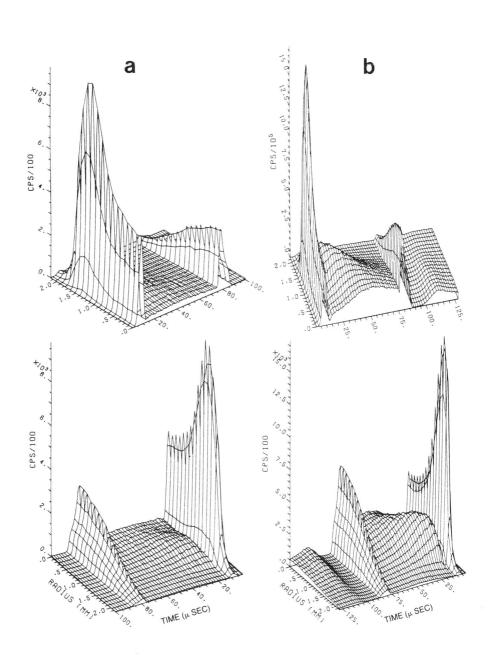

Fig. 5.16 – Emission surfaces of the Cu(I) (a) 202.4 nm and (b) 239.3 nm lines [9]. (Reprinted by permission from *Spectrochim. Acta*, **37B**, P. B. Farnsworth and J. P. Walters, Excitation Processes in an RF-boosted, Pulsed Hollow Cathode Lamp, Copyright 1982, Pergamon Press, Ltd.).

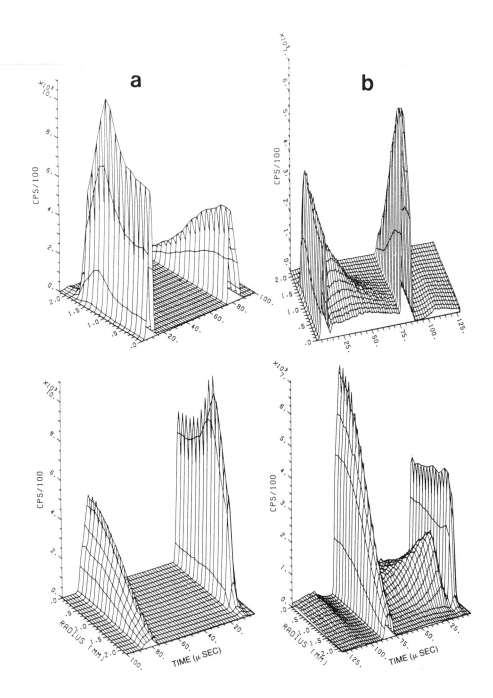

Fig. 5.17 – Emission surfaces of the Cu(I) (a) 218.2 nm and (b) 22.8 nm lines [9]. (Reprinted by permission from *Spectrochim. Acta,* **37B**, P. B. Farnsworth and J. P. Walters, Excitation Processes in an RF-boosted, Pulsed Hollow Cathode Lamp, Copyright 1982, Pergamon Press, Ltd.).

The four lines in Figs. 5.16 and 5.17 show varying levels of afterglow between the current pulse and the RF burst and following the RF burst. The intensity of the afterglow relative to that during the current pulse and RF burst appears to increase with increasing energy of the upper state involved in the transition. This trend is illustrated more dramatically in Fig. 5.18, which shows the time-dependent intensity of a series of lines from the $5p$, $6p$, $7p$, and $8p$ single-electron doublet states. No attempt was made to measure absolute intensities from these transitions. It appears, however, that the trend with increasing excitation energy is one of decreasing intensity during the current pulse and RF burst and fairly constant intensity during the afterglow.

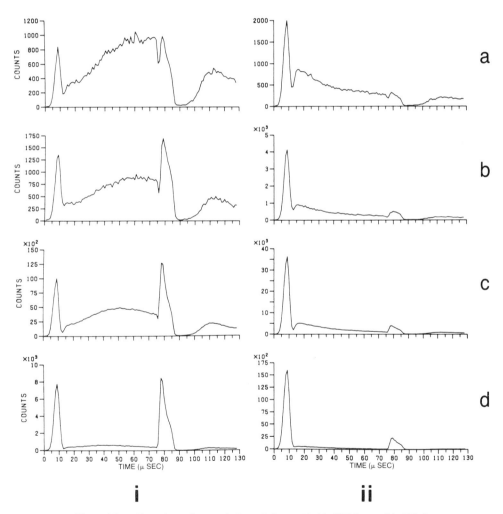

Fig. 5.18 – Time-dependent emission of the Cu(I) (a) 217.0 nm, (b) 223.6 nm, (c) 239.3 nm and (d) 202.4 nm lines: i, centre of cathode bore, ii, 0.4 mm from cathode surface [9]. (Reprinted by permission from *Spectrochim. Acta*, **37B**, P. B. Farnsworth and J. P. Walters, Excitation Processes in an RF-boosted, Pulsed Hollow Cathode Lamp, Copyright 1982, Pergamon Press, Ltd.).

The data above suggest that the neutral spectrum is excited by electron impact during the current pulse and RF burst and by ion–electron recombination during the current pulse and EF burst and by ion–electron recombination during the afterglow periods. This conclusion is supported by the dips in afterglow emission that follow the current pulse and precede and follow the RF burst. These regions of suppressed afterglow, similar to the one observed in the Ne(I) emission, represent periods when the electron temperature is too high to favour recombination yet too low for efficient excitation by electron impact.

The recombination data point to features of the discharge that affect its performance during the RF burst. It is significant that the afterglow following the RF burst returns to the same level it would have had in the absence of the RF. This suggests that copper is not ionized by the RF burst. The Cu(II) emission during the RF burst must result from the excitation by the RF of ions produced during the current pulse and afterglow. The shapes of the emission surfaces shown in Figs. 5.16b and 5.17b are also revealing. They show the region of maximum recombination emission moving from the surface of the cathode to the centre of the bore. Although the position of the emission maximum depends on several factors, including the spatial distribution of neon ion-density and electron temperature, it provides an indirect indication of the rate at which the cathode vapour is moving across the cathode. This movement is seen more clearly in Fig. 5.19, which shows plots of the time at which the recombination intensity peaks as a function of radial position in the cathode, for lines from the two sections of the Cu(I) term system. The slopes of the lines correspond to an average rate of inward diffusion of the vapour of about 3500 cm/sec. At this rate clouds from opposite sides of the bore merge in the middle after about 60 μsec. This picture of vapour transport, although simplistic, provides a qualitative explanation of the radial emission profiles during the RF burst and explains why the optimum time for the application of the RF is 50–75 μsec after the start of the current pulse.

The two sets of recombination maxima plotted in Fig. 5.19 are separated by about 0.35 mm or 10 μsec. The separation suggests that recombination into the two halves of the Cu(I) term system occurs either from different states or by different mechanisms. On the basis of arguments too lengthy to be included here, Farnsworth and Walters [9] conclude tentatively that the latter is the case. Recombination into the two-electron series is by two-electron recombination (the reverse of autoionization), while recombination into the hydrogen-like states is by three-body recombination.

The effect on the Cu(I) emission of changing the buffer gas to argon is illustrated in Fig. 5.20. Comparison of these surfaces with those in Fig. 5.16b reveals some interesting differences between them. The movement of vapour is noticeably slower in the argon-filled lamp than in the neon-filled lamp. This reflects the inverse dependence of the diffusion coefficient for copper atoms on the atomic mass of the buffer gas [20]. The afterglow returns sooner after the RF burst in argon than in neon, indicating that the electron temperature is falling faster. The electrons dissipate their energy primarily through inelastic collisions with buffer gas atoms at a rate that depends on the distribution of excited states in the buffer gas atom [21]. With its excited states at lower energies than the corresponding states in neon, argon will moderate the electron temperature more rapidly than will neon A final difference is in the level of the afterglow following the RF burst. In the argon-filled lamp, the recombination afterglow following the RF burst is significantly more intense than it was before the RF was applied. This points to an increase in either the electron density or the copper ion density. It may be that in the argon-filled lamp, Penning ionization is producing ground-state copper ions.

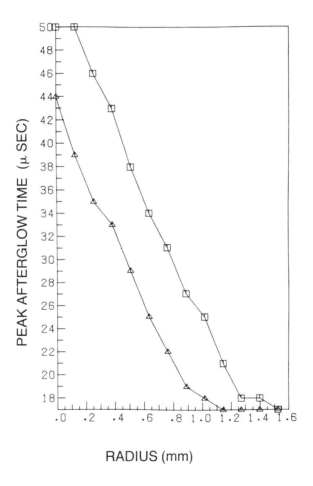

Fig. 5.19 – Time (in μsec) at which the afterglow reaches peak intensity, plotted against radial position in the cathode bore: (Δ) Cu(I) 222.8 nm, (□) Cu(I) 239.3 nm [9]. (Reprinted by permission from *Spectrochim. Acta*, **37B**, P. B. Farnsworth and J. P. Walters, Excitation Processes in an RF-boosted, Pulsed Hollow Cathode Lamp, Copyright 1982, Pergamon Press, Ltd.).

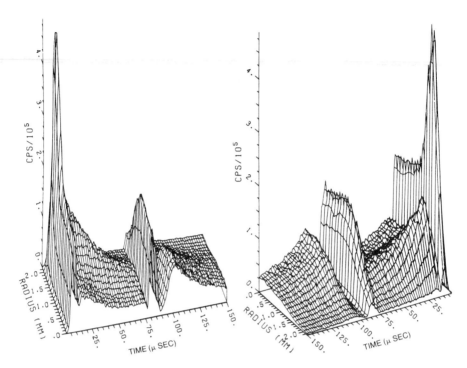

Fig. 5.20 – Emission surfaces of the Cu(I) 239.3 nm line in argon [9]. (Reprinted by permission from *Spectrochim. Acta*, **37B**, P. B. Farnsworth and J. P. Walters, Excitation Processes in an RF-boosted, Pulsed Hollow Cathode Lamp, Copyright 1982, Pergamon Press, Ltd.).

5.4.5 Summary of excitation mechanisms

In the neon-filled lamp the current pulse samples the cathode material and at the same time creates an energetic environment that continues to influence the lamp's output long after the pulse is over. Neon ions created by electron impact during the current pulse react in the pulse afterglow with copper atoms to produce excited copper ions. After radiative relaxation to the ground state, the copper ions recombine with electrons by two distinct pathways, giving rise to an afterglow in the neutral spectrum. During the RF burst, the Cu(I) and Cu(II) spectra result from electron-impact excitation of ground-state atoms and ions respectively. There is no significant sampling of the cathode by the RF, nor is there appreciable ionization of the vapour that is already present. Recombination is suppressed by the RF burst, so that ionization during the current pulse and pulse afterglow diminishes the population of neutral atoms available for excitation by the RF and results in diminished intensity of the analytically important neutral resonance lines.

5.5 ANALYTICAL PERFORMANCE

5.5.1 Atomic absorption and fluorescence measurements

In conjunction with the preliminary lamp characterization by Araki *et al.* [8] a series of experiments was conducted in which the atomic-absorption working curves obtained during the RF burst in a cadmium hollow-cathode lamp were compared with those obtained during the current pulse. Working curves obtained with the Cd 228.8 nm line are shown in Fig. 5.21. The current pulse had a duration of 20 μsec and a peak current of 200 mA. The RF burst was delayed from the beginning of the discharge by 50 μsec and had an amplitude of 400 V. The dashed line in the figure was obtained with a boxcar integrator sampling the entire period of the RF burst. The solid lines were obtained with the boxcar sampling the indicated portions of the current pulse. The current pulse produces a linear working curve only for the leading edge of the current waveform. The curves taken at later times show the effect of increasing self-absorption. The linearity of the curve taken early in time is possible only at the expense of a poorer signal to noise ratio. The emission intensity on the rising portion of the current pulse is low and the sampling period is unacceptably short. In contrast, a nearly linear curve results when the entire RF burst is sampled, and the peak intensity from the RF excitation is five times that from the current pulse. The

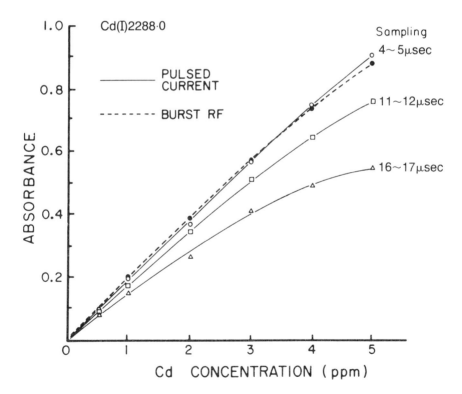

Fig. 5.21 – Working curves for Cd atomic-absorption analysis, comparing performance with pulsed-current excitation (solid lines) and RF excitation (dashed line) [9]. (Reprinted by permission from *Spectrochim. Acta,* **37B**, P. B. Farnsworth and J. P. Walters, Excitation Processes in an RF-boosted, Pulsed Hollow Cathode Lamp, Copyright 1982, Pergamon Press. Ltd.).

combination of high intensity and long sampling time results in improved signal to noise ratios. Similar benefits were realized when the RF-boosted lamp was used as an excitation source for atomic-fluorescence measurements on luminous samples.

5.5.2 Prospects for further development
At its present stage of development, the RF-boosted lamp offers distinct advantages over conventional pulsed or d.c. hollow-cathode lamps. However, the studies of the lamp described above point to several directions for possible improvement if a lamp were designed specifically for use with RF excitation. An obvious starting point would be a lamp capable of operating at higher RF voltages. The linear relationship between RF voltage and intensity suggests that an increase in voltage above the 700-V limit reported by Araki *et al.* [8] would result in a proportional increase in intensity during the RF burst. The experiments also suggest that if the emission spectrum from the lamp is to be dominated by the neutral resonance lines, as is desirable for most atomic-absorption and atomic-fluorescence applications, the buffer gas should be selected solely for its sampling capability. The buffer gas does not appear to contribute to excitation during the RF burst. Ionization of the cathode material by collisions with the buffer gas during the current pulse and afterglow decreases the number of neutral atoms available for excitation by the RF burst. Neon is used in most commercial hollow-cathode lamps because of the efficiency with which it excites the cathode vapour. The heavier noble gases should give better performance in the RF-boosted lamp. Another factor favouring the use of buffer gases other than neon is the lower rate of diffusion of the cathode material through the heavier gas. The lower the diffusion rate, the longer the residence time of the cathode vapour in the interelectrode region, where it is efficiently excited by the RF. Finally, the geometries and spacing of the electrodes should be varied to find the optimum configuration for RF excitation. Once a lamp design has been selected, the RF burst should be selected to coincide with the maximum cathode vapour concentration in the interlectrode region. The optimum timing and duration for the RF burst will depend on the electrode configuration, the cathode composition, and the buffer-gas composition.

Clearly, the potential of the RF-boosted, pulsed hollow-cathode lamp has only been superficially tapped. It is a promising source of intense pulsed atomic line emission free from the effects of self-absorption broadening.

REFERENCES
[1] J. B. Dawson and D. J. Ellis, *Spectrochim. Acta,* 1967, **23A**, 565.
[2] D. A. Katskov, G. C. Lebedev and B. V. L'vov, *J. Appl. Spectrosc., Engl. Transl.,* 1969, **10**, 215.
[3] H. Prugger, R. Grosskopf and R. Torge, *Spectrochim. Acta,* 1971, **26B**, 191.
[4] J. O. Weide and M. L. Parsons, *Anal. Lett.,* 1972, **5**, 363.
[5] H. G. C. Human, *Spectrosc. Lett.,* 1973, **6**, 719.

[6]   N. Omenetto, G. D. Boutilier, S. K. Weeks, B. W. Smith and J. D. Winefordner, *Anal. Chem.*, 1977, **49**, 1078.

[7]   G. J. De Jong and E. H. Piepmeier, *Spectrochim. Acta*, 1974, **29B**, 159.

[8]   T. Araki, J. P. Walters and S. Minami, *Appl. Spectrosc.*, 1980, **34**, 33.

[9]   P. B. Farnsworth and J. P. Walters, *Spectrochim. Acta*, 1982, **37B**, 773.

[10] P. B. Farnsworth and J. P. Walters, *Anal. Chem.*, 1982, **54**, 885.

[11] H. Shindo, S. Imazu and T. Inaba, *J. Quant. Spectrosc. Radiat. Transfer*, 1981, **25**, 77.

[12] G. F. Sauter, R. A. Gerber and H. J. Oskam, *Physica*, 1966, **132**, 1921.

[13] M. A. Biondi, *Phys. Rev.*, 1963, **129**, 1181.

[14] J. R. McNeil, G. J. Collins, K. B. Persson and D. L. Franzen, *Appl. Phys. Lett.*, 1976, **28**, 207.

[15] L. Csillag, M. Jánossy, K. Rósza and T. Salamon, *Phys. Lett.*, 1974, **50A**, 13.

[16] F. J. de Hoog, J. R. McNeil, G. J. Collins and K. B. Persson, *Appl. Phys.*, 1977, **48**, 3701.

[17] K. C. Smyth, B. L. Bentz, C. G. Bruhn and W. W. Harrison, *J. Am. Chem. Soc.*, 1979, **101**, 797.

[18] J. M. Green and C. E. Webb, *J. Phys. B*, 1974, **7**, 1698.

[19] A. R. Turner-Smith, J. M. Green and C. E. Webb, *J. Phys. B*, 1973, **6**, 114.

[20] R. D. Present, *Kinetic Theory of Gases*, McGraw-Hill, New York, 1958.

[21] H. Falk and H. Lucht, *J. Quant. Spectrosc. Radiat. Transfer*, 1976, **16**, 909 .

6

Hollow-cathode discharge in a magnetic field

N. K. Rudnevsky and D. E. Maksimov

6.1 GENERAL LAWS OF MAGNETIC FIELD EFFECT ON ELECTRIC DISCHARGE PLASMA

Among the theoretical and experimental works on electric discharges the study of the discharge characteristics in a magnetic field is of great interest, mainly because a magnetic field affects the motion of charged particles in a plasma and thus greatly changes its properties [1, 2].

Charged particles move in an electric field according to laws resembling the usual laws of motion in a gravitational field. The electric force acting on the charged particle is in this case:

$$\vec{F_e} = q\vec{E} \tag{6.1}$$

where q is the particle charge and E the electrical field intensity. When a magnetic field is applied to a discharge, charged-particle motion is changed substantially as a result of the so-called Lorentz force:

$$\vec{F_H} = \frac{q}{c} \ \vec{v}, \vec{H} \tag{6.2}$$

where q and v are the charge and particle velocity, respectively, H is the magnetic field intensity, c is the speed of light.

The Lorentz force is always perpendicular to the magnetic vector and does not influence the particle motion if the velocity vector is parallel to the magnetic field. If the particle velocity vector and the direction of the magnetic lines form an angle α, only the perpendicular velocity component $v_\perp = v\sin\alpha$ will be changed, while the parallel component $v_\parallel = v\cos\alpha$ remains unchanged. Thus:

$$F_H = \frac{qvH}{c}\sin\alpha \tag{6.3}$$

Particle motion has a simpler character in a homogeneous magnetic field, in which the lines of force will be parallel and the intensity value the same throughout. In this case the particle moves in the magnetic field in a plane perpendicular to the vector H along a curved path with constant centripetal acceleration, i.e. along a closed circle with radius r_H (the Larmor radius). The Larmor radius at $\alpha = 90°$ may be calculated from the formula:

$$r_H = \frac{mvc}{qH} = 1 \times 10^{-14}\,\frac{\sqrt{(mW)}}{zH} \tag{6.4}$$

where z is the particle charge multiplicity, m is the mass in g, W is the energy in eV, and H is in Oe; r_H is in cm.

For the electron ($z = 1$, and $m = 9 \times 10^{-28}$g):

$$r_H = \frac{3.4\sqrt{(W)}}{H} \tag{6.5}$$

The particle motion becomes more complex if simultaneously influenced by the magnetic and the electric fields. If the fields are parallel ($E\|H$), the particle motions will be accelerated or slowed down in the direction of the electric field; this will also happen in the absence of a magnetic field. The particle path will therefore be either a gradually lengthened or gradually compressed helix. If E is perpendicular to H the situation is quite different. In this case the particle path consists of periodically repeated identical arcs called cycloids, with height expressed by the formula:

$$h = \frac{2\,m\,c^2\,E}{q\,H^2} \tag{6.6}$$

and the time spent by the particle in an individual cycloid is:

$$t = \frac{2\pi mc}{q\,H} \tag{6.7}$$

This value coincides with the period of rotation on the Larmor circle. Charged particle motion on cycloids can be divided into rotary and translational components, and is the addition of rotation on the circle with radius $h/2$ to longitudinal motion with velocity cE/H.

The motion of charged particles in non-uniform magnetic fields is more complicated. The value and direction of the H vectors in such fields change from point to point. Therefore the particle motion has a complex geometric form in non-uniform magnetic fields. In this case it is difficult to find common laws allowing its mathematical expression. However, the problem is greatly simplified if we consider only those particles with a Larmor radius relatively small in comparison with the distance over which the magnetic field is noticeably changed. Particles with small Larmor radius have time to make many revolutions around a line of force before they pass into the area where the field has essentially changed.

The path of the particles is distorted by their collisions and determined by the relation of the Larmor radius and the free-path length, l. In a weak magnetic field, where $l \ll r_H$, the particle path is only slightly changed between collisions. In a strong magnetic field $l \gg r_H$ and the particles revolve several times between collisions. After each collision the particle will take a new path, the axis of which is shifted from the original one by approximately r_H. Charged particle mobility and diffusion decrease significantly in the transverse direction. Thus, when a magnetic field is applied to an electric discharge, the motion charac-teristics of the charged particles are changed, mainly resulting in alteration of the plasma energy parameters as a whole.

This phenomenon can be used for plasma-oriented control for practical purposes and in particular in a variety of areas of spectroscopy.

6.2 INFLUENCE OF A MAGNETIC FIELD ON PHYSICAL PROCESSES IN THE PLASMA OF THE HOLLOW-CATHODE DISCHARGE

From the elementary plasma processes discussed above it is possible to select a set of effects that influence the characteristics of electrical discharges (including hollow-cathode discharge), when a magnetic field is applied, e.g. change in the excited levels of the atom [3]; change in Coulomb interactions [4], variation in energy of the electron distribution function [5].

The first effect is connected with changes in the atom wave-function in the magnetic field and has a slight effect on strong magnetic fields ($H > 10^5$ Oe).

Coulomb interactions in the magnetic field plasma are greatly changed if the Larmor radius (r_H) is less than the Debye radius (r_D):

$$ r_H = \frac{mvc}{eH} < r_D = \sqrt{\frac{kT_e}{4\pi e N_e}} \tag{6.8} $$

where m, e, v, N_e, T_e are the mass, charge, velocity, concentration and tempera-ture of the electron respectively, k is the Boltzmann constant, c is the speed of light. By substituting in (6.8) the value of the most probable velocity $\bar{v} = \sqrt{(2kT/m)}$, which corresponds to the mean energy of the low-velocity in the plasma, it is seen that the magnetic field might affect the Coulomb interactions considerably if

$$ H > c\sqrt{8\pi N_e m/e} \tag{6.9} $$

The electron concentration of the hollow-cathode discharge plasma under normal conditions is equal to $\sim 10^{13}/\text{cm}^3$ [6, 7]. From Eq. (6.9) it follows that

these electron concentrations the magnetic field would affect the Coulomb interactions considerably only for $H > 10^4$ Oe.

Let us discuss possible changes in the energy characteristics of charged
particles in the plasma hollow-cathode discharge when a magnetic field is applied.
The external magnetic field cannot directly change the electron and ion energy.
Change in the ion flow condition is possible only in strong magnetic fields,
because of the large mass of ions. However, the curving of the electron trajectory
in a magnetic field of low intensity can change the dependence of the electron
energy distribution on the spatial coordinates. The electron energy distribution
for the hollow cathode, as shown in [8-11], is essentially different from the
Maxwell distribution owing to an excess of high-speed electrons. The magnetic
field causes the charged particles to travel along the arcs of Larmor circles,
leading to fast flows of high-velocity electrons which have escaped from the
cathode drop zone, deflecting them to the peripheral areas of the glow zone. The
central part of the plasma is depleted of high-velocity electrons and its electron
temperature is decreased. The increase in the relative concentration of low-
velocity electrons at the centre of the hollow-cathode plasma results in increased
population of low energy levels, thereby leading to increased intensity of the
spectral lines of low excitation potentials. In the plasma bordering on the
cathode dark space the number of high-velocity electrons is increased. As a result,
at the cathode wall the intensity of lines with high excitation potential (including those of the carrier gas) is increased. This was shown experimentally in
[12-15].

The influence of a magnetic field on the hollow-cathode discharge was first
identified and partially studied by Somesan and co-workers [16-22].

In [17] the influence of a transverse field ($H = 300$ Oe) on a cylindrical
molybdenum hollow-cathode discharge at a carrier-gas (Ne) pressure of 133 Pa
was studied. It was found that when the magnetic field was applied the discharge
current and brightness of the negative glow were significantly increased, and the
cathode drop value was constant. When the magnetic field intensity was increased
from 0 to 300 Oe, the current density increased 150-fold, to as much as 600
mA/cm^2 (at 330 V).

In a study of the hollow-cathode discharge in a longitudinal magnetic field
[18,19] it was found that the discharge current and the intensity of the spectrum of the cathode material (molybdenum, lead) were significantly increased
when the magnetic field intensity was increased, but the intensity of the working
gas (neon and other inert gases) lines remained unchanged.

To explain these experimental results, it was suggested [20] that the hollow-
cathode discharge should be considered as the opposite movement of electrons
in the thermal plasma (a condition that corresponds to so-called 'dual beam
instability'). The magnetic field action forces into a beam the cathode electrons
that penetrate into the zone of negative glow, resulting in increased possibility of
atom excitation in the hollow-cathode discharge plasma [16]. However, this
supposition is not sufficiently supported, as the intensity of the magnetic
field applied to the discharge to focus the electron beam is very low (some
hundreds of oersteds). It is more probable that the greater excitation of cathode

material atoms than of carrier-gas atoms, when the magnetic field is applied to the discharge, is due to the predominance of low-energy excitation processes over high-energy ionization processes.

The effect of a longitudinal magnetic field $\vec{H} \parallel \vec{E}_k$ on ionization waves for the hollow-cathode discharge in a neon atmosphere was also investigated [21]. The discharge current was plotted vs. the pressure of the discharge gas. Between the zones of ionization-wave generation there was a zone without oscillations, the width of which was determined by the intensity of the magnetic field applied to the discharge.

In [22] the main physical processes occurring during application of the magnetic field to the hollow-cathode discharge were analysed. It was found that at the optimal magnetic field intensity in the axial direction there was a great increase in the sputtering speed, and decrease of self-absorption.

In [23, 24] the magnetic field was applied to a cylindrical hollow-cathode discharge (30 mm diameter) in pure He and its mixture with N_2 ($P = 13$–400 Pa). Unlike the earlier results [16,20,21] there was a significant cathode drop of the potential on increase of the magnetic field intensity up to 800 Oe. At the same time there was a noticeable redistribution of the glow intensity in the cathode cavity during application of the magnetic field: in the centre the intensity of the He line was decreased while the relative intensity of the cathode lines and some molecular bands of N_2 was increased. Electron-temperature measurement by a dual probe showed that application of the magnetic field resulted in temperature decrease in the cathode centre, while at the temperature the edges remained unchanged.

The above-mentioned works deal mainly with problems deriving from the influence of the magnetic field on the physical characteristics of the hollow-cathode discharge. However, no detailed study of the spectral characteristics and the possibilities of using this source in spectroanalytical practice has been made. An overall evaluation of the results obtained by us in 1967–1983 [25–43] is presented below.

6.3 EQUIPMENT AND EXPERIMENTAL TECHNIQUE

6.3.1 Modes of operation

The equipment is shown in a block diagram in Fig. 6.1. It is comprised of a discharge tube; a system for pumping and feeding working gas into the tube; the electric power supply to the tube; a magnetic field source with a unit for electric power supply and intensity measurement; a spectral unit.

The discharge tube design is shown in Fig. 6.2. The tube case, with a water cooling-circuit, is made of molybdenum glass. The hollow-cathode emission passes from the tube through a thin optical quartz window attached with picein to the tube front. At the end of the tube there is a ground-joint stopper with a 2-mm diameter rod soldered in molybdenum for mounting the cathodes. The anode is made of molybdenum foil (0.01–0.05 mm in thickness) in the form of a cylinder with a diameter equal to the tube inner diameter; it is mounted on the

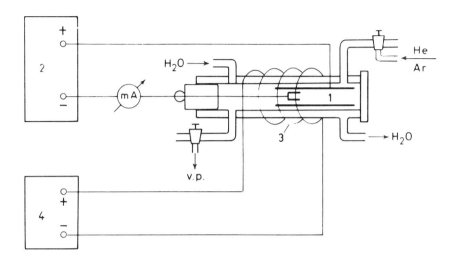

Fig. 6.1 – Equipment block diagram: 1 – discharge tube; 2 – electric power supply unit for the tube; 3 – magnetic field source; 4 – electric power supply unit for the magnetic field source.

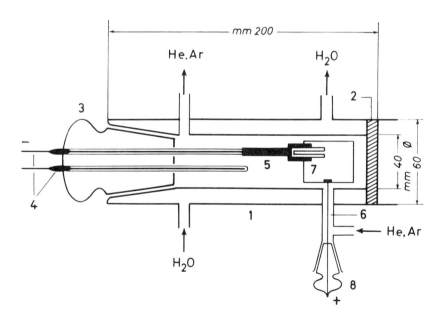

Fig. 6.2 – Discharge tube: 1 – tube case; 2 – optical quartz window; 3 – stopper with molybdenum rods (4) for mounting cathodes (5); 6 – molybdenum rod soldered in the stopper (8) for mounting anodes (7).

end of the thin molybdenum rod in the stopper which fits in a ground-in joint in the side-arm of the tube. The cathode and the anode are arranged coaxially. There are two ports in the tube for carrier gas input and output; in addition there is a cooling-water input and output. Hollow cylinders of various materials, open at one end, are used as cathodes. The configurations and dimensions of the more commonly used cathodes are given in Fig. 6.3.

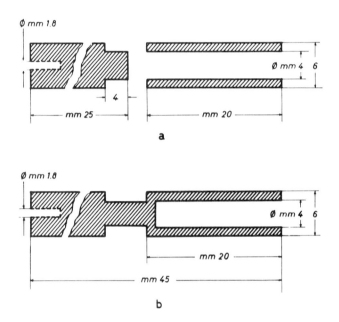

Fig. 6.3 – Dimensions and shape of hollow cathodes used in spectral analysis: (a) demountable carbon cathodes; (b) metal cathode not subjected to demounting (dimensions in mm; scale 2:1).

The system for pumping and feeding working gas into the tube is shown in Fig. 6.4. It comprises a pump which pumps air and noble gas into the tube; a mercury manometer for working-gas pressure-measurement; three glass stopcocks (a) to permit gas to leak from the tube, (b) to cut off the gas supply and (c) to leak air into the tube; a metal needle valve to control the gas pressure.

The tube and pump are connected by means of a rubber vacuum hose. Since inert gases of high purity are used there is no necessity for additional cleaning. The flow system used to supply working gas to the tube is simple to manufacture and allows quick cathode change.

The electric power supply of the discharge tube is provided by a high-voltage silicon diode bridge rectifier of ~4 kW. There is a ballast resistor ($R = 600-1000$ Ω) in the circuit for improved stability when operating the discharge tube. The rectifier provides voltage up to 1000 V at the tube with current up to 2 A.

In some cases use can be made of a combined pulse and electric power supply to the discharge tube (in steady state with an applied pulse) from the

generator circuit shown in Fig. 6.5. Several lamps (output of each 0.075 W) connected in parallel are used as modulators. The generator design permits the direct
and mean pulse current to be varied up to 2 A, the pulse rate from 20 to 10000
Hz, and the pulse duration from 5 to 1000 μsec. The generator circuit provides a
square-wave pulse.

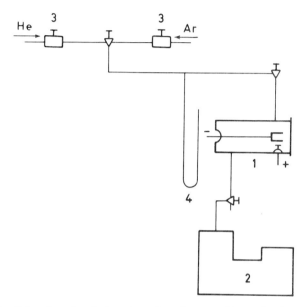

Fig. 6.4 – Running feed system of carrier gas without cleaning: 1 – discharge
tube; 2 – pumping system; 3 – metal stopcock for working gas pressure control;
4 – mercury manometer.

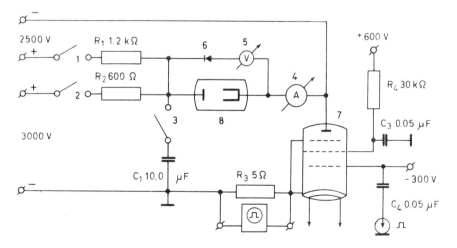

Fig. 6.5 – Pulse and combined electric power supply, schematic diagram of
discharge tube: 1, 2, 3 – high-voltage switches; 4 – ammeter; 5 – voltmeter;
6 – silicon diodes; 7 – parallel-connected electronic tubes, type GU-50; 8 –
discharge tube.

A magnetic field of intensity up to 1500 Oe in the discharge region is created by two types of sources (Fig. 6.6). A solenoid is used as the source in the first type (Fig. 6.6a). Basically it is a coil (3) of 2000 turns of 1-mm copper wire, wrapped on a brass former (1). The inner diameter of the solenoid is 100 mm, which is large enough to accommodate the tube. The length is more than twice the inner diameter and consequently the tube cathode (2) is in the region of the homogeneous magnetic field. The solenoid is screened by soft iron (4) to reduce diameter and consequently the tube cathode (2) is in the region of the homogeneous magnetic field. The solenoid is screened by soft iron (4) to reduce magnetic field dissipation. In this case the direction of the magnetic field lines is parallel to the longitudinal axis of the cathode and perpendicular to the direction of the electric field lines in the region of the cathode voltage drop (Fig. 6.7a). The source of the second type (Fig. 6.6b) is a four-section coil with 60-mm clearance in the middle for inserting a discharge tube. The coil is in the

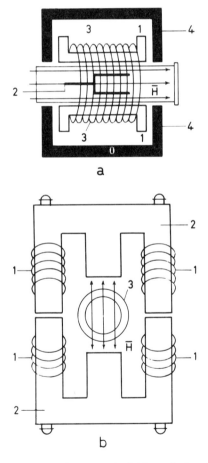

Fig. 6.6 – The source circuits for magnetic fields applied to the hollow-cathode discharge: (a) solenoid, (b) coil with two E-shape cores.

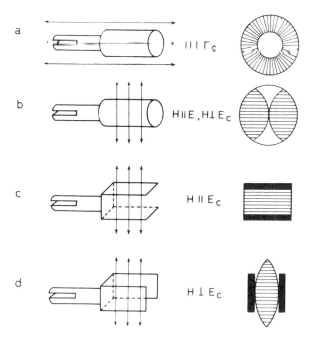

Fig. 6.7 – Various magnetic field orientations relating to the electrical field in the region of the cathode potential drop and the corresponding appearance of the luminous plasma at the front face of the hollow cathode.

form of two interconnected E-shaped cores made from iron transformer plates. Each coil section contains 1000 turns of 1-mm copper wire. The two coils on a core are connected in series to the electric power supply and two pairs of coils are connected in parallel. Here the direction of the magnetic field lines is perpendicular to the longitudinal axis of the cathode. In this case the vectorial orientation of the magnetic and electric fields depends on the cathode design and their arrangement (Fig. 6.7 b, c, d). With a cylindrical cathode, the magnetic field is parallel to one part of the electric field and perpendicular to another. The orientation of the magnetic field vector of flat parallel cathodes, relative to an electric field, is defined by the arrangement of the cathodes in the tube.

The right-hand side of Fig. 3.7 shows the end-on view of the luminous plasma obtained with various configurations of the magnetic field applied to the discharge.

The electric power for these magnetic field sources is supplied by with d.c. semiconductor diode rectifiers.

The magnetic field intensity was measured with a Hall germanium transducer calibrated against a constant magnetic field of a known intensity. Taking into account the calibration accuracy, the measurement error is about 10%.

Spectrographs with an average dispersion in the ultraviolet region, a visible region spectrograph with a camera ($F = 270$ mm), and a crossed dispersion apectrograph were employed. For spectral survey the hollow-cathode negative glow plasma was focused on the spectrograph slit. The slit-width used was 15-25 μm. The spectra were photographed with suitable spectral photoplates and the intensity of the spectral lines was measured with Zeiss MF-2 and GII microphotometers.

6.3.2 Procedure

Powder samples were placed in the cathode cavity; solution samples were dropped into the bottom of the cavity, covered beforehand with a polystyrene film, and then dried. The cathodes were placed in the discharge tube, which was then exhausted down to 1 Pa, after which the working gas was fed in. Helium or argon or a mixture of the two was used as carrier gas. The helium pressure was 2.666-4.0 kPa and the argon pressure 667-933 Pa. Before the spectral survey the cathodes (containing the samples) were run at 50-200 mA to stabilize the discharge (during this gas desorption took place from the cathodes and the polystyrene was ashed). The current was then increased up to the working value (usually 500-1000 mA) and the spectral survey run.

6.4 MAGNETIC FIELD EFFECTS ON THE SPECTROSCOPIC, ELECTRIC AND TEMPERATURE CHARACTERISTICS OF THE HOLLOW-CATHODE DISCHARGE

6.4.1 Selection of the optimum pattern for the magnetic field

The mutual orientation of the electric and magnetic fields appreciably affects the plasma behaviour of a gas discharge [1, 2]. Selection of the optimum magnetic field pattern, i.e. the orientation relative to the electric field in the area of cathode potential drop and longitudinal axis, that will give the highest intensity for the spectral lines excited in the hollow cathode, has been studied [28]. The dependence of the intensity of the cathode-material lines on the magnetic field intensity was investigated for the four patterns shown in Fig. 6.7. For the axial pattern with respect to the longitudinal axis of the cylindrical cathode $(\vec{H} \perp \vec{E}_c)$ the solenoid coil was used (Fig. 6.6a). For the other three patterns the twin-core four-coil system (Fig. 6.6b) was employed. The cathodes were made of copper, with wall thickness 1 mm and depth 20 mm and run at 150 mA. Helium was used as carrier gas. Spectra were photographed with an exposure time of 1 min.

Figure 6.8 shows the line intensity of copper [Cu (I) 324.7 nm] as a function of magnetic field intensity of the patterns under investigation. The line intensity increases most when the magnetic field axial to the cathode longitudinal axis is applied to the discharge.

The line-intensity gain factor (ratio of intensity at $H_{opt.}$ to intensity at H_o) depends on the product of the carrier-gas pressure (P) and the cathode cavity diameter or distance between the plane-parallel plates of the slot cathodes. As can be seen in Fig. 6.9, the amplification of line intensity is maximal in the range $Pd = 11 - 16 \times 10^3$ Pa.mm. Similar results were achieved with cathodes made of other materials, as well as for the impurity element lines [Ag (I) 328.1 nm and Cd (I) 326.1 nm] used as representing solution residues.

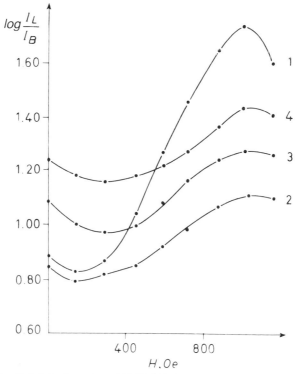

Fig. 6.8 – Relativity intensity of Cu(I) 324.7 nm line vs. the strength of various patterns of magnetic field: 1 – axial with longitudinal axis and transversal electrical field; 2 – transversal-longitudinal; 3 – longitudinal; 4 – transversal (1, 2 – cylindrical cathodes, 3, 4 – slit plane-parallel cathodes). (I_1 = intensity of line, I_b = intensity of background).

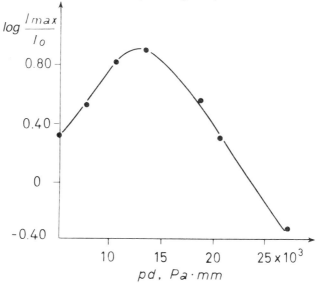

Fig. 6.9 – Coefficient of intensity amplification of the Cu(I) 324.7 nm line in a magnetic field axial with the longitudinal axis of cylindrical cathodes, vs. product of working-gas (He) pressure and cavity diameter.

Further investigations were made with He, Ar and an He–Ar mixture as carrier gases, cylindrical cathodes with 4-mm cavity diameter, and the magnetic field applied axially to the cathode longitudinal axis.

6.4.2 Spectral line intensity distribution

The radiation intensity of different plasma discharge areas is known to be more uniform in the hollow cathode than in arc and spark excitation sources. Due to this fact, sharp focusing of the discharge glow on the spectrograph slit is typical in photography of the spectra radiated by the hollow cathode. However, from the appearance of the hollow-cathode discharge plasma in the magnetic field it can be presumed that the distribution of spectral line intensity over the cross-section is not uniform. In this connection the effect of magnetic field intensity on the intensity distribution of some spectral lines in the cross-section of the hollow cathode has been investigated [12]. Figure 6.10 shows the line intensity distribution of He (I) (318.8 nm) ($P = 4.0$ kPa) with maximum line intensity at the centre of the cathode in the absence of the magnetic field. When a magnetic field is applied to the discharge, the line intensity in different plasma areas is

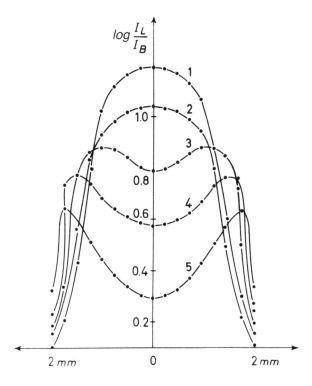

Fig. 6.10 – Relative intensity distribution of the spectral line He(I) 318.8 nm along the cross-section of the cathode cavity at various magnetic field intensities: $1 - H = 0$, $2 - H = 600$ Oe, $3 - H = 680$ Oe, $4 - H = 850$ Oe, $5 - H = 1150$ Oe (I_1 = intensity of the line, I_b = intensity of background, r = radius in mm).

redistributed. The maximum value is at the cavity walls, while at the centre there is a trough which becomes deeper with increase in field intensity. The same result was observed when the line intensity distribution of He (II) (320.3 nm) was studied. The results of these investigations [12] are confirmed by the data obtained [13-15] with different carrier-gas pressures and cavity diameters.

The line intensity distribution of impurity elements (representing residues from evaporation of solutions) was also investigated. Figure 6.11 shows the distribution for In (I) (325.6 nm), with maximum line intensity at the centre of the cathode. As the field intensity increases up to 850 Oe the intensity of the line grows over the whole cathode cross-section. At higher field intensities it slightly decreases again. Similar results were obtained for the Na (I) (330.2 nm) and K (I) (404.4 nm) lines.

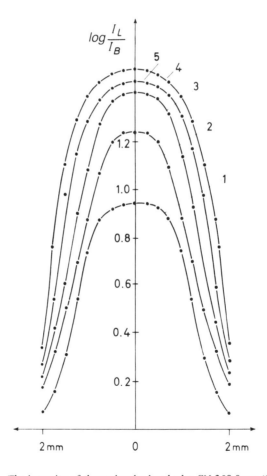

Fig. 6.11 – The intensity of the molecular band edge CN 359.0 nm (1) and of the along the cross-section of the cathode cavity at various magnetic field intensities: 1 – H = 0, 2 – H = 600 Oe, 3 – H = 680 Oe, 4 – H = 850 Oe, 5 – H = 1150 Oe. (I_1 = intensity of line, I_b = intensity of background, r = radius in mm).

Studies of the line intensity distribution over the cathode cross-section when a magnetic field is applied to the discharge, permit us to choose the optimum conditions for cavity-glow focusing on a spectrograph slit, i.e. sharp focusing of the cathode front with the plasma central zone appearing as a diaphragm in it, so that the maximum value of the line intensity of the element under investigation is recorded.

6.4.3 Dependence of the carrier gas line intensity, cathode materials, molecular bands and continuous background on the magnetic field intensity

Investigations have been done with helium and argon (P_{He} = 3.33–4.0 kPa, P_{Ar} = 667–933 Pa) as carrier gases. Figure 6.12 shows the atomic and ionic line intensities of He (I) 318.8 nm ($V_{exc.}$ = 23.7 eV), He (II) 320.3 nm ($V_{exc.}$ = 52.23 eV), Ar (I) 317.2 nm ($V_{exc.}$ = 15.45 eV) and Ar (II) 294.3 nm ($V_{exc.}$ = 21.35 eV) as functions of magnetic field intensity. It is seen that the intensity of these lines, all having high excitation potentials, drops as the field intensity increases, the effect being greater for helium.

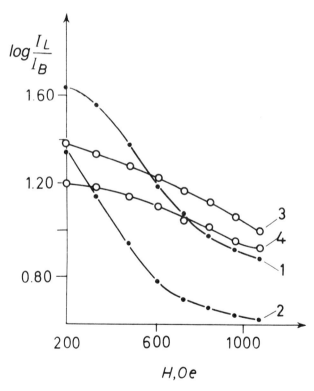

Fig. 6.12 – Relative intensities of He and Ar lines vs. magnetic field intensity applied to the hollow-cathode discharge: 1 – He(I) 318.8 nm (V_{exc} = 23.7 eV), 2 – He(II) 320.3 nm (V_{exc} = 52.2 eV), 3 – Ar(I) 317.2 nm (V_{exc} = 15.45 eV), 4 – Ar(II) 294.3 nm (V_{exc} = 21.35 eV). (I_1 = intensity of lines, I_b = intensity of background).

Studies of magnetic field effects on the line intensity of cathode materials (iron, copper, molybdenum) show that the intensity of lines with low excitation potentials [Cu (I) 324.7 nm, 3.8 eV, Mo (I) 315.8 nm, 3.9 eV; Fe (I) 302.0 nm, 4.11 eV] grows with increased magnetic field intensity up to a maximum and then drops. The intensity of lines with higher excitation potential [Fe (II) nm, 5.51 eV; Cu (II) 271.3 nm, 10 eV] decreases (Fig. 6.13). It should be noted that the increase in intensity of lines with low excitation potentials is slightly greater with helium as carrier gas than with argon. The magnetic field effect on the stability of discharge in the hollow cathode has also been evaluated. The relative standard deviation calculated from 100 measurements of the Cu (I) 324.7 nm line intensity is 4% when the field is applied and 6% without it. Thus, magnetic field application to some extent improves the stability of the hollow-cathode discharge.

The magnetic field effect on the intensity of the continuous background and molecular bands, excited in the hollow-cathode discharge, has been examined for a carbon cathode discharge in a helium atmosphere ($P = 3.33–4.0$ kPa).

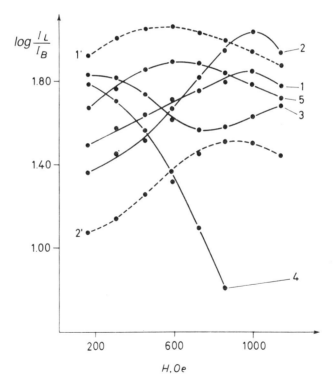

Fig. 6.13 – Relative intensity of lines of the cathode material vs. the magnetic field intensity applied to the hollow-cathode discharge in an atmosphere of He (1–5) and Ar (1', 2'): 1,1' – Fe(I) 302.0 nm ($V_{exc} = 4.11$ eV); 2,2' – Cu(I) 324.7 nm ($V_{exc} = 3.80$ eV); 3 – Fe(II) 273.9 nm ($V_{exc} = 5.51$ eV); 4 – Cu(II) 271.3 nm ($V_{exc} = 10.0$ eV); 5 – Mo(I) 315.8 nm ($V_{exc} = 3.93$ eV). (I_1 = intensity of background).

Figure 6.14 shows molecular (CN 359.0 nm band edge) and continuous back-ground (250-300 nm region) intensity as a function of magnetic field intensity. As can be seen in the diagram, the molecular background intensity decreases noticeably with increase in magnetic field intensity, whereas the continuous background intensity remains unchanged.

The data obtained show that application of a magnetic field can broaden the analytical capabilities of the hollow cathode, because the decrease in intensity of the carrier-gas molecular band lines can reduce or even eliminate their super-position on the analytical lines of the test elements.

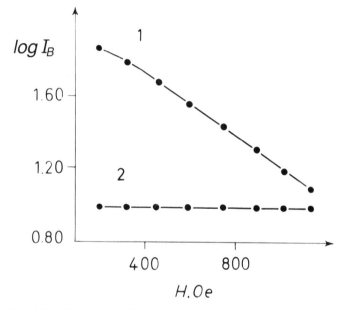

Fig. 6.14 – The intensity of the molecular band edge Cn 359.0 nm (1) and of the complete background-region at 300.0 nm (2) vs. intensity of the magnetic field applied to the hollow-cathode discharge.

6.4.4 Dependence of the line intensity of trace elements on magnetic field intensity

The effect of the magnetic field on the line intensities of a great many elements in the first six groups of the periodic table (including the lanthanides) and of manganese, iron, cobalt and nickel, when these are excited in the hollow-cathode discharge, has been examined.

Cylindrical-section hollow cathodes (cavity depth 20 mm, diameter 4 mm, wall thickness 1 mm) made of special purity graphite were used. Solutions of salts of the elements were applied to the bottom of the cavity and evaporated to dryness. The discharge was run in atmospheres of helium or argon, and mixtures of helium–argon, helium–nitrogen, helium–air and helium–carbon dioxide. Direct current was used (500-1200 mA), in some cases combined with a current pulse.

As an example, Figs. 6.15 and 6.16 show the dependence of the spectral line intensity of several elements, excited in the hollow-cathode discharge, on the magnetic field intensity. With magnetic field intensity up to approximately 850 Oe the intensity of atomic and ionic lines having excitation potentials of less than 5 eV first increases and then drops. On the other hand, the intensity of lines with excitation potentials over 5 eV drops continuously, except for those of Mg (II) 279.8 nm ($V_{exc.}$ = 8.86 eV) and Mg (II) 279.0 nm ($V_{exc.}$ = 8.86 eV) which do not change when the magnetic field is applied.

It should be noted that the increase in the intensity of lines with low excitation potentials, when the magnetic field is applied, is greater when an atmosphere of pure helium is used than it is with pure argon or a mixture of these two gases. When a helium–nitrogen or helium–air mixture is used, and a magnetic field, the line intensity increase is due to a decrease in the molecular background level (CN, NO, NO_2 bands). The line intensity does not change if the discharge occurs in a mixture of helium and carbon dioxide.

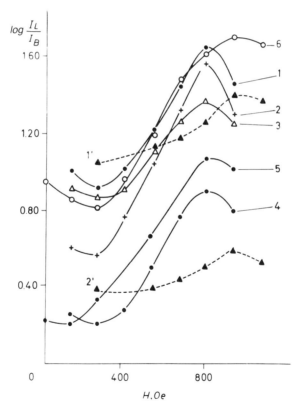

Fig. 6.15 – Relative intensity of trace element line vs. the strength of magnetic field applied to the hollow-cathode discharge in an atmosphere of He (1–6) and Ar (1', 2'): 1,1' – Cu(I) 324.7 nm (V_{exc} = 3.82 eV; 2, 2' – In(I) 325.6 nm (V_{exc} = 4.06 eV); 3 – Ca(I) 294.4 nm (V_{exc} = 4.29 eV); 4 – Fe(I) 302.0 nm (V_{exc} = 4.11 eV); 5 – Ag(I) 328.1 nm (V_{exc} = 3.78 eV); 6 – Cd(I) 326.1 nm (V_{exc} = 3.82 eV). (I_1 = intensity of lines, I_b = intensity of background).

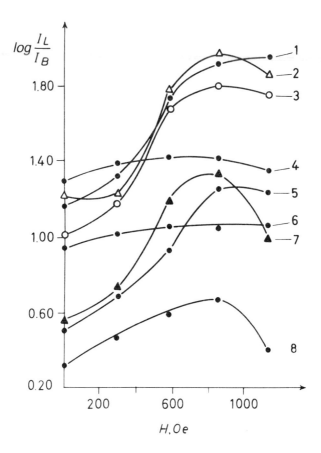

Fig. 6.16 – Relative intensity of trace element lines of the Group II of the Periodic Table vs. intensity of the magnetic field applied to the hollow-cathode discharge in an atmosphere of He: 1 – Mg(II) 280 nm (V_{exc} = 4.42 eV); 2 – Mg(II) 297 nm (V_{exc} = 4.43 eV); 3 – Mg(I) 285.2 nm (V_{exc} = 4.34 eV); 4 – Mg(II) 299.8 nm (V_{exc} = 8.86 eV); 5 – Ba(II) 455.4 nm (V_{exc} = 2.72 eV); 6 – Mg(II) 279.0 nm (V_{exc} = 8.86 eV); 7 – Ba(II) 493.4 nm (V_{exc} = 2.51 eV); 8 – Ca(I) 422.5 nm (V_{exc} = 4.68 eV). (I_1 = intensity of lines, I_b = intensity of background).

6.4.5 Some electric and temperature characteristics

The relation between the electric parameters of the discharge (voltage drop and electric force) is usually expressed by volt-ampere curves [44–49]. The form and position of the discharge depend on the nature and pressure of the carrier gas, the cathode material and shape, the ballast resistance, cathode-anode spacing and so on.

The magnetic field effect on the volt-ampere characteristics of the hollow-cathode discharge, used as a light-source in atomic spectroscopy, has been measured in an atmosphere of helium (P = 4.0 kPa). Cathodes with a 4 × 20 mm cavity and made of special purity graphite were used. Figure 6.17 shows a group of discharge volt-ampere characteristics at different intensities of the

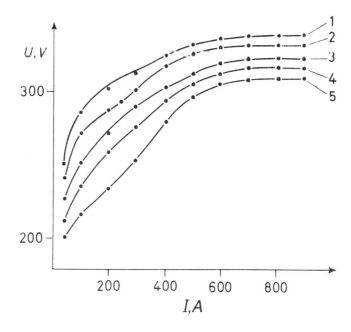

Fig. 6.17 — Current–voltage characteristics of the hollow-cathode discharge at various of magnetic field intensities applied to it: 1 − H = 0, 2 − H = 300 Oe, 3 − H = 600 Oe, 4 − H = 850 Oe, 5 − H = 1100 Oe. (U = cathode potential drop, I = current intensity).

magnetic field. It can be seen that with increase in magnetic field intensity, the voltage of discharge decreases at a fixed current value. As a result, the discharge resistance and the power resulting at the cathode diminish and this can result in decreased cathode wall temperature. Temperature measurements at different current values, taken with an optical pyrometer, show that increasing the magnetic field intensity up to 850-900 Oe results in a slight reduction of the cathode wall temperature (by approximately 100°C).

6.4.6 Discussion of experimental results

The experimental data given in Sections 6.4.1–6.4.5 show that a magnetic field has a fundamental effect on the hollow-cathode discharge plasma, changing its optical and energy characteristics. The most important of these effects, from a practical point of view for atomic spectroscopy, is the increase in analytical line intensity for a number of elements. The following factors may be possible causes of this: higher rate of transport of specimen material into the discharge zone; longer residence time for trace element atoms in the cathode cavity; change in the character of excitation of atomic and ionic spectral lines. Let us consider these in turn.

As shown in Section 6.4.5, application of a magnetic field to the discharge results in a slight reduction of cathode temperature. We can therefore conclude that the magnetic field does not increase the rate of evaporation; on the contrary, it decreases it slightly.

The magnetic field does not lengthen the residence time of neutral atoms in the discharge zone, as they are not influenced in any way. There is no real change in ion mobility under conditions of magnetic field pattern and intensity used in our experiments.

The most probable reason for the change in spectral line intensity when a magnetic field is applied to the discharge, is the change in excitation conditions, which is obviously related to the change in the energy distribution function in different areas of the plasma. This was discussed in Section 6.2.

The increased concentration of slow electrons, with energy less than 5 eV, in the centre of the hollow-cathode plasma when the magnetic field is applied, results in increased intensity of spectral lines with excitation potentials of less than 5 eV. However, it should be kept in mind that this explanation of the magnetic field effect on the hollow-cathode discharge characteristics is only valid if we consider the excitation and ionization processes to be caused by collisions with electrons. This mechanism of trace element excitation is typical for the hollow-cathode discharge in helium [50]. For a discharge in argon and other molecular gases or metal vapours (Hg, Cd, Zn), collisions (of the second kind) of atoms of the test elements with metastable atoms of the carrier gas acquire a significant role [51-55].

The magnetic field enhancement of the intensity of atomic and ionic lines with low excitation potentials can be used to improve the detection limits for a large number of elements in spectral analysis.

6.5 SPECTROANALYTICAL APPLICATION OF THE HOLLOW CATHODE DISCHARGE IN THE MAGNETIC FIELD

6.5.1 Detection limits and accuracy

The theoretical calculations made by Mandel'shtam and Nedler [7] showed that spectrum excitation in the hollow-cathode discharge can provide lower detection limits of elements than an arc source can.

The decrease in trace detection limits when the hollow cathode is used, compared to those with excitation sources operating in an open atmosphere, is due to the atoms of the elements remaining in the discharge plasma for a longer time. There is then multiple participation of the same atoms in producing the luminous radiation, and this leads to an increase in the utilization factor for the test substance. Experimental evidence for this has been given [56]. The authors demonstrated that the time spent by atoms in the hollow-cathode plasma is some tenths of a second, which is greater by two orders of magnitude than that in an arc discharge [57].

This improvement of detection limits is also due in part to the low pressure of the working gas, which increases the probability of population and depletion of the energy levels of the test elements.

Recombination and Bremsstrahlung background is significantly less, because of the lower electron concentration in the hollow cathode ($10^{13}/cm^3$, compared to

$10^{15}/cm^3$ in an arc discharge). As the solid continuum brightness is proportional to the square of the electron concentration, it is less by four orders of magnitude than that in the arc discharge, leading to a significant increase in the signal/background ratio and hence to lower detection limits.

It is essential, for obtaining low detection limits with the hollow-cathode discharge, to excite the spectrum of the sample in an isolated volume and an inert atmosphere. Besides eliminating the molecular bands which are characteristic of open sources and cover considerable areas of the spectrum (thereby making them analytically unsuitable), this also prevents introduction of contaminants into the sample from the ambient atmosphere.

In this connection it is worth noting the techniques of fractional distillation of the sample components in a non-cooled hollow cathode and of selective sputtering in a cooled cathode, which lower the detection limits for volatile and easily sputtered elements respectively.

The detection limits obtainable for trace elements by using the conventional hollow-cathode discharge and standard spectral equipment are 10^{-4}-10^{-6}% (10^{-9}-10^{-11} g), depending on the nature of the element and the sample. By preconcentration of the impurity elements from large samples it is possible to obtain detection limits of 10^{-6}-10^{-8}% [42, 58-60].

The hollow-cathode discharge has high glow stability. The hollow-cathode tubes used in atomic-absorption spectroscopy give intensity fluctuations of the radiated spectral lines of only about 0.1%, which is significantly lower than that in other light sources [61]. As is shown by experiment, however, the relative standard deviations of results obtained with non-cooled hollow-cathode tubes and the arc discharge are virtually the same (for low concentrations of the trace elements they are 10-40%). This can be explained as mainly due to the fact that in the non-cooled hollow cathode it is difficult to stabilize the transport of specimen material into the discharge zone. The cooled hollow-cathode discharge or the Grimm lamp is better, the relative standard deviation being not more than 1% [62-64].

Although the sensitivity and accuracy of analysis with these excitation sources are sufficiently high, they do not entirely meet the requirements of modern science and production in such industries as semiconductor radioelectronics, thermonuclear energetics, space exploration, etc.

There are several methods for improving the detection limits and accuracy of determination with the hollow-cathode discharge. The most interesting are the use of cathodes of special construction [65-69], separation of impurity elements in the excitation and evaporation zones [70, 71], thermochemical reactions in the discharge plasma [72, 73], use of the dual hollow cathode [74, 75], introduction of special additives into a sample [76, 77], and improvement of the discharge-tube power supplies [78-82].

Application of the magnetic field to the hollow-cathode discharge appears to be most suitable for obtaining a reduction in trace element detection limits. The development of procedures for spectral analysis of solutions and powder samples by using the hollow-cathode discharge in a magnetic field is dealt with in the next section.

6.5.2 Analysis of solution residues

The analysis of residues produced by evaporation of the sample solution in the cathode has been used [25-33] for evaluation of the effect of the magnetic field on the hollow-cathode discharge as a means of lowering the detection limits for a series of ultratrace elements.

The discharge has been operated in He ($P = 4.0$ kPa), Ar ($P = 933$ Pa) and a mixture of He and Ar ($P_{He} = 3066$ Pa, $P_{Ar} = 933$ Pa) in sectional graphite cathodes with a 4×20 mm cavity. The cathodes were made of special purity graphite and were preheated at a current of 1500 mA for 10 min to free them from contaminants. Solutions of the elements (volume 40 μl) were placed in the bottom of the sectional cathode, which had been pretreated with two drops of 0.7% solution of polystyrene in benzene, and then heating under an infrared lamp in an isolated box; the cathode was then placed in a discharge tube. The tube was powered by direct ($i_d = 500$-1000 mA), pulsed ($i_{mean\ p.} = 500$-1000 mA) and

Table 6.1 – Detection limits (in g) of several elements in the form of solution residues in the d.c. hollow-cathode discharge

Carrier gas	The element to be determined, wavelength (nm), (excitation potential eV)	Detection limits	
		In a magnetic field (850 Oe)	In the absence of a magnetic field
	Ag(I) 328.0 (3.8)	3×10^{-12}	4×10^{-11}
	Cd(I) 326.1 (3.8)	2×10^{-10}	2×10^{-9}
	Cu(I) 324.7 (3.8)	6×10^{-12}	3×10^{-10}
	Ga(I) 294.4 (4.3)	1.5×10^{-10}	1.5×10^{-9}
	In(I) 325.6 (4.1)	1×10^{-10}	1×10^{-9}
	Li(I) 670.7 (1.9)	3×10^{-11}	3×10^{-10}
Helium	Na(I) 589.5 (2.1)	1×10^{-10}	9×10^{-10}
	K(I) 404.4 (3.1)	3×10^{-10}	3×10^{-9}
	Mg(I) 285.2 (4.3)	5×10^{-12}	3×10^{-11}
	Ba(I) 455.4 (2.7)	4×10^{-10}	2.5×10^{-9}
	La(II) 394.9 (3.5)	1.5×10^{-7}	8×10^{-7}
	Sn(I) 317.5 (4.3)	1.5×10^{-8}	1×10^{-7}
	Pb(I) 283.3 (4.4)	4×10^{-8}	2.5×10^{-7}
	Sn(I) 317.5 (4.3)	6.5×10^{-9}	6.5×10^{-9}
Argon	Pb(I) 283.3 (4.4)	4×10^{-8}	4×10^{-8}
	Cu(I) 324.7 (3.8)	8×10^{-12}	1.5×10^{-11}
	In(I) 325.6 (4.1)	3×10^{10}	1×10^{-9}
Mixture of argon + helium	La(II) 394.9 (3.5)	2×10^{-8}	1×10^{-7}
	Sn(I) 317.5 (4.3)	6×10^{-9}	3×10^{-8}
	Pb(I) 283.3 (4.4)	3×10^{-8}	1×10^{-7}

combined ($i_{sum} = i_d + i_{mean\ p.}$ = 500–1000 mA) currents. The exposure time corresponded to a total burn-out of the trace elements. Standard solutions were prepared by dissolving metals and their oxides in hydrochloric or nitric acids of high purity, followed by dilution with demineralized water distilled twice in a quartz still. Calibration graphs were plotted as ($\log I_1/I_b$) vs. $\log c$, [I_1 = line intensity, I_b = background intensity (both as relative values), c = trace contents in g]. The detection limits of elements in residues of their salt solutions, when the hollow-cathode discharge is used in the absence ($H = 0$) and presence ($H = 850$ Oe) of a magnetic field, are given in Tables 6.1 and 6.2.

The tables show that when the magnetic field is applied, the detection limits are lower by an order of magnitude for the discharge in He, a factor of 2–3 for that in Ar and a factor of 4–5 for He-Ar mixture, than the detection limits in the absence of a magnetic field. In both cases the relative standard deviations are approximately 20–30%, depending on the element and its concentration.

6.5.3 Analysis of powder samples
The hollow-cathode discharge in the magnetic field has been used to determine the trace elements in tungsten powder, semiconductor silicon, and aluminium and chromium oxides [34–43].

The powder samples are placed in the 4 × 25 mm cavity of the cathodes, made of special purity graphite and preheated for 10 min at a current of 1.5 A.

The discharge was operated only in He of special purity, as use of Ar or its mixtures with He resulted in high sputtering of the sample, and hence to instability of the discharge. The tube was powered by a d.c. supply (current 600–800 mA). The exposure time was 4–5 min and corresponded to the time of total burn-out of the traces from the sample. To improve the discharge stability it was necessary, before spectrum survey, to preheat the cathode (plus sample) at a current of 100 mA for 3 min.

Table 6.2 – Detection limits of rare-earth elements in the form of solution residues in the hollow cathode discharge, with various power supplies

Element, line (excitation potential, eV)	Intensity of the magnetic field applied to the hollow cathode discharge (Oe)	Detection limits (g)		
		Steady	Pulse	Combined
La(II) 412.3 nm (3.3)	0	–	–	1×10^{-8}
Gd(II) 365.6 nm (3.5)		6×10^{-8}	6×10^{-9}	4×10^{-9}
Yb(I) 398.8 nm (3.1)		4×10^{-9}	1×10^{-9}	6×10^{-10}
La(II) 412.3 nm (3.3)	850	–	–	3×10^{-9}
Gd(I) 365.6 nm (3.5)		2×10^{-8}	3×10^{-9}	2×10^{-9}
Yb(I) 398.8 nm (3.1)		2×10^{-9}	5×10^{-10}	2×10^{-10}

Standard samples were prepared by introduction of the oxides or salts of the elements to be determined into a clean matrix in which the concentrations of these elements were less than their detection limits. A series of standard samples with various contents of the elements was prepared by means of successive dilution with the pure matrix. When no pure matrix was available for the preparation of standard samples, the method of standard additions [83] was used. Calibration graphs similar to those used in analysis of solution residues were plotted as $\log I_1/I_b$ vs. $\log c$.

Table 6.3 — Detection limits of trace elements in tungsten powder, semiconductor silicon, aluminium and chromium oxides, with the hollow-cathode discharge as excitation source, carrier gas He

Substance analysed	Elements, analytical line (nm), (excitation potential, eV)		Detection limits (%)	
			Without the magnetic field	In the magnetic field (850 Oe)
Tungsten powder (100 mg)	Cd(I)	326.1 (3.08)	1×10^{-5}	2×10^{-6}
Semi-	Ag(I)	328.0 (3.78)	2×10^{-6}	5×10^{-7}
conductor	Cu(I)	324.7 (3.82)	3×10^{-6}	8×10^{-7}
silicon (50 g)	In(I)	325.6 (4.08)	3×10^{-6}	1×10^{-6}
Aluminium	Mn(I)	279.48 (4.42)	3×10^{-5}	1×10^{-5}
oxide (40 mg)	Fe(I)	302.06 (4.11)	1.5×10^{-4}	5×10^{-5}
	Cr(I)	357.86 (3.46)	1×10^{-5}	5×10^{-6}
	Ga(I)	294.3 (3.29)	2×10^{-5}	4×10^{-6}
	Cd(I)	326.1 (3.80)	4×10^{-6}	1×10^{-6}
	Ge(I)	303.9 (4.96)	2×10^{-5}	5×10^{-6}
	Cu(I)	327.4 (3.78)	3×10^{-5}	1×10^{-5}
	In(I)	325.6 (4.10)	8×10^{-6}	2×10^{-6}
	Sn(I)	283.9 (4.78)	8×10^{-4}	3×10^{-4}
	Ag(I)	328.0 (3.78)	2.5×10^{-6}	3×10^{-7}
	Pb(I)	283.0 (4.40)	1×10^{-5}	4×10^{-6}
Chromium	Cu(I)	327.4 (3.78)	1×10^{-6}	3×10^{-7}
oxide	In(I)	325.6 (4.10)	1×10^{-5}	2×10^{-6}
(40 mg)	Ni(I)	305.1 (4.09)	3×10^{-2}	5×10^{-3}
	Ag(I)	328.06 (3.78)	2.5×10^{-6}	3×10^{-7}
	Cd(I)	326.1 (3.8)	4×10^{-5}	1×10^{-6}
	Ga(I)	299.4 (4.29)	8×10^{-6}	2×10^{-6}
	Mn(I)	279.48 (4.42)	1×10^{-4}	6×10^{-5}
	Pb(I)	283.3 (4.4)	1×10^{-4}	3×10^{-5}

Information on the limits of detection of trace elements in tungsten powder, semiconductor silicon, chromium and aluminium oxides with and without application of the magnetic field is given in Table 6.3. As shown, the detection limits for powder samples are lower by a factor of 3–10 with a magnetic field (850 Oe) applied than without it. The relative standard deviation is also slightly lower when the magnetic field is used, ranging from 20 to 30%, depending on the element and its concentration.

6.6 INVESTIGATION OF SPECTRAL RESPONSE CHARACTERISTICS OF HOLLOW-CATHODE LAMPS USED IN ATOMIC-ABSORPTION AND ATOMIC-FLUORESCENCE SPECTROSCOPY WITH A MAGNETIC FIELD

Hollow-cathode lamps are the most popular emitting sources used in atomic-absorption and atomic-fluorescence analysis. The main drawback of these lamps (fed by direct current) is the low intensity of the lines emitted. It is not advisable to increase the discharge current for the purpose of increasing resonance-line intensity, since there would be significant line-broadening [61]. High-current pulse discharge also has the same effect. Therefore research on methods of increasing the intensity of spectral line intensity without broadening them is of interest.

Several spectral response characteristics of hollow-cathode lamps fed by direct and pulsed current in a magnetic field have been studied [84]. The LSP-1 full-scale lamps produced in the USSR were used, with the magnetic field applied by means of the solenoid type coil (Section 6.2). Relative intensity measurements of the resonance lines emitted by the hollow-cathode lamps run with and without application of the magnetic field were made by use of a VMS-2 monochromator and a U2-6 amplifier. Application of the magnetic field to the hollow-cathode lamp discharge sometimes increased the resonance-line intensity by as much as 50–100% (Table 6.4).

Table 6.4 – Line intensity amplification factor in the magnetic field
$(I_{H=1000\,Oe}/I_{H=0})$

Line (nm)	Lamp type	Current (mA)	Amplification factor		
			Direct current	Pulsed current $\nu = 480$ Hz $\tau = 50\ \mu$sec	Pulsed current $\nu = 4800$ Hz $\tau = 5\ \mu$sec
Fe(I) 248.3	LS–1	15	1.2	2.0	1.3
Co(I) 240.7	LS–1	15	1.3	2.0	1.2
Ni(I) 232.0	LS–1	15	1.3	2.0	1.25
Mg(I) 294.2	LS–1	15	1.4	2.5	0.8
Cu(I) 324.7	LS–1	15	1.2	2.1	1.0
Zn(I) 213.8	LS–1	12	1.3	1.6	0.9
Cr(I) 357.9	LSP–1	20	1.0	1.2	1.1
Ag(I) 328.1	LS–1	10	1.0	1.4	1.0
Mo 313.3	LS–1	15	1.0	1.4	1.0
V(I) 318.4	LSP–1	30	1.1	1.2	0.9

As can be seen from this table the greatest increase of line intensity is given by use of a magnetic field, low-frequency pulsed current and long pulse duration, whereas high pulse rates and short duration in the magnetic field give a decrease in the intensity of some of the lines.

When the magnetic field is applied to the hollow-cathode lamp discharge, the line-width generally remains unchanged, and sometimes even decreases.

Thus when such lamps are used in atomic-absorption and atomic-fluorescence analysis there may be a lowering of the detection limits for some elements, but at the expense of increasing resonance-line emission intensity and as a consequence there may be less possibility of increasing the signal to noise ratio.

On the basis of the results discussed above, we can draw the conclusion that the application of a magnetic field to the hollow-cathode discharge greatly increases the potentialities in spectral analysis and specifically in the analysis of high-purity substances. The limits of trace element detection attainable are sufficient for solving various analytical problems in modern science and technology.

REFERENCES

[1] L. A. Artsymovich, *Elementarnaya fizika plasmy*, Atomizdat, Moscow, 1969.

[2] A. V. Chernetsky, *Vvedenie v fisiku plasmy*, Atomizdat, Moscow, 1969.

[3] B. M. Smirnov, *Atomnye stolknoveniya i elementarnye protsessy v plazme*, Atomizat, Moscow, 1968.

[4] B. I. Moytes and G. E. Pikus, *Termoemissionnye preobrazovateli i nizko-temperaturnaya plazma*, Nauka, Moscow, 1973.

[5] B. M. Smirnov, *Fizika slaboionizovanogo gaza*, Nauka, Moscow, 1972.

[6] K. Hirnquist, *RCA Rev.*, 1958, **19**, 35.

[7] S. L. Mandel'shtam and V. V. Nedler, *Opt. Spektrosk.*, 1961, **10**, 390.

[8] V. S. Borodin and Yu. M. Kagan, *Zh. Tekh. Fiz.*, 1966, **36**, 181, 1198.

[9] Yu. M. Kagan, R. I. Lyagushchenko and S. N. Khvorostovsky, *Zh. Tekh. Fiz.*, 1972, **42**, 1686.

[10] Yu. M. Kagan, R. I. Lyagushchenko, A. S. Taroyan and S. N. Khvorostovsky, *Zh. Tekh. Fiz.*, 1973, **43**, 1488.

[11] Yu. M. Kagan, R. I. Lyagushchenko and S. N. Khvorostovsky, *Opt. Spektrosk.*, 1972, **33**, 430.

[12] T. M. Shabanova, L. P. Lazareva, D. E. Maksimov and N. K. Rudnevsky *Tr. Khim. Khim. Tekhnol., Fiziko-Khim. Metody Issled. Anal., Gorky*, 1973, **3**, No. 34, 79.

[13] V. Z. Krasil'shchik, *Khim. Reaktivy Preparaty, IREA*, 1970, **32**, 253.

[14] V. H. Pacheva and D. Z. Zhechev, *Dokl. Bolg. Akad. Nauk*, 1971, **24**, 1617.

[15] V. M. Tkachenko and V. B. Tyutyunnik, *Izv. Vyssh. Ucheb. Zaved., Radiofiz.*, 1972, **15**, 631.

[16] E. Badareu, C. Popovici and H. Somesan, *Rev. Roum. Phys.*, 1967, **12**, 3.

[17] C. Popovici and M. Somesan, *Electron Lett.*, 1965, **1**, 31.

[18] C. Popovici and M. Somesan, *Appl. Phys. Lett.*, 1966, **8**, 103.

[19] M. Someşan and C. Popovici, *Appl. Phys. Lett.*, 1966, **9**, 65.

[20] C. Popovici, M. Somesan and V. Nistor, *Phys. Lett.*, 1966, **22**, 587.

[21] C. Popovici, V. Kreici and O. Stirand, *Rev. Roum. Phys.*, 1968, **13**, 423.

[22] M. Somesan, *Proc. 9th Intern. Conf. Phenomena Ioniz. Gases, Bucharest*, 1969, p. 119.

[23] V. M. Tkachenko and V. B. Tyutyunnik, *Opt. Spektrosk.*, 1969, **26**, 896.

[24] V. M. Tkachenko and V. B. Tyutyunnik, *Zh. Tekh. Fiz.*, 1972, **42**, 67.

[25] N. K. Rudnevsky, D. E. Maksimov and T. M. Shabanova, in *Tezisy dokl. na Vsessoyuzn. Symp. po spektr. analizu na malye soderzhaniya i sledy elementov*, Tbilisi, p. 66.

[26] N. K. Rudnevsky, D. E. Maksimov and T. M. Shabanova, *Zh. Prikl. Spektrosk.*, 1970, **13**, 199.

[27] N. K. Rudnevsky, D. E. Maksimov, T. M. Shabanova and L. P. Lazareva, *Zh. Prikl. Spektrosk.*, 1972, **16**, 356.

[28] N. K. Rudnevsky, D. E. Maksimov, T. M. Shabanova and L. P. Lazareva, *Zavodsk. Lab.*, 1972, **38**, 1338.

[29] N. K. Rudnevsky, N. G. Pichugin, D. E. Maksimov and E. E. Kachan, in *Sb. poluchenie i analiz vechestv osoboy chistoty*, p. 215, Nauka, Moscow, 1978.

[30] N. K. Rudnevsky, D. E. Maksimov and L. P. Lazareva, *Zh. Analit. Khim.*, 1974, **39**, 1422.

[31] N. K. Rudnevsky, D. E. Maksimov and L. P. Lazareva, *Zh. Prikl. Spektrosk.*, 1976, **24**, 136.

[32] L. P. Lazareva, T. M. Shabanova, D. E. Maksimov and N. K. Rudnevsky, in *Mezhvuz. Sb. Fiz. Khim. Met. Anal., Gorky*, No. 4, p. 42, 1979.

[33] N. K. Rudnevsky, D. E. Maksimov and L. P. Lazareva, *Zh. Prikl. Spektrosk.*, 1978, **29**, 916.

[34] N. K. Rudnevsky, D. E. Maksimov, T. M. Shabanova and L. V. Bakhareva, *Tr. Khim. Khim. Tekhnol., Gorky*, 1973, No. **4**, 102.

[35] T. M. Shabanova, D. E. Maksimov and N. K. Rudnevsky, *Tr. Khim. Khim. Tekhnol., Gorky*, 1975, No. 1, 65.

[36] N. K. Rudnevsky, D. E. Maksimov, A. N. Tumanova and T. M. Shabanova, *Zh. Prikl. Spektrosk.*, 1982, **37**, 722.

[37] N. K. Rudnevsky, D. E. Maksimov, T. M. Shabanova and L. P. Kruglova, *Zh. Prikl. Spektrosk.*, 1981, **34**, 1114.

[38] D. E. Maksimov, A. N. Rudnevsky and T. M. Shabanova, *Mezhvuz. Sb. Fiz. Khim. Met. Anal., Gorky*, 1982, 55.

[39] D. E. Maksimov and N. K. Rudnevsky, *Zh. Prikl. Spektrosk.*, 1983, **39**, 5.

[40] D. E. Maksimov and N. K. Rudnevsky, *Spektralny analiz s primeneniem razryada v polom katode*, Izd. GGU, Gorky, 1979.

[41] D. E. Maksimov, N. K. Rudnevsky, A. N. Rudnevsky and T. M. Shabanova, *Spektralnu analiz s primeneniem razryada v polom katode*, Izd. GGU, Gorky, 1983.

[42] D. E. Maksimov, V. G. Pimenov, A. N. Rudnevsky, T. M. Shabanova and V. N. Shishov, in *Tezisy dokladov XIX Vsesoyuzn. syezda po spektroskopii,* Chap. 5, p. 172, Tomsk, 1983.

[43] D. E. Maksimov, A. N. Rudnevsky and T. M. Shabanova, *Proc. 9th ICAS/ XXII CSI, Tokyo, 1981,* p. 505.

[44] A. Lompe, R. Seeliger and E. Wolter, *Ann. Phys.,* 1939, **36**, 9.

[45] I. Roig and M. Becart, *Compt. Rend.,* 1952, **234**, 1606.

[46] A. N. Shteinberg, *Opt. Spektrosk.,* 1965, **18**, 16.

[47] A. N. Shteinberg, *Zh. Prikl. Spektrosk.,* 1965, **2**, 385.

[48] S. Caroli and P. Delle Femmine, *Spectrosc. Lett.,* 1978, **11**, 299.

[49] S. Caroli, A. Alimonti and O. Senofonte, *Spectrosc. Lett.,* 1980, **13**, 457.

[50] H. Falk, *Ann. Phys.,* 1965, **16**, 160.

[51] R. A. Sawyer, *Phys. Rev.,* 1930, **36**, 44.

[52] A. Ferkhmin and S. E. Frish, *Phys. Z. Sowjetunion,* 1936, **9**, 466.

[53] V. A. Konovalov and S. E. Frish, *Phys. Z. Sowjetunion,* 1936, **10**, 111.

[54] S. E. Frish and Yu. M. Kagan, *Vest. Leningrad. Univ.,* 1948, No. 1, 12.

[55] D. E. Maksimov and A. N. Rudnevsky, *Dokl. Akad. Nauk SSSR,* 1981, **256**, 628.

[56] I. A. Berezin and I. N. Sten'gach, *Zh. Prikl. Spektrosk.,* 1969, **11**, 399.

[57] V. D. Malykh and M. D. Serd, *Opt. Spektrosk.,* 1964, **16**, 368.

[58] Kh. I. Zil'bershtein, N. I. Kaliteevsky, A. N. Razumovskii and Yu. F. Fedorov, *Zavodsk Lab.,* 1962, **28**, 43.

[59] G. A. Pevtsov and V. Z. Krasil'shchik, *Zh. Analit. Khim.,* 1963, **18**, 1314.

[60] N. K. Rudnevsky, A. N. Tumanova, D. E. Maksimov and L. V. Lomzilova, *Zh. Prikl. Spektrosk.,* 1969, **11**, 783.

[61] B. V. L'vov, *Atomic Absorption Spectroscopy,* Hilger, London, 1970.

[62] A. I. Drobyshev and Yu. I. Turkin, *Zh. Prikl. Spektrosk.,* 1969, **11**, 783.

[63] W. Grimm, *Spectrochim. Acta,* 1968, **23B**, 443.

[64] A. Alimonti, S. Caroli and O. Senofonte, *Spectrosc. Lett.,* 1980, **13**, 307.

[65] F. Birks, *Spectrochim. Acta,* 1954, **6**, 169.

[66] A. Monfils, I. Ottelet and B. Rosen, *Ind. Chim. Belge,* 1951, **16**, 675.

[67] V. L. Sabatovskaya, I. A. Kuzovlev and I. G. Yudelevich, *Zh. Prikl. Spektrosk.,* 1977, **26**, 207.

[68] D. E. Maksimov, L. P. Lazareva, L. D. Nizyakova and T. M. Shabanova, *Zh. Analit. Khim.,* 1979, **24**, 1045.

[69] V. G. Pimenov, V. N. Shishov and N. V. Larin, *Zh. Analit. Khim.,* 1981, **26**, 1019.

[70] G. A. Pevtsov and V. Z. Krasil'shchik, *Zh. Analit. Khim.,* 1966, **21**, 863.

[71] G. A. Pevtsov and V. Z. Krasil'shchik, *Zh. Prikl. Spektrosk.,* 1968, **9**, 504.

[72] G. A. Pevtsov, V. Z. Krasil'shchik and A. F. Yakovleva, *Zh. Analit. Khim.,* 1969, **24**, 234.

[73] N. K. Rudnevsky, A. N. Tumanova, L. V. Kutergina and A. N. Pozdnyakova, *Zh. Prikl. Spektrosk.,* 1968, **8**, 571.

[74] Yu. B. Atnashev, V. N. Muzgin and F. F. Gavrilov, *Zh. Prikl. Spektrosk.,* 1973, **18**, 183.

[75] A. G. Zhiglinskii, N. N. Zaretskaya and Yu. I. Turkin, *Zh. Prikl. Spektrosk.*, 1973, **18**, 903.

[76] D. E. Maksimov and A. N. Rudnevsky, *Zh. Prikl. Spektrosk.*, 1981, **34**, 406.

[77] A. N. Rudnevsky and D. E. Maksimov, *Mezhvuz. sb. poluch. i anal. vesechestv osoboy chistoty, Gorky,* 1981, 37.

[78] N. K. Rudnevsky, N. G. Pichugin and D. E. Maksimov, *Zh. Prikl. Spektrosk.*, 1973, **19**, 5.

[79] N. K. Rudnevsky, D. E. Maksimov, N. G. Pichugin and R. Khasyanov, *Zh. Prikl. Spektrosk.*, 1974, **20**, 707.

[80] Yu. B. Atnashev and V. N. Muzgin, *Zh. Prikl. Spektrosk.*, 1974, **21**, 414.

[81] A. I. Drobyshev and Yu. I. Turkin, *Zh. Prikl. Spektrosk.*, 1975, **22**, 755.

[82] V. J. Gladushchak and E. Ya. Shreider, *Zavodsk. Lab.*, 1964, **30**, 47.

[83] N. K. Rudnevsky, L. N. Ivagin and L. N. Ivagina, *Izv. Akad. Nauk SSSR, Fiz.,* 1950, **14**, 698.

[84] V. T. Demarin, D. E. Maksimov and N. G. Pichugin, *Tr. Khim. Khim. Tekhnol., Gorky,* 1975, No. 1, 62.

7

Principles and use of a boosted hollow-cathode discharge source for atomic spectroscopy

Zs. Szilvássy

7.1 INTRODUCTION

In recent decades, low-pressure gas-discharge tubes have gained increasing importance in emission spectroscopy. One of most important of these spectral sources is the hollow-cathode lamp. The negative glow discharge, drawn into the cathode cavity, acts as a radiating plasma in hollow-cathode discharge (HCD) tubes.

Compared with those of heat-generated plasmas, the most important characteristics of glow-discharge plasma are the lack of thermodynamic equilibrium, even local, and the big difference (more than several orders of magnitude) in electron, ion and neutral gas temperatures. Another important point is that the atoms to be determined are transferred to the discharge space by the sputtering effect of the working gas. These atoms are excited and ionized by electron impact and secondary impact. This plasma then has all the advantages of hollow-cathode excitation. Characteristically, high-energy electrons are present in glow-discharge plasmas, and consequently all elements are susceptible to excitation by this method. Due to a reduction in or a total lack of thermal effects, fractional distillation and interelement effects are less severe.

Another advantage of HCD tubes is that solid or liquid samples of conducting or non-conducting substances can be directly analysed, without any pretreatment, by placing them in the cathode cup or, if a gaseous sample is to be analysed, mixing it with the working gas. Samples as small as 0.1 mg can be analysed.

The main drawbacks are the handling of the vacuum system connected to the discharge tube, and the presence of interfering molecular bands in the spectra, caused by impurities in the vacuum system and working gas.

The modified HCD lamp described hereafter was devised in order to:

(i) increase the concentration of atomic particles and create more favourable excitation conditions for elements with low ionization-potential;

(ii) decrease interference caused by the initial stabilization period;

(iii) decrease the relatively high standard deviation of determination when extremely volatile elements are determined.

Several variants of Schüler and Gollnow's original discharge lamp [1] were built and tested experimentally. Best results were obtained with hot hollow cathodes, arranged perpendicularly to the axis of the water-cooled discharge tube.

7.2 BACKGROUND OF HOLLOW-CATHODE RADIATION SOURCES

7.2.1 Major hollow-cathode discharge tube designs

HCD tubes belong to the family of low-pressure gas discharge tubes, filled with noble gases, which are operated at d.c. voltages of 1-2 kV.

On the basis of the intensity of the d.c. current in the tube, two different types can be distinguished. The term HCD tube is generally used when the applied current intensity is in the range 0.1-1 A. When the current is 10-100 A (and the tubes are operated at a lower voltage than the HCD tubes), the system is called a hollow-cathode arc (HCA) lamp [2].

Only HCD tubes — and their variants — will be discussed in this chapter.

7.2.2 HCD radiation sources and their applications in spectroscopy

Schüler and Gollnow [1] built and used the first analytically-oriented HCD systems. The discharge tubes were constructed in metal, with double-wall, water-cooled cathode and anode. The tubes were filled with gas at a pressure of 10-1000 Pa. Since the cathode and the anode are very close to each other in this particular type of tube, the positive column of layered gas-discharge cannot develop, and the discharge section consists, for all practical purposes, of the cathode glow, Hittorf's dark space and the negative glow discharge. Owing to the special geometry of the hollow cathode, the negative glow discharge is drawn into the cup of the cathode, and becomes much brighter. The emission intensity is increased almost a hundredfold. The closed gas-circulation system is operated with a mercury-diffusion pump. This radiation source has been used for studies of the hyperfine structure of spectra and for the determination of trace impurities in radioactive materials. The structure of the discharge is shown in Fig. 7.1.

The major advantages of HCD tubes — i.e. sharp emission lines, absence of Doppler and Stark broadening, excitation in a closed space, permitting the analysis of toxic and radioactive materials — were established in these first experiments.

HCD tubes became more widely used and investigated, during the 1950s.

Birks [3] introduced a modified version of the Schüler and Gollnow system, A removable quartz window was mounted on the front of the lamp, facilitating rapid replacement of the sample. Most of the mercury-diffusion pump vacuum system was retained, several traps and cold baffles were added.

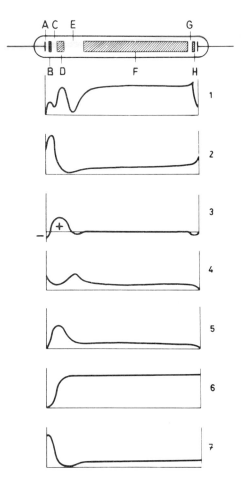

Fig. 7.1 – Layered gas discharge in a long discharge tube. 1. Light intensity.
2. Field strength. 3. Resulting space charge. 4. Negative charges. 5. Positive charges.
6. Electron current. 7. Ion current.
A – Aston's dark space; B – first cathode layer; C – Hittorf's dark space; D –
negative glow discharge; E – Faraday's dark space; F – positive column; G –
positive glow discharge; H – anode dark space.

Rosen [4] designed a special system for the determination of oxygen in steel. The tube was made of copper and a window was added to the anode block, for observing excitation phenomena in the cavity without interfering with the main radiation beam.

Milazzo [5,6] used water-cooled metal HCD tubes as radiation sources in vacuum spectrographs. Excellent results were obtained in trace impurity analysis for halogens. The same type of lamp was used by Caroli et al. [7–10] for the analysis of biological samples. An important modification, the use of an external microwave field, was also devised by Caroli et al. [11]. A typical tube design is shown in Fig. 7.2.

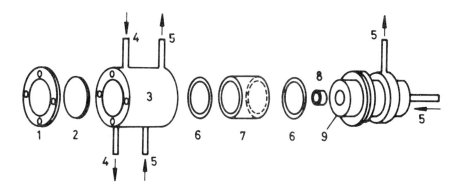

Fig. 7.2 – Scheme of the water-cooled metal HCD lamp: 1, fastening ring; 2, quartz window; 3, anode unit; 4, gas inlet; 5, water cooling; 6, sealing ring; 7, glass chamber; 8, cathode cup; 9, cathode unit.

In trace metal analysis, the detection limits obtained with an HCD source can be improved by applying an external magnetic field. The longitudinal axis of the tube is parallel to the field and therefore the field is perpendicular to the velocity vector of the electrons emitted by the cathode wall [12]. Owing to the Lorentz force, the electron concentration is increased in front of the cathode wall, and both the positive space-charge and the potential drop at the cathode decrease. This leads to reduced electron temperature, increased intensity of the atomic lines and decreased intensity of the ion lines.

Falk *et al.* [13,14] attained spatial separation of atomization and excitation processes, thereby improving detection limits considerably.

Another modification, developed in our laboratory [15-18], permits both the spatial and time-separation of atomization and excitation processes. A secondary discharge increases the particle density, improving the detection limits for metals, and delayed switching of the secondary discharge decreases the standard deviation of the relative concentration of volatile elements.

7.2.3 Cooled hollow cathodes

Depending on the method of cooling, we can divide HCD lamps into hot (no cooling), water-cooled and liquid-air-cooled types. There are two important consequences of a decrease in cathode temperature:

 (i) the gas temperature in the plasma is decreased and the Doppler broadening of spectral lines is reduced;
(ii) thermal evaporation of the sample is reduced or eliminated.

Hot hollow cathodes were first used for the determination of radioactive metals, halogens and sulphur, non-conducting oxides and carbonates in various matrices [19-22].

Czakow [23] made an important modification of hot hollow cathodes in developing the microcavity hollow-cathode lamp. In this case, the diameter of the cathode cavity is 1–2 mm, compared with the conventional 5–10 mm. The smaller cathode bores resulted in higher cathode wall temperatures (up to 2000°C), influencing the physical, chemical and thermal processes which take place in the tube. High cavity temperatures, combined with the presence of reducing atmospheres, result in fractional distillation of the sample. This phenomenon can be utilized in the determination of elements of different volatility. Fluorine, chlorine, selenium and other elements can be determined. Because of stability problems, the pulsed method gives better results.

Water-cooled HCD sources are the most widely used. By a proper choice of material and magnitude of the heat-transfer coefficient of the cathode cup, cathode wall temperatures of several hundred degrees centigrade can be obtained. This is well below the melting point of most elements; consequently thermal effects can be eliminated and the sample applied to the wall of the cathode enters the discharge space as a result of the sputtering effects of the working gas.

Török and Záray have developed a deep-cooled twin hollow-cathode lamp [24] which has been used before for the determination of isotope ratios [25–36].

7.3 ENERGY CONTROL POSSIBILITIES

Most of the electric energy introduced into the hollow-cathode discharge tube is recovered, through excitation processes, as radiation.

The electric field inside the discharge tube accelerates both the electrons released by the cathode and the ions (present and formed) in the gas phase. The electron and ion beams, moving in opposite directions, undergo both elastic and inelastic impacts.

Elastic impacts between electrons and gas atoms increase the kinetic energy of the latter. The elastic impacts of ions and neutral gas molecules increase the kinetic energy of the neutral particles. Charge exchange can also accompany the impacts of ions and neutral molecules. This process also increases the number of high-energy neutral species. These high-energy neutral atoms, in turn, ionize the gas and/or release secondary electrons.

Electrons released by the cathode are accelerated across the potential drop in front of the cathode. These electrons represent the fast-electron component of the electron beam. Low-energy slow electrons are left behind by these impacts. The energy of fast electrons can be increased in two ways: by increasing the energy of the ions which impinge upon the cathode, or by increasing the potential drop at the cathode.

Excited, ionized and metastable species are generated in inelastic impacts with fast electrons. Excited atoms return to their ground state in about 10^{-8} sec, and release their excitation energy in the form of radiation. The lifetime of metastable states is of the order of 10^{-4} sec in gas discharge systems. Therefore, the presence of metastable states increases the probability of ionization. Metastable atoms lose their energy by secondary impacts, creating new excited and ionized species. Metastable states can be formed and eliminated in the following processes:

Formation: $A + e_{fast}^- \rightarrow A^* + e_{slow}^-$ (7.1)

Elimination: $A^* + e_{slow}^- \rightarrow A + e_{slow}^-$ (7.2)

$A^* + B \rightarrow A + B^*$ (7.3)
(energy resonance)

$A^* + B \rightarrow A + B^{+*} + e^-$ (7.4)
(ionization and excitation)

(A is the carrier gas, B the foreign species and * indicates the metastable state).

Metastable states are most often eliminated by means of reaction (7.2). If the probability of formation of metastable states is to be decreased, the number of fast electrons has to be reduced.

Inelastic impacts of slow electrons and ions lead to recombination. Here, excess of energy and momentum is released in the form of photons. Photon energy represents the difference between the initial kinetic energy and the bond energy. Photons thus created reach the cathode by a rapid process of radiation diffusion, i.e. fast absorption and emission processes. There they either generate new electrons or appear directly as radiation.

The energy conversion processes involved in gas discharge are shown in Fig. 7.3.

Part of the radiation is a continuous radiation, as a result of Bremsstrahlung. The larger and more important part of the radiation consists of a series of discrete-wavelength photons in the ultraviolet, visible and infrared spectral ranges.

The energy-releasing processes involved in the gas discharge have to be controlled if the number and/or intensity of atomic lines in the spectra are to be increased.

Electron velocities can be controlled by the voltage applied to the discharge tube or by suitable choice of noble gas as the working gas.

When the spectra are recorded on photographic emulsions the intensities of the emission lines are derived indirectly, from the degree of blackening of the spectral lines on the plate or film. The blackening S is defined by $S = \log (I_0/I)$, where I_0 is the intensity of the incident light and I is the intensity of the transmitted light at any spectral line.

In the case of HCD radiation sources, rather long exposures are needed, assuming that the other experimental parameters (such as current intensity, voltage, temperature and type and pressure of the working gas) have been optimized. The application of an external magnetic field, however, improves the sensitivity of the method. The effects of an external magnetic field on the performance of a new water-cooled HCD system developed in our laboratory have been investigated. The discharge tube is shown schematically in Fig. 7.4.

Since the energy conversion processes of the glow discharge can be influenced to a certain extent by the external magnetic field, the effects of field strength on the discharge mechanism and the line intensity have been elucidated.

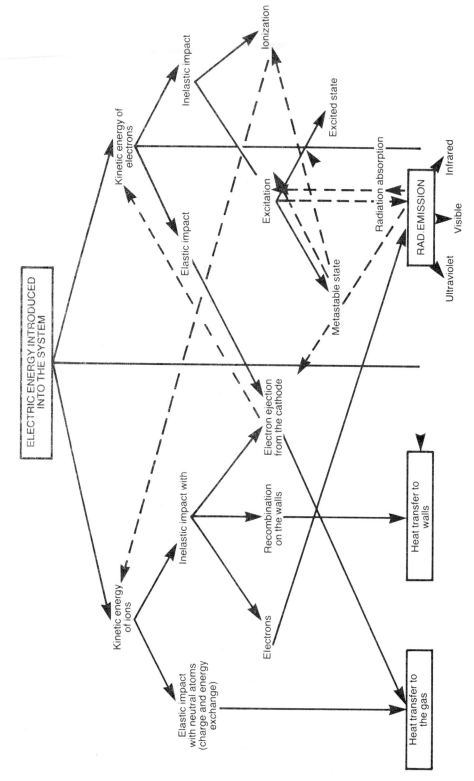

Fig. 7.3 – Energy conversion process occurring in a glow-discharge plasma.

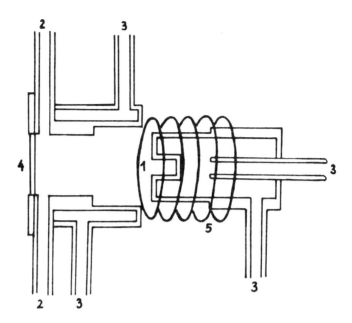

Fig. 7.4 – Scheme of the discharge tube with external magnetic field perpendicular
to the electric field:
1, cathode cavity; 2, gas inlet; 3, water cooling; 4, quartz window; 5, solenoid.

The solenoid body and the discharge tube were made of copper, the cathode
cup of graphite. None of these materials influences the intensity of the magnetic
field. The magnetic susceptibilities are $\kappa_{Cu} = -8 \times 10^{-7}$ and $\kappa_C = -8 \times 10^{-6}$,
respectively.

The magnetic field influences the structure of the glow discharge. In the
absence of an external magnetic field, the glow discharge is evenly distributed in
the cathode cup, but in its presence a dark spot appears in the centre of the cup,
increasing in size with the strength of the field. This observation can be explained
as follows. Electrons leaving the wall of the cathode at right angles enter a
magnetic field having its induction vector perpendicular to their velocity vectors.
Therefore, the electrons are deflected by a force depending on the strength of
the magnetic field and their velocities. This deflection force is the Lorentz
force **F**:

$$\mathbf{F} = e(\mathbf{v} \times \mathbf{B}) \tag{7.5}$$

where e is the charge on the electron.

Since the Lorentz force is always perpendicular to the velocity vector **v**, the
magnetic field will influence the direction of the velocity vector, but not its
magnitude. Therefore the electrons follow a path in plane-circular motion.
However, electrons emitted from the cathode wall are influenced simultaneously
by the magnetic field and an electric field perpendicular to the magnetic field.

Thus, the differential equation describing the motion of the electron is:

$$m \frac{d\mathbf{v}}{d\mathbf{E}} = e(\mathbf{E} + \mathbf{v} \times \mathbf{B}) \tag{7.6}$$

where m is the mass of the electron.

If we consider a coordinate system with its X axis aligned with the electric field $\mathbf{E}$, and Y axis with the magnetic field $\mathbf{B}$, and also assume that the electron starts its motion at time zero from the origin of the coordinate system, with zero velocity, then the path of the particle is a cycloid, the result of the superposition of a motion with constant velocity on a circular motion. If an elementary section of the cathode wall is in the XY plane, then the electron emitted by the wall, between two successive impacts, follows part of the cycloid rather than a stright line. This results in curved electron trajectories and reduced electron density in the centre of the cup, and consequently in the appearance of a dim spot.

It has been shown that the strength of the magnetic field does not influence the magnitude of the electron velocity, but the trajectories become curved. Therefore, the electron concentration is increased in the Hittorf dark space, and consequently the magnitude of the positive space charge and the potential drop are decreased.

When the relationship between line intensity and magnetic field strength was investigated, it was found that with low ionization-potential elements the line intensity becomes maximized at a certain field strength, as shown in Fig. 7.5.

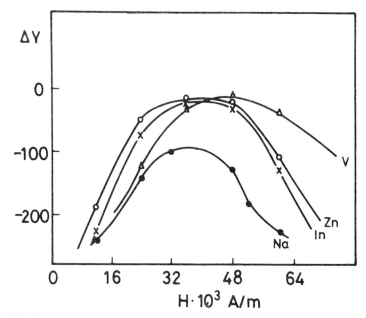

Fig. 7.5 – Relationship between line intensity and the strength of the magnetic field.

7.4 HOLLOW-CATHODE DISCHARGE COMBINED WITH SECONDARY DISCHARGE

7.4.1 Modified plane-cathode discharge tubes

Lowe [37] described a modified plane-cathode Grimm discharge tube with a secondary discharge of high current density. Negative glow discharge was induced between the anode and the plane-surface sample connected as the cathode. Secondary discharge was created between the anode and the thorium-coated electron-emitting tungsten incandescent cathode. The radiation tube was made of glass and filled with flowing argon working gas at a pressure of 666 Pa. Glow discharge was maintained by a square-wave modified amperostatic power supply (30 mA, 500 V), and the secondary discharge was maintained by an amperostatic d.c. power supply (750 mA, 30 V).

In this system, the secondary discharge increased the electron concentration, and this in turn improved the excitation of the sample atoms sputtered by the positive ions. Intensities of the spectral lines of trace metals were improved significantly.

Sullivan and Gough [38] built an improved metal glow discharge tube in which argon served as the flowing working gas at a pressure of 400 Pa. The combined power supply maintained the heating current of the electron-emitting incandescent filament, the glow discharge at 100 mA and 900 V, and the secondary discharge at 750 mA and 120 V. Because of the high intensity of the emitted resonance lines, trace metals could be detected at very low concentrations.

These discharge tubes act as extremely stable emission sources. With this radiation source, relative standard deviations as low as 1% could be achieved in determination of both the alloying components and the main components of various metals.

7.4.2 Modified hollow-cathode discharge (MHCD)

7.4.2.1 Discharge Tubes Modified by an Electron Source

As discussed above, excitation in hollow-cathode discharge tubes results from impacts with high-energy electrons. Metastable atoms of the working gas, obtained in first-order type impacts, also play an important role in the maintenance of the discharge. These metastable atoms increase the probability of excitation of atoms in the higher energy levels.

In our experiments, an auxiliary electron source was installed in the discharge tube, perpendicular to its main axis. At first a tungsten filament, then a tungsten plate was used [39], both powered from a separate supply. The potential fields, current and voltage characteristics of the modified discharge tube and the changing line intensities were examined.

It could be concluded that in the modified discharge tube higher currents were achieved but the slopes of the curves were unaltered.

The time-dependent changes of the current density can be expressed as

$$\left(\frac{dN}{dt}\right) = \left(\frac{dN}{dt}\right)_i + \left(\frac{dN}{dt}\right)_M + \left(\frac{dN}{dt}\right)_\gamma + \left(\frac{dN}{dt}\right)_E - \left(\frac{dN}{dt}\right)_R \qquad (7.7)$$
$$ a b c d e$$

where: term *a* represents the current of electrons expelled from the cathode
by the impinging ions;

term *b* represents the current of electrons expelled from the cathode
by the impinging metastable atoms;

term *c* represents the current of electrons expelled from the cathode
by the photoelectric effect;

term *d* represents the current of electron emission from the secondary
cathode;

term *e* represents the current of electrons consumed in the recombination reactions.

It was expected that the increased current density resulting from the change
in design would decrease the number of fast electrons and increase the probability
of lower energy excitation processes.

The effects of the modified design on the intensities of the spectral lines of
the excited atoms and ions of yttrium were investigated in pure Ar and mixed
He–Ne working gases. It was found that with the He–Ne gas mixture the modified
design did not afford increased line intensity. With Ar, the line intensity of
yttrium increased slightly but not significantly.

7.4.2.2 Improved HCD Tube

In non-thermal radiation sources the atoms of the sample enter the discharge
space as a consequence of the sputtering effect of the working gas. Thus,
evaporation processes are eliminated or at least greatly reduced.

The effects of cathode wall temperature on the excitation of volatile
elements [15] in water-cooled hollow-cathode tubes have been studied. It was
found that the intensity of an element's spectral lines decreased rapidly, even in
the first minutes of the discharge, when the element melting point was lower
than the cathode wall temperature.

Therefore, a new device was designed for determination of volatile elements,
with small standard deviations, by releasing the analyte atoms into the gas phase
after the initial stabilization of the discharge.

It has been found that for elements with melting points close to the cathode
wall temperature the spectral lines of an element appear early in the first period
of stabilization. During the stabilization period the voltage and current values
fluctuate widely, and no glow discharge forms. There are irregular light flashes
between the anode and the cathode. Current flowing through the tube heats the
cathode cup, the sample begins to vaporize and the random flashes of glow
discharge excite the atoms. This means that spectra also appear during this
period. With the old type of discharge tube two choices are possible: either to
exclude the stabilization period from the recorded exposure or to start photo-
graphing at the time of switching on the voltage. Both solutions lead to errors.
With the first, some of the excited atoms are not included in the detection
processes; in the second the length of the illumination period varies, depending
on the length of the stabilization period. Consequently the standard deviation is
also increased.

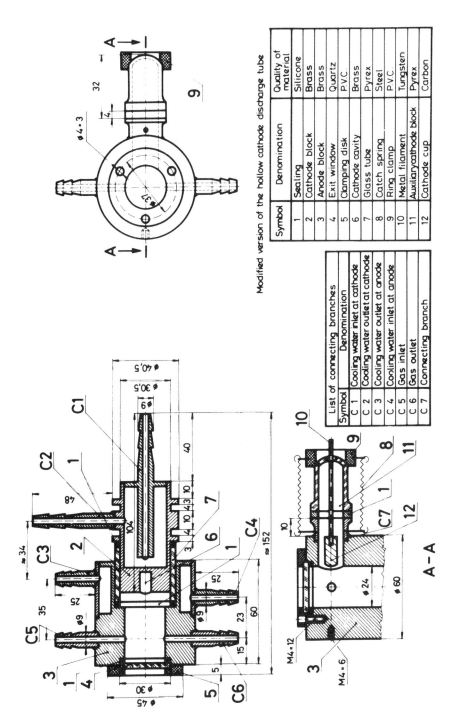

Modified version of the hollow cathode discharge tube

Symbol	Denomination	Quality of material
1	Sealing	Silicone
2	Cathode block	Brass
3	Anode block	Brass
4	Exit window	Quartz
5	Clamping disk	P.V.C.
6	Cathode cavity	Brass
7	Glass tube	Pyrex
8	Catch spring	Steel
9	Ring clamp	P.V.C.
10	Metal filament	Tungsten
11	Auxiliarycathode block	Pyrex
12	Cathode cup	Carbon

List of connecting branches

Symbol	Denomination
C 1	Cooling water inlet at cathode
C 2	Cooling water outlet at cathode
C 3	Cooling water outlet at anode
C 4	Cooling water inlet at anode
C 5	Gas inlet
C 6	Gas outlet
C 7	Connecting branch

A – A

Fig. 7.6 — Scheme of the modified HCD tube (reproduced from [17] by permission of Akadémiai Kiadó, Budapest).

Therefore, the design was modified, with a secondary hollow cathode (without cooling) perpendicular to the main axis of the discharge tube (Fig. 7.6). The secondary cathode could be switched on after an appropriate delay once the main discharge had stabilized.

The new discharge tube was mounted on the optical axis of a PGS II Zeiss plane-grating spectrograph. A vacuum system (as described previously [17]) was connected to the apparatus, with a dual-stage rotating-vane pump to maintain the vacuum at constant pressure. The discharge tube was connected between two cold traps. The pressure was read with a Pirani-type vacuum tube. A 2-kW d.c. power supply (2000 V, 1 A) was connected to the discharge tube.

7.5 ELEMENTARY PROCESSES OF THE IMPROVED HOLLOW-CATHODE RADIATION SOURCE

7.5.1 Electron temperature in the plasma

The modification in the design of the discharge tube, i.e. the application of a secondary discharge, results in

(a) increase in the number density of the particles;
(b) decrease in the energy of the electrons and improvement in the detection limits for trace metals;
(c) decrease in the relative standard deviation of the concentration measurements for volatile elements.

The secondary discharge increases the electron density in the HCD tube, which therefore shows increased current intensity following application of the secondary discharge, as shown in Fig. 7.7.

There is no overall or local thermodynamic equilibrium in the glow discharge plasma. Consequently, neither the Saha equation nor the approximations which assume the existence of local thermodynamic equilibria will apply. Therefore the method proposed by Rompe and Steenbeck [40] was used to measure the electron temperature (T_e). This method makes use of the intensity ratio of two helium lines which have different excitation functions.

The 504.1 nm singlet and the 471.3 nm triplet lines of He were used for measurements. For this pair of spectral lines the excitation functions are the same over the 0.12–13 Pa pressure range. By use of known constants in Eq. (7.8), the $I_{He\ 504.7}/I_{He\ 471.3}$ vs. T_e relationships were evaluated by computer for both the original and the modified HCD tubes.

$$\frac{I_1}{I_2} = \frac{Q_{m1}\ \nu_1}{Q_{m2}\ \nu_2} \times \frac{\displaystyle\int_{E_{g1}}^{\infty} Q_1(E)E^{\frac{1}{2}} \exp\left(-\frac{E}{T_e}\right) dE}{\displaystyle\int_{E_{g2}}^{\infty} Q_2(E)E^{\frac{1}{2}} \exp\left(-\frac{E}{T_e}\right) dE} \tag{7.8}$$

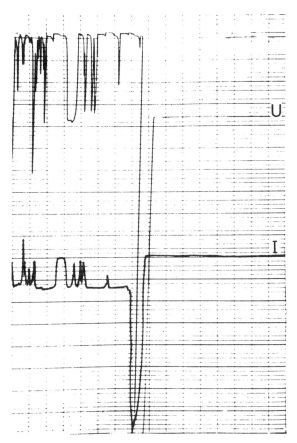

Fig. 7.7 – Changes in the current and tube voltage when the secondary discharge
is applied.

If Fabrikant's approximation* is used to describe the excitation functions,
then the calculations outlined in Eq. (7.8) simply become

$$Q(E) = Q_{\mathrm{m}} \frac{E - E_{\mathrm{g}}}{E_{\mathrm{m}} - E_{\mathrm{g}}} \exp\left(1 - \frac{E - E_{\mathrm{g}}}{E_{\mathrm{m}} - E_{\mathrm{g}}}\right) \qquad (7.9)$$

where E is the energy of the electron, E_{g} the excitation energy and E_{m} the
electron energy at the maximum of the excitation function.

From Eqs. (7.8) and (7.9) we obtain

$$\frac{I_1}{I_2} = \alpha \frac{\dfrac{a_1 - 1}{a_1^3}\left(2 + a_1\dfrac{3E_{\mathrm{g1}}}{2T_{\mathrm{e}}}\right)\exp\left(-\dfrac{3E_{\mathrm{g1}}}{2T_{\mathrm{e}}}\right)}{\dfrac{a_2 - 1}{a_2^3}\left(2 + a_2\dfrac{3E_{\mathrm{q2}}}{2T_{\mathrm{e}}}\right)\exp\left(-\dfrac{3E_{\mathrm{g2}}}{2T_{\mathrm{e}}}\right)} \qquad (7.10)$$

* V. Fabrikant, *Compt. Rend. Acad. Sci. URSS,* 1937, XV, 451.

where

$$a = \frac{2T_e}{2\,(E_m - E_g)} + 1 \tag{7.11}$$

$$\alpha = \frac{Q_{m1}\,\nu_1}{Q_{m2}\,\nu_2} \tag{7.12}$$

Thus, by using the intensities of the two lines mentioned, the effects of the modified design on the electron temperature could be calculated. The main conclusions are as follows:

(a) the electron temperatures change with current intensity;
(b) the electron temperatures are in the range $3-5 \times 10^6$ K;
(c) in the modified discharge tube the electron temperatures are lower by 10–30%.

7.5.2 Potential decreases
It can be seen in Fig. 7.7 that the potential decreases when the secondary discharge is activated. It is apparent from the Laplace equation that this decrease will reduce the magnitude of the positive space charge:

$$\Delta U = \frac{\rho}{\epsilon_0} \tag{7.13}$$

where Δ is the Laplace operator, U the potential, ρ the charge density and ϵ_0 the dielectric constant of a vacuum.

$$\phi(r) = U_c \left[2\,\frac{D-r}{d} - \frac{(D-r)^2}{d^2} \right] \tag{7.14}$$

where $\phi(r)$ is the potential distribution, U_c the potential drop in the Hittorf dark space, D the inner radius of the cathode, d the length of the Hittorf dark space and r the independent parameter. Expressing $\nabla^2\phi$ as $\Delta\phi$, and setting $r = D$, we get

$$\Delta\phi(r)_{(r=D)} = -\frac{2U_c}{d^2}\left(1 + \frac{d}{D}\right) \tag{7.15}$$

$$\rho = \epsilon_0\,\frac{2U_c}{d^2}\left(1 + \frac{d}{D}\right) \tag{7.16}$$

If U_c is smaller, then ρ is smaller and the positive space charge is decreased. This also means that the number of fast electrons, and consequently, the number of positive ions formed, decreases as the number density of the particles increases.

This phenomenon is responsible for the increased intensity of the lower energy spectral lines when the secondary discharge is switched on.

7.5.3 Motion of atoms evaporated in the secondary discharge

It can be seen from Fig. 7.6 that the secondary discharge glows in a carbon cup, located on a tungsten wire. When the current is switched on, the cup is heated (Fig. 7.8 a,b). The sample is evaporated and an inhomogeneity occurs in the plasma. Diffusion of the particles formed in the hot hollow cathode is super-imposed on the motion of the charged particles:

$$\bar{J} = -D \operatorname{grad} n \tag{7.17}$$

where $\bar{J}$ is the diffusion current density, D the diffusion constant and n the number of particles in unit volume.

$$D = \frac{v\lambda}{3} \tag{7.18}$$

where v is the mean velocity of the particles and λ their mean free path.

$$D\Delta n = \partial n/\partial t \tag{7.19}$$

For the stationary state $\partial n/\partial t = 0$, so the Laplace equation has to be solved for $\Delta n = 0$. It is satisfied by

$$n = C/r$$

where C is a constant and r is distance from the source.

C can be evaluated from $J = -D \operatorname{grad} n$, Eq. (7.17):

$$\bar{J} = \frac{DC}{r^2} \bar{r_o}$$

$$C = \frac{M}{4\pi D}$$

where M is the total mass transported by diffusion through a sphere of radius r:

$$M = \frac{DC}{r^2} 4 r^2 \pi = 4\pi DC \tag{7.20}$$

and finally

$$n = M/4\pi Dr \tag{7.21}$$

When the fundamental equations of diffusion are applied to the motion of the particles, the approximate solution shows that the number of particles leaving the hot cathode is inversely proportional to the distance. Therefore, the increased line intensity is due partly to the fact that the atoms of the sample within the space of the secondary discharge are evaporated and some of these atoms reach — by diffusion — the space of the water-cooled primary discharge.

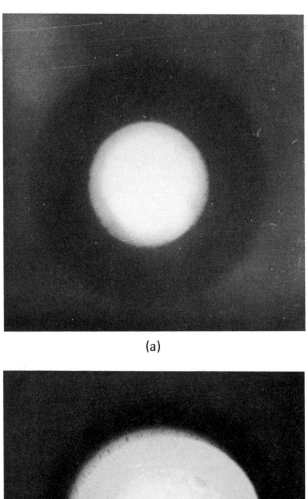

(a)

(b)

Fig. 7.8 – Sample evaporation in the hot cathode cavity.

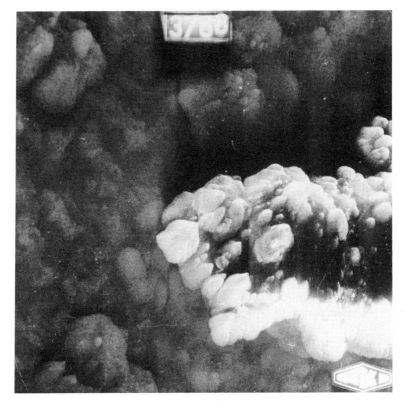

Fig. 7.9 – Aluminium cathode wall under excitation for 3 min.

7.6 ANALYTICAL APPLICATIONS

7.6.1 Spectrographic determination of micro-alloying rare-earth metals in steel samples by using MHCD tubes

Rare-earth metals are used as micro-alloying components in steel, for their deoxidation and desulphurization effects. They also profoundly influence the crystallization processes. Therefore, precise determination of micro-alloying rare-earth metals is of special importance, both in product development and routine production control.

There are numerous papers on the theoretical and practical problems of the determination of trace rare-earth metals [e.g. 41, 42] Methods which make use of the visible range of the spectrum are the least affected by various interferences. Since the sensitive lines of rare-earth metals overlap with the cyanide bands, either metal electrodes or nitrogen-free atmospheres are used. Owing to its high electron density the modified HCD tube developed in this project is especially suitable for the determination of low ionization-potential rare-earth metals [18]. In the noble-gas working atmosphere used, no nitrogen is present. Consequently, no cyanide radicals are formed. Because of the sharp lines from HCD tubes, rare-earth spectrum lines can be well detected even in the crowded spectrum of steel. Table 7.1 sets out the working conditions.

Table 7.1 − Experimental conditions

Excitation: 2 kW d.c. power supply, connected to a modified water-cooled hollow-cathode discharge tube

Hollow cathode: material of the cathode cups at the primary and the secondary discharges: aluminium and carbon, respectively
diameter of cathode cavity: 5.5 mm
depth of cathode cavity: 10.0 mm

Working gas: argon at a pressure of 800 Pa

Discharge current: 500 mA
voltage: 900 V

Exposure time: 5 min

Spectrograph: PGS−2, plane-grating

Illumination of spectrograph: intermediate focusing

Entrance slit: 0.02 mm

Step filter: 100/50/10% average light transmission

Spectrum plate: Agfa-Gevaert Scientia 34B50

Developer: GP 201

Development time: 4 min

Development temperature: 19 °C

Microdensitometer for spectroscopy: MF2

Measured lines: Ce 320.17 nm/Fe 319.95 nm
Y   332.78 nm/Fe 332.89 nm
La 408.67 nm/Fe 408.53 nm
Dy 421.17 nm/Fe 421.03 nm

Equal amounts of the sample are weighed into both cathode cups (primary and secondary discharge cathodes). Thus, through sputtering and diffusion the number of atoms entering the plasma of the primary discharge is increased. This results in improved detection limit and signal-to-noise ratio. The optimum analysis parameters are determined experimentally. A desk-top calculator is used for data processing. Synthetic powder standards containing Ce, Dy, La and Y in the 0.0001-1% concentration range are used. Figures 7.10-7.13 illustrate the corresponding analytical plots.

The detection limits, accuracy and reliability of the method have been determined. Results obtained with the original water-cooled HCD lamp and the modified HCD tube are compared in Table 7.2.

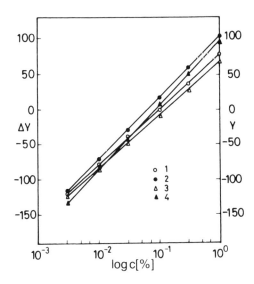

Fig. 7.10 – Calibration graphs for Ce in steel; values of Y for use of (1) the HCD, (2) the modified HCD, and values of ΔY for use of (3) the HCD, (4) the modified HCD ($Y = \log I$).

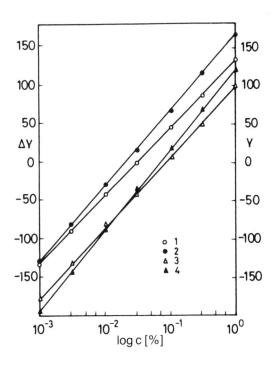

Fig. 7.11 – Calibration graphs for yttrium in steel; values of Y (= $\log I$) for use of (1) the HCD, (2) the modified HCD, and values of ΔY for use of (3) the HCD, (4) the modified HCD.

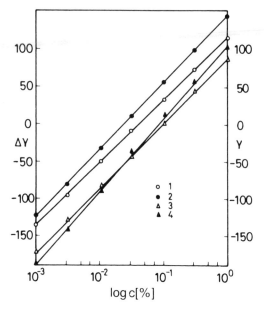

Fig. 7.12 – Calibration graphs for La in steel; values of Y for use of (1) the HCD, (2) the modified HCD, and values of ΔY for use of (3) the HCD, (4) the modified HCD ($Y = \log I$).

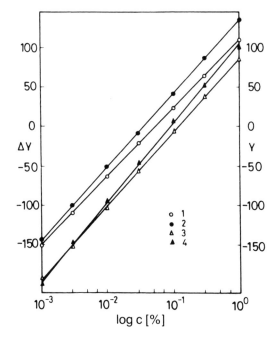

Fig. 7.13 – Calibration graphs for Dy in steel; values of Y for use of (1) the HCD, (2) the modified HCD, and values of ΔY for use of (3) the HCD, (4) the modified HCD ($Y = \log I$).

Table 7.2 — Comparison of the results obtained with the original and modified versions of the HCD tube

Analytical lines (nm)	HCD					modified HCD				
	r	b	a	$s_{\Delta Y}$	$s_{c,rel}\%$	r	b	a	$s_{\Delta Y}$	$s_{c,rel}\%$
Ce 320.17	0.97	0.78	0.80	0.043	12.7	0.98	0.87	1.06	0.032	9.0
Ce 320.17/Fe 319.95	0.98	0.95	0.69	0.038	11.7	0.99	0.92	1.00	0.025	6.3
Y 332.79	0.98	0.88	1.34	0.040	10.5	0.99	0.99	1.68	0.033	7.7
Y 332.79/Fe 332.89	0.99	0.92	1.00	0.035	8.8	1.00	1.05	1.23	0.031	6.8
La 408.67	0.98	0.83	1.18	0.037	10.3	0.99	0.90	1.48	0.032	8.2
La 408.67/Fe 408.53	0.99	0.87	0.90	0.033	8.7	0.99	0.98	1.08	0.028	6.6
Dy 421.17	0.98	0.86	1.10	0.039	10.4	0.99	0.94	1.36	0.031	7.6
Dy 421.17/Fe 421.03	0.99	0.92	0.85	0.034	8.5	0.99	1.01	1.06	0.026	5.9

r = correlation coefficient
a, b = parameters of calibration equation ($\Delta Y = a + b \log c$; c = concentration)
s = standard deviation
$s_{c,rel}\% = 230 \, s_{\Delta Y}/b$

7.6.2 Spectral analysis for volatile elements with the MHCD tube

Owing to the increased interest in the balneological utilization of spas, determination of their trace element composition is of importance [43].

The modified HCD tube has been used for the determination of the volatile elements present in natural water samples, with delayed switch-on of the secondary discharge following stabilization of the electric parameters. Table 7.3 lists the working parameters.

Table 7.3 — Experimental conditions used in the analysis of the water samples

Sample preparation:	evaporation to dryness at 80°C, in a Teflon beaker
Spectrograph:	PGS-2 plane-grating, operated with the first-order spectrum
Blazing wavelength:	330 nm
Spectral range:	230–410 nm
Illumination:	intermediate
Slit width:	20 μm
Stop filter:	100/50/10% average transmission
Electrode:	carbon cup (Johnson-Matthey)
Spectral plate:	ORWO blau extrahart WU-3
Developer:	Kodak D-19 (19°C, 4 min)
Excitation:	water-cooled HCD tube
Working gas:	He–Ne mixture (75% He, 25% Ne) at 666.5 Pa
Voltage:	1100 V
Current:	350 mA
Exposure time:	5 min

Direct analysis of the sample is not sensitive enough, however. Therefore, the water sample was concentrated by evaporation in a Teflon beaker, at 80°C, and the dry residue placed in the cathode cup. On the average, 1.5 g of solid residue was obtained per litre of natural water sample tested. The water-cooled HCD lamp was used and the main components, the contaminants and 31 trace elements were determined. For determination of the trace elements, calibration standards representing the composition of the dry residue were prepared. Seven standards were used, with metal oxide concentrations in the 0.00001–0.1% range in a $CaCO_3$ matrix. The homogenized samples were weighed (3-mg portions) into the hollow-cathode cup (made of spectral graphite). The logarithm of the degree of blackening, corrected for background intensity, was plotted against concentration.

The detection limits for several elements, with both the HCD and the modified HCD lamps, are shown in Table 7.4.

Table 7.4 – Detection limits ($\mu g/l$.)

Element	HCD	Modified HCD	Element	HCD	Modified HCD
Al	8	5	Mg	0.5	0.1
As	0.3	0.07	Mn	0.2	0.1
B	5	3	Mo	4	2
Ba	4	2	Na	0.03	0.01
Ca	0.1	0.07	Ni	6	4
Fe	1	0.4	Rb	0.2	0.03
Ga	0.5	0.02	Sn	0.4	0.01
K	30	5	Ti	10	8
Li	2	0.6	V	20	10

7.7 CONCLUSIONS

On the basis of the data presented above it can be concluded that:

(a) the analytical curves are linear over a wide concentration range, for both radiation sources;

(b) with the latest version of the HCD tube, the slope of the linear analytical curves (i.e. the sensitivity of the method) is greater than that obtained with the original radiation sources and is near the optimum value of 1.0;

(c) the reproducibility [represented by the relative standard deviation (rsd) of the concentration, determined from replicate measurements at the average concentrations] is lower for the modified version of the radiation source than for the original one;

(d) the analytical efficiency of the method with the modified tube is better than that with the original one;

(e) in most cases, acceptable analytical results are obtained from the corrected absolute intensity of the analytical lines, as a consequence of the high discharge stability.

Modification of the HCD offers several advantages such as fine-tuning of the electron energies, and obtention of optimum experimental conditions for the atomic lines of lower excitation-energy metals by decreasing the electron energy.

On the one hand, the metastable levels of the argon working gas lie around 11 eV, a value which is too high for the optimum excitation of the 2-5 eV lines. On the other hand, delayed switching of the secondary excitation offers a major advantage for the user. By this technique, the atoms of the sample can be introduced into the discharge space after the primary discharge has been stabilized, without disturbing the vacuum system. By use of two secondary hollow cathodes, two parallel measurements can be made without opening the vacuum system. The use of a hot hollow cathode in the secondary discharge is especially advantageous when volatile elements are excited and some of the sample material evaporates during the stabilization period. In this case, use of the modified hollow-cathode tube significantly decreases the standard deviation of the measurements.

Acknowledgements – The author is indebted to Professors T. Lengyel and E. Házi, Institute for Radiochemistry and Physics, University of Chemical Engineering, Veszprém, Hungary, for their encouragement and interest in this work. The contribution of Anna Györfiné-Buzási to the development of the modified hollow-cathode discharge tube and some of experiments is also gratefully acknowledged.

REFERENCES

[1] H. Schüler and H. Gollnow, *Z. Phys.*, 1935, **93**, 611.

[2] J. L. Delcroix, H. Minoo, and A. R. Trindade, *J. Phys. (Paris)*, 1968, **29**, 605.

[3] F. T. Birks, *Spectrochim. Acta*, 1954, **6**, 169.

[4] B. Rosen, *Rev. Univ. Mines Liège*, 1953, 445.

[5] G. Milazzo and N. Sopranzi, *Appl. Spectrosc.*, 1967, **21**, 172.

[6] G. Milazzo and N. Sopranzi, *Appl. Spectrosc.*, 1967, **21**, 256.

[7] S. Caroli and P. Delle Femmine, *Spectrosc. Lett.*, 1978, **11**, 299.

[8] S. Caroli, A. Alimonti, and O. Senofonte, *Spectrosc. Lett.*, 1980, **13**, 457.

[9] S. Caroli, A. Alimonti, P. Delle Femmine and S. K. Shukla, *Anal. Chim. Acta*, 1982, **136**, 225.

[10] A. Buzási, S. Caroli, A. Alimonti and O. Senofonte, *Acta Chim. Hung.*, 1983, **113**, 295.

[11] S. Caroli and A. Alimonti, *Proc. Euroanalysis IV, Helsinki*, 1981.

[12] Zs. Szilvássy, *Proc. XVII CSI, Florence, 1973*, Vol. II, 465.

[13] H. Falk, E. Hoffmann and Ch. Lüdke, *Spectrochim. Acta*, 1981, **36B**, 767.

[14] H. Falk, E. Hoffmann, I. Jaeckel and Ch. Lüdke, *Spectrochim. Acta*, 1979, **34B**, 333.

[15] Zs. Szilvássy, *Proc. XXV Ungarische Tagung für Spectralanalyse, Sopron*, 1982, 46.

[16] Zs. Szilvássy and I. Buzási, *Spectrochim. Acta*, 1983, **38B**, *Supplement* (Abstracts 23 CSI, Amsterdam, 1983), 326.

[17] A. Buzási and Zs. Szilvássy, *Acta Chim. Hung.*, 1983, **113**, 285.

[18] A. Buzási and Zs. Szilvássy, *Acta Chim. Hung.*, 1983, **113**, 279.

[19] J. S. Dobrosavljević and M. Marinković, *Spectrochim. Acta*, 1974, **29B**, 87.

[20] V. Afanas'eva, A. Lukin and K. Mustafin, *Zh. Tekh. Fiz.*, 1966, **26**, 526.

[21] V. S. Borodin and Yu. M. Kagan, *Zh. Tekh. Fiz.*, 1966, **26**, 181.

[22] W. C. Kreye, *J. Phys. B, Atom. Molec. Phys.*, 1979, **12**, 1953.

[23] J. Czakow and J. Glinsky, *Proc. Euroanalysis II, Budapest*, 1975.

[24] Gy. Záray, T. Török and N. Rehák, *Spectrochim. Acta*, 1984, **39B**, 57.

[25] J. Litomisky, *Sympozium o metodach stanovenia nizkych koncentracii prvkov v nerastnych surovinach*, Smolence, 1969, 171.

[26] W. Setz and J. Maierhofer, *Z. Angew. Phys.*, 1970, **28**, 168.

[27] Zs. Szilvássy, *Proc. V Kongress für Materialprüfung, Budapest*, 1970.

[28] Zs. Szilvássy, *Proc. 1st National Conference on Analytical Chemistry, Varna*, 1971, 9.

[29] Zs. Szilvássy, *2nd International Symposium on Analytical Chemistry, Ljubljana*, 1972.

[30] Zs. Szilvássy, *Proc. VII Hüttenmännischen Materialprüfertagung, II, Balatonszéplak*, 1973, 121.

[31] Zs. Szilvássy, *Proc. Euroanalysis II, Budapest*, 1975, 9.

[32] Zs. Szilvássy and Gy. Straub, untersuchung der Hohlkathoden-Anregungsprozesse aus der Erhöhung de Genauigkeit. *Wiss. Tech. Inform. Berlin*, 1976, 17 June 217.

[33] Zs. Szilvássy, *Proc. XX CSI, Prague*, 1977, 513.

[34] Zs. Szilvássy, *VI Polish Spectroanalytical Conference, Bialowieza*, 1981, **A3**, 10.

[35] A. Buzási and Zs. Szilvássy, *VI Polish Spectroanalytical Conference, Bialowieza*, 1981, **B13**, 30.

[36] Zs. Szilvássy and A. Buzási, *Proc. Analytiktreffen, Neubrandenburg*, 1982.

[37] R. M. Lowe, *Spectrochim. Acta*, 1976, **31B**, 257.

[38] D. S. Gough and J. V. Sullivan, *Analyst*, 1978, **103**, 887.

[39] Zs. Szilvássy and A. Buzási, *Proc. XXIV Hungarian Annual Conference on Spectral Analysis, Miskolc*, 1981, 29, 37.

[40] R. Rompe and M. Steenbeck, *Ergebnisse der Plasmaphysik und der Gaselektronik*, Akademie Verlag, Berlin, 1967.

[41] K. Zimmer and Zs. Bassa, *Magy. Kém. Foly.*, 1970, **76**, 170.

[42] K. Zimmer, Bewertung der Leistungsfähigkeit von spektrographischen Verfahren durch Anwendung der statistischen Methoden mit programmierter Rechenmaschine, *Wiss. Tech. Inform. Berlin*, 17 June 1976.

[43] Zs. Szilvássy, M. Horváth and K. Evele, *Balneologia*, 1982, **III**.

8

Conical bottom modified hollow-cathode discharge

D. Zhechev

8.1 SPECTROSCOPIC PECULIARITIES OF THE CONICAL BOTTOM HOLLOW-CATHODE DISCHARGE (CBHCD)

8.1.1 Introduction

The broad energy spectrum of the hollow-cathode discharge, historically the first of its peculiarities to be noticed [1], encouraged the subsequent thorough investigations and applications of this spectral source. Two main approaches for interpreting its specific characteristics can be outlined: the first is based on electron parameters [2,3], and the second on the interaction processes between the charged and neutral particles in the negative glow, taking into account the plasma composition, the atomic cross-section and the probabilities of transitions [4-9]. It is not so easy to make a similar differentiation for the scientific and applied aspects of the hollow-cathode discharge (HCD). Investigations on the measurement of the relaxation constants of atomic and ionic levels [10-14], calculation of nuclear moments and hyperfine and isotopic spectral line structure [15-17], inverse population of the levels [18-20], alignment of the excited states [21-23], as well as other purely scientific studies, create many problems, most of which are similar to those in applied research. These problems, more or less specific for the HCD, can be solved in different ways. The use of pulse [24-26] and high frequency [27-29] regimes, for example, together with parameter optimization in a classical d.c. discharge mode, significantly broadens the possibilities of the HCD while allowing the simultaneous regulation of some processes, in particular, atomization of the substance with subsequent atomic excitement [30, 31]. The application of the HCD as a laser medium [32-34] accentuates some additional characteristic features.

By modification of the conventional cylindrical hollow cathode the HCD can be given certain desirable spectral, electrical and other characteristics. The existing concepts for formulation of the electron energy distribution [6–9], the temperature of the gas phase, the atomized substance concentration and the spectral intensities in the HCD [35] allow us, by changing the cathode–anode construction, to operate with a hollow-cathode source with preselected defined features. The spiral cathode [36], for example, combines the high-voltage discharge with the more easily regulated diffusion of the metal vapours, plus the possibility to vary the working voltage by changing the pitch of the spiral. Except for a laser system [37, 38], this construction can be successfully applied to hollow-cathode discharge lamps for atomic-absorption spectral analysis [39]. In another case the replacement of the cylindrical cathode cavity with three separate coaxial cylinders with different diameter and length [40] favours the spatial separation of the atomization and excitation processes. The detection limit of some elements in emission spectral analysis is lower with this type of HCD modification.

The aforementioned examples give only an indication of the possibilities afforded by constructional modification of the discharge, but underline the problem of not overstepping the limits at which its HCD character is altered. Since various HCD criteria differ, in this case it is best to establish a general criterion limiting the volume ratio between the cathode cavity and the cathode discharge region [41]. The expression 'hollow cathode' will be taken as meaning a cathode with negative curvature of the working surface (or consisting of separate electrically connected surfaces which limit part of the gas discharge surface and create a cavity). According to this criterion the cathode should be a cavity with dimensions similar to those of the cathode discharge, and the hollow cathode discharge is then always significantly different from the plate electrode discharge.

In the work described here we investigated a new modification of the HCD, with the cathode bottom in the form of a re-entrant cone (Fig. 8.1) and the geometrical dimensions of the cavity satisfying the criterion above.

Some plasma characteristics of the new construction differ significantly from those of the classical flat-bottom hollow-cathode discharge (FBHCD) and, as we shall see later, are advantageous, but the experimental work done so far does not offer a complete picture of this type of discharge.

The physical processes occurring in the conical-bottom hollow-cathode discharge (CBHCD) are discussed below, together with its spectral properties and several aspects of its analytical application.

8.1.2 CBHCD effects on the spectral lines of Al, Zn, Cu, Fe, Mo, Si, Ca, Ba and Mg

Initial data on spectroscopic effects in the CBHCD [42] have been obtained for aluminium, with helium as the working gas. The discharge tube used is illustrated in Fig. 8.1. The cylindrical cathode is made of aluminium, with inner diameter (d) 6 mm, length (L) 15 mm and cone height 7.5 mm. Line intensities for this type of hollow cathode are compared with those for a hollow cathode with a flat

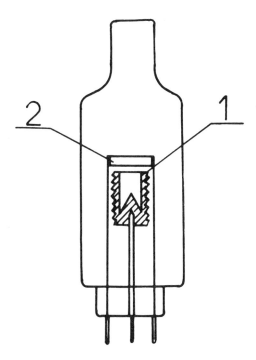

Fig. 8.1 – Hollow-cathode discharge tube: 1 – cathode, 2 – anode.

Table 8.1 – I^c/I^f ratio of Al spectral line intensities ($d = 6$ mm, $L = 15$ mm, $h = 7.5$ mm). $I^c/I^f = \Phi(p_{He}, i)$. (Reproduced from [42] by permission of the Publishing House of the Proc. 2nd Nat. Conf. Physics Industry, Kazanlak, 1977, Bulgaria).

p_{He}, Pa	385.70			305.90			232.75			152.95	
λ (nm)\\i(mA)	10	20	30	10	20	30	10	20	30	10	20
Al(I) 309.3	40	20	16	5	44	3	3	4	4	5	–
Al(II) 281.6	34	40	25	20	12	10	12	26	18	10	–
Al(II) 466.6	2	4	8	5	6	9	–	6	10	2	4

bottom (same diameter and length for both type of cathode) in Table 8.1, which gives some I^c/I^f ratios (I^c and I^f are the spectral line intensities obtained with the conical and flat bottom cathodes, respectively) for several pressures (p_{He}) and discharge currents (i). $I^c/I^f > 1$ is observed for the resonance line Al(I)

309.3 nm as well as for the ion lines Al(II) 281.6 nm and Al(II) 466.6 nm; for the first two lines the ratio can be as high as 40. The ratio is dependent on both the helium pressure and the discharge current.

For the line Al(III) 276.2 nm there is no improvement in the signal, but a positive effect has been found for the Al(II) 396.2 nm emission line [43].

We should point out that the comparison was made for equal values of the discharge current i, but as the current density j_i is always lower in the HCDCB, comparison at equal discharge currents gives I^c/I^f ratios that are even more favourable for the new modification.

The line intensities for other elements – Fe, Mo, Si – with hindered atomization in the CBHCD has been reported [44]. The cathodes were made from the element concerned, or completely surfaced with it, and the discharge tube was filled with neon at various pressures. Table 8.2 shows that the ratio I^c/I^f generally increased with gas pressure and current density for the lines examined.

Table 8.2 – I^c/I^f ratio of Mo, Fe and Si spectral line intensities ($d = 3$ mm, $L = 17$ mm, $h = 8$ mm); $I^c/I^f = \Phi\,(p_{Ne}, j_i)$. (Reproduced from [44] by permission of the Publishing House of *Elektropromishlenost i Priborostroene*, Bulgaria)

		I^c/I^f					
λ(nm)		Mo(I) 379.8			Fe(I) 372.0		Si(I) 251.6
p_{Ne} (Pa) $\diagdown$ $j_i(\mu A/mm^2)$		14.8	32.6	44.5	14.8	32.6	14.8	32.6
146		1.9	2.0	2.3	1.2	1.8	2.7	3.7
200		2.0	2.4	2.5	1.3	1.9	2.6	3.9
266		2.1	3.1	3.2	1.4	2.1	2.8	3.8
332		2.0	3.5	3.8	1.6	2.2	3.1	3.9
400		2.1	3.8	3.9	1.5	2.4	3.8	3.9
440		2.3	3.8	4.3	1.7	2.5	4.0	4.2

A similar effect for cathodes with the same geometry was also found for Zn and Mg. As mentioned, there seems to be no direct connection between this effect and the increase in area of the emitting surface. Copper also gives increased light emission in the CBHCD [45]. Here to attain the aim of the experiment – crossing the self-alignment atomic levels – required not only a sufficiently high degree of coherence but also a spectral line intensity suitable for the threshold sensitivity of the recording system. In fact, the increase in intensity of the lines Cu(I) 324.7 nm, Cu(I) 515.3 nm and Cu(I) 402.3 nm, when the CBHCD is used, was studied. The necessity for low gas pressure in the discharge tube (a condition due to the depolarizing effect of atom–atom interaction and connected with the correct extrapolation of the signal width) requires the Cu-cathode dimensions to be $d = 8$ mm, $L = 40$ mm, $h = 16$ mm. An increase of about 2.6 times in the spectral line intensity of the non-resonance line Cu(I) 324.7 nm is observed. Moreover, there is charge stabilization and, in particular, stability of light-emission. The importance of this result goes beyond the pertinence of energy-level crossing experiments.

All the data given so far refer to lines characterizing the atomized cathode material (cathode inner surface). An analogous effect for a sample located in the cathode has been reported [43]. A sample in the form of copper chips was in the conical bottom ($d = 3$ mm, $L = 17$ mm, $h = 8$ mm). The behaviour of the function $I^c/I^f = \Phi(p_{Ne}, j_i)$ was studied and for this purpose the measurements were repeated with the CBHCD. Table 8.3 illustrates the significant (up to 6-fold) positive effect of the CBHCD as well as the dependence of I^c/I^f on the gas pressure but not on the current density. At the same time the I^c/I^f data for the Al(I) 309.3 nm line are not influenced by the presence of the sample in the cathode. This result broadens the analytical possibilities of the CBHCD and to some extent affects the choice of conditions for modification of the discharge.

An intensity increase was also observed for Ca, Ba and Zn lines excited in CBHCD for the purposes of crossing level spectroscopy.

Table 8.3 – Copper chip in aluminium cathode ($d = 3$ mm, $L = 17$ mm, $h = 8$ mm); I^c/I^f ratio of Cu(I) 324.7 nm. (Reprinted from [43] by courtesy of Marcel Dekker, Inc.)

				I^c/I^f			
j_i ($\mu A/mm^2$) \ p_{Ne} (Pa)	146	200	266	332	400	440
14.8	3.5	3.8	4.3	5.4	5.9	6.0
32.6	3.0	3.3	3.8	4.5	5.8	6.1

8.1.3 The CBHCD effect on the spectral lines of He, Ar and Ne atoms

Comparing the lines of the working gas with those of the atomized cathode surface (or sample) shows two substantial differences: (a) production of the lines is not preceded by atomization, i.e. the line intensity in an optically thin plasma is determined by the excitation process balance: (b) in principle, there is a higher excitation potential, U_e, and a maximum, F_{max}, of the optical excitation function $F(U)$.

Analogous comparative measurements have been made for Ne lines and especially for He lines [42, 43], in order to investigate this effect in detail, and also the highly distinctive optical-excitation functions $f(U)$ of the upper level transition for the singlet and triplet He lines. The analysis of the experimental data demonstrates that use of the conical-bottom HCD makes $I^c/I^f < 1$ for most of the lines investigated, though the decrease in intensity is not very great.

The intensity ratios of two line pairs, namely $(I_{\lambda_1}/I_{\lambda_2}; I_{\lambda_3}/I_{\lambda_1})^c$ and $(I_{\lambda_1}/I_{\lambda_2}; I_{\lambda_3}/I_{\lambda_1})^f$ were compared in order to find a correlation between the characteristics of the lines and their behaviour in the BCHCD [42]. The lines from the first pair, $\lambda_1 = $ He(I) 471.3 nm, $\lambda_2 = $ He(II) 468.6 nm, differ greatly in F_{max} and U_e [$F_{max} = 27.00$ eV, $U_e = 23.58$ eV for He(I) 471.3 nm, $F_{max} = 170$–190 eV, $U_e = 51.01$ eV for He(II) 468.6 nm] while those from the second pair, $\lambda_3 = $ He(I) 388.9 nm and λ_1, are close to each other [$F_{max} = 28.00$ eV, $U_e = 23.01$ eV for He(I) 388.9] [46]. The data are summarized in Table 8.4. The values for the second line pair ($\sim$1) are practically constant, while for the first pair the ratio $(I_{\lambda_1}/I_{\lambda_2})^f/(I_{\lambda_1}/I_{\lambda_2})^c$ varies between 1.3 and 2.0 for the various discharge-current/helium-pressure combinations.

Table 8.4 – $I_{\lambda_1(\lambda_3)}/I_{\lambda_2(\lambda_1)}$ ratios for the CBHCD (C) and FBHCD (F). $\lambda_1 = $ He(I) 471.3 nm, $\lambda_2 = $ He(II) 468.6 nm, $\lambda_3 = $ He(I) 388.9 nm (Reprinted from [42] by permission of the Publishing House of the Proc. 2nd Nat. Conf. Physics-Industry, Kazanlak, 1977, Bulgaria)

p_{He} (Pa) \ i(mA)	$I_{\lambda_1}/I_{\lambda_2}$						$I_{\lambda_3}/I_{\lambda_3}$			
	10		20		30		10		20	
	F	C	F	C	F	C	F	C	F	C
385.70	6.3	4.8	2.8	2.1	2.3	1.5	1.1	1.1	1.1	1.1
305.90	5.8	2.9	2.9	1.9	2.3	1.7	1.1	1.1	1.0	1.1
232.75	6.0	3.3	2.8	2.0	2.3	1.6	1.1	1.0	1.0	1.0
152.75	5.3	2.8	2.8	1.7	2.3	1.3	1.1	1.0	1.0	1.0
126.35	5.3	–	2.8	–	2.3	–	1.0	–	1.0	–

Taking into account the fundamental role of electron–atom collisions for atomic-level excitation in the HCD [6, 35], this result is at least a logical indication for differences in the electron-energy distribution in the CBHCD and FBHCD. A more explicit connection would require more experimental data, and a quantitative relation would need a direct investigation of the electron energy function distribution (EEFD).

8.2 OTHER CHARACTERISTICS OF THE CBHCD

8.2.1 General behaviour

The spectroscopic effect in the CBHCD is integral in character and is reflected in the improved intensity of the emitted spectral lines, mainly those of the cathode material and the sample. In order to apply this effect it is necessary to have information on the factors determining its magnitude.

The absolute intensity of the spectral line from the kth level in the HCD can be compared with the number β_k of excitations to this level:

$$\beta_k = \frac{4\pi N_0 n_e}{m^2} \int_{U_e^k}^{\infty} F(U)Q(U)U\mathrm{d}U \tag{8.1}$$

$$\beta_k + \beta_{ks} = N_k \left(\sum_{k-1}^{} A_{ki} + A_d \right) \tag{8.2}$$

where N_0 is the ground-state atom concentration, n_e the volume electron concentration, m the mass of the electron, $Q(U)$ the cross-section for direct excitation to level k from the ground state, U_e^k the excitation potential of level k, U the excitation potential, β_{ks} the number of the stepwise excitations to level k, N_k the atom concentration of the k level, A_{ki} the probability of transition from level k to level i, A_d the transition probability of non-radiative transition [in Eq. (8.2), the balance equation, the cascade transitions are not taken into account]. This relation is significantly more complicated for the spectrum of an atomized metal. The complexity is conditioned by the fact that the excitation process is secondary to a certain extent, i.e. it develops after formation of the concentration N_0 of metal atoms in the plasma. The interpretation of this requires, in particular, the quantitative estimation of these processes for the system 'gas–metal', for example, the degree of cathode sputtering, heat interaction of the gas atoms with the cathode surface, physical and chemical adsorption, and their dependences on cathode temperature. The characteristics of all these processes, together with the ion–electron emission, photoemission, work function, etc., depend significantly on the cathode surface temperature [47–53] and, to a considerable extent, on the gas layer adsorbed at the surface [54–58].

For each specific case it is particularly important to have suitably optimized discharge parameters. For this purpose, some spectroscopic and electrical characteristics of the plasma in the CBHCD [43] (in particular, the axial distribution of the spectral line intensities as well as the role of the height and type of the conical bottom, and the influence of the working gas on the integral spectroscopic effect), have been investigated in detail.

A discharge tube with a hollow cathode similar geometrically to the one in Fig. 8.1, with dimensions $d = 7$ mm, $L = 23$ mm and $h = 5, 11, 18$ mm was used. Four outlets (diameter 1.5 mm) located along the cathode cylinder (Fig. 8.2a) allowed registration of the spectral emission from four regions along its length. The tube was filled successively with helium, neon and argon. A photomultiplier was used as the light detector. The experimental values of $I^c/I^f = \Phi(p_{Ne}, h)$ for the Al(I) 396.2 nm line are summarized in Table 8.5 and confirm the relation found in the majority of CBHCD experiments reported so far, that I^c/I^f is maximal when h is in the range from $L/2$ to $2L/3$.

In connection with the shape of the bottom we would like to add that a change in the height of the cone does not noticeably influence the I^c/I^f ratio. The curves for the axial distribution for the Al(I) 396.2 nm line (Fig. 8.2b)

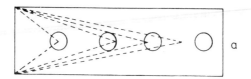

Fig. 8.2(a) – Schematic view of the cathode showing the outlets and positions of
the cones (dashed lines) of various heights.

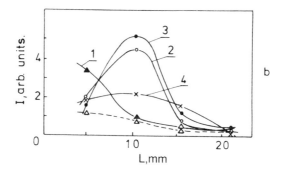

Fig. 8.2(b) – Axial distribution of the Al(I) 396.2 nm spectral line intensity in
the FBHCD (dashed line) and in the CBHCD, with $h = 5$ mm (1), $h = 11$ mm (2),
$h = 15$ mm (3), $h = 18$ mm (4). (Reproduced from [43] by courtesy of Marcel
Dekker, Inc.)

Table 8.5 – I^c/I^f ratio of Al(I) 396.2 nm spectral line intensities; $I^c/I^f =
\Phi(p_{Ne}, h)$ at $j_i = 1.41 \times 10^{-2}$ mA/mm^2. (Reprinted from [43] by courtesy of
Marcel Dekker, Inc.)

		I^c/I^f		
p_{Ne} (Pa) \ h (mm)	5	11	15	18
133	2.8	2.6	2.9	2.6
200	2.6	2.7	3.0	2.5
266	2.9	3.8	3.7	3.3
332	4.3	6.8	6.1	5.4
400	5.2	9.8	8.9	7.1
466	5.1	10.1	10.6	7.0

illustrate mainly a significant inhomogeneity in the CBHCD ($I^c_{max}/I^c_{min} \cong 15\text{-}17$)
in comparison to the FBHCD ($I^f/I^f_{min} \cong 6$). We do not wish to go into detail on
the behaviour of the curves; however, we stress the importance of the cone
height h, as well as the magnitude and location of I_{max}, in determining the

character of this distribution. We point out especially that in all cases the maximum of the axial emission distribution is not located at the point of the cone. The same behaviour is observed with He and Ar as the working gas, as with Ne.

A detailed study of the axial distribution of emission intensity in the FBHCD [59, 60] has revealed a correlation between this distribution for atomized-metal lines and the axial distribution of the ion-current. Both distributions reach their maximum at a third of the cathode length away from the bottom of the cathode, i.e. the excitation of these spectral lines is localized in the part of the cathode that is bombarded by ions. The use of a cone in the cylindrical cavity significantly changes the ion-current distribution along the axis of the cathode.

The experimental results for I^c and I^f as a function of gas presssure, for the Al(I) 309.3 nm line in He, Ne and Ar, show that for all three gases $I^c > I^f$; however, even the maximum increase (with He) has no practical significance, because of the low spectral line intensity.

A high cathode fall potential U_{cf} is typical of the HCD. The U_{cf} limits the maximum energy in the EEFD [5] and is an important parameter in creating theoretical models of the EEFD [6, 7] and for the spectral line intensity in the HCD [6, 8]. The total voltage between the anode and the cathode U_{ca}, is the experimental parameter that is measured, and as $U_{ca} \sim U_c$ can be taken as a measure of U_{cf}.

The curve for U_{ca} as a function of the gas pressure used (p_{Ne}), Fig. 8.3, (the absolute values confirm the HCD character of the discharge) indicates that the conical bottom gives a lower cathode fall potential, the difference being as much

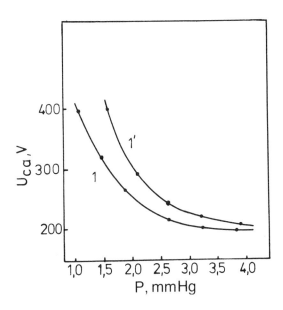

Fig. 8.3 — Cathode-anode fall potential as a function of working gas pressure, $U_{ca}(p_{Ne})$, for the CBHCD (1) and FBHCD (1'). (Reproduced from [43] by courtesy of Marcel Dekker, Inc.)

as 25%, depending on p_{Ne}. Comparative measurements of U_{ca} in other working gases and with various cathodes (differing in materials and dimensions) demonstrate similar deviations in results. It is reasonable to interpret this as meaning that the CBHCD gives higher intensity with consumption of less energy.

8.2.2 Typical features

Comparison of the experimental results in Sections 8.1 and 8.2 allows us to draw some conclusions about the character of CBHCD.

The conical form of the cathode bottom enhances the spectral intensity of the lines characterizing the cathode probe. This effect is not directly due to the increase in the emitting surface area of the cathode cavity or to the electrode phenomena around the top of the cone.

This new configuration of the cathode cavity is characterized by the axial distribution of the ion current i_i^c and of the spectral intensity, I^c, which differs from that in the conventional hollow cathode with a flat bottom.

The shape of the bottom slightly influences the working-gas line-intensity, leading to a general intensity decrease. Comparative measurements at equal pressures of working gases exclude N_o in Eq. (8.1) as a possible factor in the behaviour of these lines. A change in the EEDF can be the only explanation. The decreased cathode fall potential in the CBHCD defines the lower initial rate of production of the primary electrons, with reduced energy in the discharge plasma. This is equivalent to a decrease of the number of fast electrons in the EEFD, at least for excitation potentials $> U_e$. As has been pointed out, a direct measurement of the EEFD should give the same character information about the CBHCD. With regard to the line intensity for the cathode and sample material, the available experimental data do not exclude another possible factor for the enhancement, namely the concentration N_o of the atomized element. Quantitative analysis of this factor requires experiment with results defined by N_o. A method [61,62], based on the Hanle-signal in HCD [45], for comparative estimation of N_o in CBHCD and FBHCD is described in the next section.

8.3 THE HANLE SIGNAL IN THE CBHCD

8.3.1 General

Level-crossing is the simplest of interference phenomena [63]. It is a resonance change in the angular distribution of degenerate emission (magnetic field $H = 0$, which in fact is the Hanle effect) or degenerate Zeeman sublevels. The dependence of the depolarization on the magnetic field, in the region of the crossing point, contains information about the relaxation constants of the atomic state as well as the physical conditions in the source. In some cases, a narrowing of the Hanle signal-width, $2 \Delta H_{\frac{1}{2}}$, is observed at a given density of the atomic ensemble, owing to its trapping. The spectroscopic enhancement ($I^c/I^f > 1$) with the CBHCD, used in Hanle experiments with self-aligned levels of copper atoms, has been reported [64]. The narrowing of the signal for the Cu(I) 324.7 nm ($4^2P_{\frac{3}{2}}$–$4^2S_{\frac{1}{2}}$) line is a starting point for developing a method for relative measurement of atomized-substance concentration in the CBHCD and FBHCD.

8.3.2 Model for complete light trapping

We shall discuss the model for complete trapping of the resonance photon of the transition $4^2P_{\frac{3}{2}}-4^2S_{\frac{1}{2}}$ in order to calculate the maximum narrowing of the corresponding Hanle signal. It is assumed that (i) the plasma volume of copper atoms is sufficient for the trapping of this transition, and (ii) this trapping does not occur in the $4^2P_{\frac{3}{2}}-3^2D_{\frac{3}{2}}$ and $4^2P_{\frac{3}{2}}-3^2D_{\frac{5}{2}}$ transitions with metastable low levels, i.e. the emitted resonance radiation Cu(I) 324.7 nm from unit volume excites ground-state Cu atoms to the $4^2P_{\frac{3}{2}}$ level, which relaxes to $3^3D_{\frac{3}{2}}$ and $3^3D_{\frac{5}{2}}$ levels or by resonance transition to $4^2S_{\frac{1}{2}}$. In the last case the photon is absorbed in the ensemble, again exciting ground-state atoms to the $4^2P_{\frac{3}{2}}$ level, etc. (Fig. 8.4).

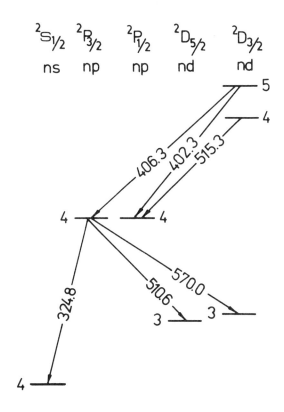

Fig. 8.4 — Scheme of the working Cu(I) levels.

The existence of such a cycle in the photon distribution is the reason for the Hanle signal, with Lorentzian shape and effective width γ_2 [65] connected with the radiation line width γ_R.

$$\gamma_2 = \gamma_R \left(1 - \sum_i \alpha_2^i\right) \tag{8.3}$$

where

$$\alpha_2^i = \frac{0.7 A_{io}}{\displaystyle\sum_k A_{ik}} \left\{ \begin{matrix} 1 & 1 & 2 \\ J_1 & J_1 & J_2 \end{matrix} \right\}^2 \Big/ \left\{ \begin{matrix} 1 & 1 & 0 \\ J_1 & J_1 & J_2 \end{matrix} \right\}^2 \tag{8.4}$$

and the summing is over all transitions from the upper state i; A_{io} is the resonance transition probability, A_{ik} the probability for every possible transition from state io, and J_1, J_2 the angular momenta of the upper (J_1) and lower (J_2) states.

In our case the levels discussed have a hyperfine structure (the nuclear momentum is $3/2$). The state $4^2P_{\frac{3}{2}}$ splits into four hyperfine components with total angular momentum quantum number $F = 0, 1, 2, 3$; state $4^2S_{\frac{1}{2}}$ into two components with $F = 1, 2$ (we shall designate them as $1°, 2°$); state $3^2D_{\frac{3}{2}}$ into four components with $F = 1, 2, 3$ ($0', 1', 2', 3'$) and state $3^3D_{\frac{5}{2}}$ into four components with $F = 1, 2, 3, 4$ ($1'', 2'', 3'', 4''$). The Hanle signal of the transition $4^2P_{\frac{3}{2}}-4^2S_{\frac{1}{2}}$ consists of signals of the corresponding F-F transitions: 3-$2°$, 2-$2°$, 1-$2°$, 2-$1°$, 1-$1°$ (the signal from 0-$1°$ does not exist, because of the symmetry in the upper state).

The signal of the transition with angular momenta J_1 and J_2 has an amplitude [66]:

$$I_{J_1 J_2}(\vec{e}) = (-1)^{(J_1 + J_2)} I_0 \sum_{\mathcal{H}} (2\mathcal{H}+1) \left\{ \begin{matrix} 1 & 1 & \mathcal{H} \\ J_1 & J_1 & J_2 \end{matrix} \right\} \sum_q (-1)^q \rho_q^{\mathcal{H}} \, \Phi_{-q}^{\mathcal{H}}(\vec{e}) \tag{8.5}$$

where

$$I_0 = k'(2J_1 + 1)^{-\frac{1}{2}} |(J_2\|d\|J_1)|^2 = k'(2J_1+1)^{-\frac{1}{2}} d_2^2 \tag{8.6}$$

and $\rho_q^{\mathcal{H}} = \mathcal{F}_q^{\mathcal{H}} (\gamma_2 - i q \Omega)$ is the statistical tensor, determined by the excitation tensor with components

$$\mathcal{F}_q^{\mathcal{H}} = (-1)^{(J_1 + J_2)} B \left\{ \begin{matrix} 1 & 1 & \mathcal{H} \\ J_2 & J_2 & J_1 \end{matrix} \right\} \Phi_q^{\mathcal{H}}(\vec{e}_o) \tag{8.7}$$

where $B = k'(J_1 + 1)^{\frac{1}{2}} d_1^2$, and

$$\Phi_q^{\mathcal{H}}(\vec{e}_o) = \sum_{q_1, q_2} (-1)^{q_2} e_{q_1} e_{q_2}^* \left\{ \begin{matrix} 1 & 1 & 2 \\ q_1 & -q_2 & -q \end{matrix} \right\} \tag{8.8}$$

d_1 and d_2 being the reduced matrix elements ($(J_1\|d\|J_2$ and $J_2\|d\|J_1$ respectively), d the diameter of the cathode cavity, $\vec{e}$ and $\vec{e}_o$ the unit polarization vectors of the observed and incident light respectively, e_{q_1} and e_q^* the circular components of the polarization vector of the exciting radiation, Ω the frequency difference between the interfering states.

In our case the statistical tensor component $\rho_q^{J_c}$ for the corresponding excited state F is:

$$F = 3 \qquad \rho_2^2 = -B_{32}^2 \begin{Bmatrix} 1 & 1 & 2 \\ 3 & 3 & 2 \end{Bmatrix} \Phi_q^{\mathcal{H}}(\vec{e}_0) \qquad (8.9)$$

$$F = 2 \qquad \rho_2^2 = -B_{22}^2 \begin{Bmatrix} 1 & 1 & 2 \\ 2 & 2 & 2 \end{Bmatrix} - B_{21}^2 \begin{Bmatrix} 1 & 1 & 2 \\ 2 & 2 & 1 \end{Bmatrix} \Phi_q^{\mathcal{H}}(\vec{e}_0) \quad (8.10)$$

$$F = 1 \qquad \rho_2^2 = -B_{12}^2 \begin{Bmatrix} 1 & 1 & 2 \\ 1 & 1 & 2 \end{Bmatrix} + B_{11}^2 \begin{Bmatrix} 1 & 1 & 2 \\ 1 & 1 & 1 \end{Bmatrix} \Phi_q^{\mathcal{H}}(\vec{e}_0) \quad (8.11)$$

and the amplitudes I:

$$I_{32^\circ} \cong - \begin{Bmatrix} 1 & 1 & 2 \\ 3 & 3 & 2 \end{Bmatrix} \rho_2^2 = (0.107)^2 \, B_{32^\circ}^2, \qquad (8.12)$$

similarly

$$I_{22^\circ} \cong (0.153)^2 \, (B_{22^\circ}^2 - B_{21^\circ}^2), \qquad I_{21^\circ} \cong -(0.153)^2 \, (B_{22^\circ}^2 - B_{21^\circ}^2), \quad (8.13)$$

$$I_{12^\circ} \cong (0.033)^2 \, (B_{12^\circ}^2 - 5B_{11^\circ}^2), \qquad I_{11^\circ} \cong -6 \times 10^{-3}(B_{12^\circ}^2 - 5B_{11^\circ}^2). \quad (8.14)$$

The signals from $F = 2$ have equal amplitudes with opposite sign, which compensate each other and do not contribute to the amplitude of the $J\text{-}J$ transition signal.

According to the resolution of the $F\text{-}F$ structure, three cases are possible: (i) unresolved structure, and then $B_{32^\circ}^2 = B_{22^\circ}^2 = B_{21^\circ}^2 = B_{11^\circ}^2 = B_{01^\circ}^2$; (ii) partially resolved structure, for example, in the low state if there is a saturation of the photon trapping, the case is identical to (i); otherwise the signal amplitudes from the F-states are defined by the statistical weight of these levels; (iii) fully resolved structure — the amplitudes are defined by the statistical weight of the F levels.

We shall apply the scheme of resonance-photon trapping proposed at the beginning to the case (i) in which all $F\text{-}F$ transitions have equal intensities and their resolution does not create any significant problems. The transitions from $F = 3$ will illustrate the scheme (Fig. 8.5): a photon is absorbed in the $2^\circ\text{-}3$ transition (the level $F = 3$ participates in radiation trapping only through this transition) and is emitted in $3\text{-}2^\circ$ or $3\text{-}3'$, $3\text{-}2'$, $3\text{-}4''$, $3\text{-}3''$, $3\text{-}2''$ transitions. Then $A_{io} = A_{32^\circ}$, $A_{ik} = A_{32} + A_{33'} + A_{32'} + A_{34''} + A_{33''} + A_{32''}$ and if we use the relative probabilities of $F\text{-}F$ transitions [67] from $J = 3/2$ to $J = 1/2; J = 3/2$

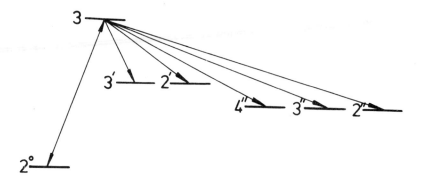

Fig. 8.5 – F-F transitions from the hyperfine level $F = 3$; [Cu(I) $4\,^2P_{3/2}$ level].

to $J = 3/2$; $J = 3/2$ to $J = 5/2$, we obtain the transition probability $A_{32^\circ} = 1.794$ (the relative probability of the F-F transitions is normalized to the probability of the corresponding J-J transition, using data from [68]); calculating the J-symbol product

$$\begin{Bmatrix} 1 & 1 & 2 \\ 3 & 3 & 2 \end{Bmatrix}^2 \Big/ \begin{Bmatrix} 1 & 1 & 0 \\ 3 & 3 & 2 \end{Bmatrix}^2 = 0.239$$

we obtain $\alpha_2^{32^\circ} = 0.1646$, which gives 0.84 as the probability for the transition from $F = 3$. Similarly $\alpha_2^{11^\circ} = 0.1691$ and $\alpha_2^{12^\circ} = 0.6385 \times 10^{-2}$ can be calculated, as well as $\alpha_2^{21^\circ} = \alpha_2^{22^\circ} = 0.2367$ ($\alpha_2^{01^\circ} = 0$, obviously, for the component from $F = 0$). Finally for the Hanle signal trapping and narrowing of the $4^2P_{\frac{3}{2}} - 4^2S_{\frac{1}{2}}$ transition we find

$F = 1,3$ – the signal is narrowed – $\gamma_2 = 0.84\,\gamma_R$;

$F = 2$ – no alignment because of the compensation of the hyperfine component signals in the 2-2° and 2-1° transitions – the signals have equal amplitudes and opposite sign.

If the hyperfine structure is partially (see [69]) or fully resolved and the transitions between the hyperfine components have different intensities, the final quantitative result might be different. The experimentally derived [64] value $\gamma_2 = 0.86\gamma_R$ coincides well with the theoretical calculation based on the model described. Although the importance of this coincidence should not be exaggerated, it might be thought that the signal deformation observed [64] is due to radiation trapping from $F = 1.3$ for the $4^2P_{\frac{3}{2}}$ Cu(I) level.

8.3.3 Hanle signal width and concentration of Cu atoms in CBHCD

The analysis above indicates the connection between the copper atom concentration N and the Hanle signal narrowing for the Cu(I) 324.7 nm spectral line in the HCD. This is the main feature of the method for comparing the concentration of the ground-state Cu atoms in the CBHCD and FBHCD. The experiment consists of a comparative measurement of the function $2\Delta H_{\frac{1}{2}}$, (i) with two cylindrical copper hollow cathodes with equal dimensions, one having a conical bottom ($d = 8$ mm, $L = 40$ mm, $h = 16$ mm). The linear dependence of N_o on i [60] is the reason for choosing i as a preliminary fixed parameter in the experiment, which is done with the same gas pressure, $p_{Ne} = 40$ Pa, for both cathodes.

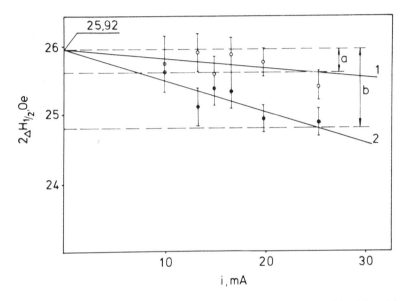

Fig. 8.6 – Hanle signal width $2\Delta H_{1/2}$ of the Cu(I) $(4^2P_{3/2}-4^2S_{1/2})$ transition: 1 – flat-bottomed cathode, 2 – conical bottomed cathode. (Reprinted from [62] by courtesy of Marcel Dekker, Inc.)

The detected Hanle signal widths are illustrated in Fig. 8.6. They are systematically smaller than those for the flat-bottom cathode. This fact indicates stronger trapping of the Cu(I) 324.7 nm resonance emission with the conical-bottom cathode, i.e. an increased copper atom concentration. The difference between the signal width at a fixed value of i and its zero value is defined as the 'narrowing magnitude' in the FBHCD (difference a) and CBHCD (difference b). Since both cathodes have approximately equal volume, we can consider that the narrowing is defined only by the concentrations N_o^c and N_o^f of the ground-state copper atoms. In both cases N_o is a linear function of i, so the ratio a/b depends on the ratio of the concentrations, namely $a/b = N_o^f/N_o^c$. For $i = 0.25$ mA, the narrowings are $a = 0.37$ Oe and $b = 1.12$ Oe, and the ratio of the sputtered-atom concentrations in the two cathodes is $N_o^f/N_o^c = 0.33$, (i.e. a three times higher concentration in the conical-bottom cathode). We note that this ratio correlates with the above-mentioned increase of the Cu(I) 402.3 nm and Cu(I) 515.3 nm spectral line intensities in the CBHCD. We can consider this correlation as an indication that of the two possible reasons for higher line intensity in the conical hollow cathode, the main one is the increased concentration N_0^c of sputtered atoms in the ground state. The limited increase in the resonance Cu(I) 324.7 nm line intensity is probably due to self-absorption in the gas discharge emission.

8.4 ANALYTICAL APPLICATIONS OF THE CBHCD

As a spectral source the HCD began to attract the attention of analytical chemists from different research fields many years ago. Although the HCD has found only limited application compared to arc, spark, and modern ICP and laser sources, it has been successfully applied to several specific analytical problems, for example determination of elements with high ionization potentials, gases, traces of certain elements, thin layer analysis [70–72]. The discharge tube with a hollow cathode is also frequently used in other analytical methods, in particular in atomic-fluorescence analysis. The most common application of the HCD, however, is as a source of monochromatic light for atomic-absorption spectrometry (AAS). In this case the discharge tube and the anode and cathode construction have special features of their own [73, 74].

The necessity continually to improve spectral analysis also implies further development of the hollow-cathode discharge systems as spectral sources. The tendency here is mainly to increase the spectral line intensity, and sometimes to decrease the line width without worsening the stability and spectral emission. It follows from Sections 8.1 and 8.2 that the characteristics of the new HCD modification described here satisfy the above-mentioned purposes. The results obtained for cathode or sample material spectral lines are helpful when it is intended to use the HCD in emission spectral analysis. In this case it is also very important that the spectral lines of the working gas are generally little influenced by the HCD modification. This selectivity implies less influence of extraneous lines and of the background near the analytical line, and hence an improved signal-to-noise ratio, and therefore higher analytical sensitivity. The requirements for the recording instrumentation are not so severe. All these advantages are easier to attain with the HBHCD than by other methods, such as use of a pulse mode [75], a dynamic filter [76], or a magnetic field [77].

Besides the enhancement of the line intensity, there is no significant increase in the line width [78], and under equal conditions the enhancement ratio I^c/I^f is much greater than the line width ratio $\Delta\nu^c/\Delta\nu^f$. The change in line width can be minimized by suitable choice of the discharge current. A possible application of the CBHCD as a monochromatic source is in lamps for AAS. In this case the intensity, stability and width of the spectral line emission are simultaneously expressed by the quality of the calibration graph. CBHCD lamps for determination of Ni, Mo, Fe, Si, Mg, Cu, Zn and Al have been reported [44, 79, 80]. The lamp construction is schematically illustrated in Fig. 8.1. Cathode 1 is a cylinder 16 mm in length, 4 mm in inner diameter, with a cone height of 7 mm. The outer cathode surface area is increased by special cutting to give more effective cooling of the discharge. Lamps for multielement analysis use cathodes prepared with suitable alloys or with a suitable inner coating. The lamps are filled with neon as working gas at a pressure of about 530 Pa. The slope of the calibration graph is used as a criterion for the optimum working current since it characterizes the competition between the increases in intensity and width of the line; the stability of the light emission is considered to be a limiting condition for the selection of the optimal current.

Use of the CBHCD instead of the FBHCD gives a steeper calibration graph at a given working current as shown in Fig. 8.7 for magnesium and in Fig. 8.8 for

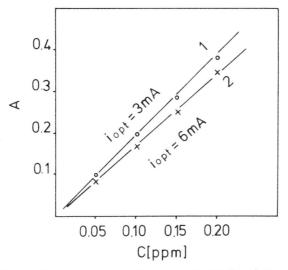

Fig. 8.7 – Calibration graphs for Mg [λ = Mg(I) 285.2 nm] : 1 – CBHCD, 2 – FBHCD. (Reprinted from [79] by courtesy of Marcel Dekker, Inc.)

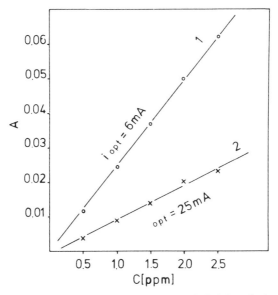

Fig. 8.8 – Calibration graphs for Ni [λ = Ni(I) 232.0 nm] : 1 – CBHCD, 2 – FBHCD. (Reproduced from [79] by courtesy of Marcel Dekker, Inc.)

nickel. Thus for AAS lamps for determination of aluminium, the optimum working current is the same for both types of hollow cathode, but the conical-bottomed type gives greater sensitivity. The newly constructed Cu-Zn double-element lamp retains the advantages of the single-element versions.

The lower optimal working current of the CDHCD also means a longer working life for the lamp, besides the improvement of the discharge and increase of the analytical detection power.

This new type of AAS lamp compares very favourably with commercial AAS lamps. The lamps we have investigated up to now give us confidence in saying we foresee no major difficulties in making lamps for other elements.

REFERENCES

[1] F. Paschen, *Ann. Phys.*, 1916, **50**, 901.

[2] A. Günterschulze, *Z. Phys.*, 1923, **19**, 313.

[3] A. Lompe, R. Seeliger and E. Wolter, *Ann. Phys.*, 1939, **36**, 9.

[4] V. S. Borodin and Yu. M. Kagan, *Zh. Tekh. Fiz.*, 1966, **36**, 181.

[5] V. S. Borodin, Yu. M. Kagan and R. I. Lyagushchenko, *Zh. Tekh. Fiz.*, 1966, **36**, 1198.

[6] Yu. M. Kagan, R. I. Lyagushchenko and S. N. Hvorostovsky, *Opt. Spectrosk.*, 1972, **33**, 430.

[7] Yu. M. Kagan, R. I. Lyagushchenko and S. N. Hvorostovsky, *Zh. Tekh. Fiz.*, 1972, **42**, 1686.

[8] Yu. M. Kagan, R. I. Lyagushchenko and S. N. Hvorostovsky, *Opt. Spektrosk.*, 1973, **35**, 422.

[9] Yu. M. Kagan, R. I. Lyagushchenko and S. N. Hvorostovsky, *Zh. Tekh. Fiz.*, 1973, **43**, 1488.

[10] F. A. Korolev, A. I. Odintsov, V. V. Lebedeva and V. M. Salimov, *Radiotekh. Elektr.*, 1969, **14**, 1519.

[11] F. A. Korolev, A. I. Odintsov and E. B. Foursova, *Opt. Spektrosk.*, 1964, **16**, 555.

[12] H. Krellman, E. Siefart and E. Wiehreter, *J. Phys.*, 1975, **B8**, 2608.

[13] E. D. Tidwell, *J. Quant. Spectrosc. Radiat. Transfer*, 1972, **12**, 431.

[14] B. van der Sijde, *J. Quant. Spectrosc. Radiat. Transfer*, 1972, **12**, 703.

[15] N. I. Kaliteevsky and M. P. Chaika, *Vestn. Leningr. Univ. Fiz. Khim.*, 1959, **16**, 51.

[16] N. I. Kaliteevsky and M. P. Chaika, *Dokl. Akad. Nauk SSSR*, 1955, **103**, 49.

[17] N. I. Kaliteevsky and M. P. Chaika, *Dokl. Akad. Nauk SSSR*, 1959, **126**, 57.

[18] V. P. Chebotaev, *Radiotekh. Elektr.*, 1965, **10**, 372.

[19] V. P. Chebotaev, *Radiotekh. Elektr.*, 1965, **10**, 374.

[20] V. P. Chebotaev and V. V. Pokasov, *Radiotekh. Elektr.*, 1965, **10**, 958.

[21] D. Z. Zhechev and M. P. Chaika, *Opt. Spektrosk.*, 1977, **43**, 590.

[22] D. Z. Zhechev and M. P. Chaika, *Opt. Spektrosk.*, 1978, **45**, 406.

[23] D. Z. Zhechev, *J. Phys. Lett.*, 1982, **43**, 67.

[24] D. A. Katskov, G. G. Lebedev and B. V. L'vov, *Zh. Prikl. Spektrosk.*, 1969, **10**, 215.

[25] B. M. Boshnyak,, E. S. Dobrosavljević. A. G. Zhiglinsky and T. N. Khlopina, *Zh. Prikl. Spektrosk.*, 1969, **10**, 554.

[26] J. B. Dawson and D. J. Ellis, *Spectrochim. Acta,* 1967, **23A**, 565.

[27] A. I. Bodrezova, B. V. L'vov and V. I. Mosichev, *Zh. Prikl. Spektrosk.*, 1966, **4**, 207.

[28] D. Z. Zhechev and R. B. Djulgerova, *Bulg. J. Phys.*, 1983, **10**, 438.

[29] G. G. Bratescu and F. Gruzsmiczki, *Rev. Roum. Phys.*, 1977, **22**, 565.

[30] Y. B. Atnashev and V. N. Muzgin, *Zh. Spektrosk.*, 1974, **21**, 414.

[31] B. M. Boshnyak and A. G. Zhiglinsky, *Proc. 7th Uralska Conf. Atom. Spectrosc.*, 1971, **1**, 19.

[32] M. F. Sem, V. V. Vainer, S. P. Zinchenko and I. G. Ivanov, *Proc. Intern. Conf. Lasers, Florida,* 1979, 445.

[33] S. P. Zinchenko, I. G. Ivanov and M. F. Sem, *Sov. J. Quantum Electr.*, 1980, **7**, 1827.

[34] V. V. Zhoukov, E. L. Latoush and M. F. Sem, *Zh. Prikl. Spektrosk.*, 1980, **32**, 738.

[35] A. G. Zhiglinsky, *Ph. D. Thesis,* LGU, Leningrad.

[36] N. Sabotinov, M. Grozeva, N. Vouchkov and P. Telbizov, 1981. *Discharge Tube for a Hollow Cathode Laser,* Inventor's certificate No. 52167, Sofia, 1981.

[37] M. Grozeva and N. Sabotinov, *Opt. Commun.*, 1982, **41**, 57.

[38] H. Koch, *Sci. Instrum.*, 1983, **16**, 122.

[39] R. Djulgerova, D. Zhechev and N. Teodosiev, *Opt. Appl.*, 1983, **13**, 355.

[40] V. G. Pimenov, V. N. Shishov and N. V. Larin, *Zh. Analit. Khim.*, 1981, **36**, 1019.

[41] B. I. Moskalev, *Hollow Cathode Discharge,* Energiya, Moscow, 1969, pp. 6-8.

[42] D. Z. Zhechev, R. B. Djulgerova and S. Valkanov, *Proc. 2nd Natl. Conf. Physics-Industry, Kazanlak,* 1977, 314.

[43] R. B. Djulgerova and D. Z. Zhechev, *Spectrosc. Lett.*, 1979, **12**, 615.

[44] R. B. Djulgerova, D. Z. Zhechev and Z. P. Savova, *Elektroprom. Pribor.*, 1980, **3**, 110.

[45] D. Z. Zhechev, *Ph. D. Thesis,* LGU, Leningrad, 1980.

[46] I. P. Zapisochny and P. V. Felzan, *Ukr. Fiz. Zh.*, 1965, **10**, 1197.

[47] H. Fetz, *Z. Phys.*, 1942, **119**, 590.

[48] G. K. Wehner, *Phys. Rev.*, 1965, **102**, 690.

[49] M. Smolouhovsky, *Ann. Phys. Chem.*, 1898, **64**, 101.

[50] B. I. Moskalev, *Zh. Tekhn.*, 1965, **35**, 1408.

[51] I. N. Slivkov, Vi. I. Mikhailov, N. I. Sidorov and A. I. Nastyukha, *Electric Breakdown and Discharge in Vacuum,* Atomizdat, Moscow, 1966, pp. 44-56.

[52] V. Orlinov and G. Mladenov, *Int. J. Elec.*, 1969, **27**, 65.

[53] T. M. Gorbounova and O. P. Semenova, *Zh. Prikl. Spektrosk.*, 1970, **12**, 17.

[54] G. A. Arifov, *Atomic Particles Interaction with Solid State Surfaces,* Nauka, Moscow, 1968. pp. 27-32.

[55] M. Kaminsky, *Atomic and Ionic Impact Phenomena on Metal Surfaces*, Mir, Moscow, 1967, pp. 13-18.

[56] F. M. Devienne, *Compt. Rend.*, 1964, **259**, 4575.

[57] G. V. Spivak and V. E. Urasova, *Izv. Akad. Nauk SSSR Fiz.*, 1956, **20**, 1184.

[58] K. B. Cheney and E. T. Pitkin, *J. Appl. Phys.*, 1965, **36**, 3542.

[59] A. G. Zhiglinsky and T. N. Khlopina, *Opt. Spektrosk.*, 1972, **32**, 645.

[60] B. M. Boshnyak, A. G. Zhiglinsky, G. G. Kund and T. N. Khlopina, *Opt. Spektrosk.*, 1972, **33**, 1033.

[61] D. Z. Zhechev, *J. Environ. Sci. Health*, 1981, **A16**, 149.

[62] D. Z. Zhechev, *Spectrosc. Lett.*, 1981, **14**, 293.

[63] W. Hanle, *Z. Phys.*, 1924, **30**, 93.

[64] D. Z. Zhechev, *Opt. Spektrosk.*, 1980, **49**, 465.

[65] E. B. Saloman and W. Happer, Jr., *Phys. Rev.*, 1966, **144**, 7.

[66] M. I. Dyakonov, *Zh. Eksp. Teor. Fiz.*, 1964, **47**, 2213.

[67] H. Kopfermann, *Kernmomente*, Izd. In. Lit., Moscow, 1960, pp. 42-45.

[68] C. B. Corliss and W. R. Bozman, *Experimental Transition Probabilities for Spectral Lines of Seventy Elements*, National Bureau of Standards, Washington D. C., 1962.

[69] M. P. Chaika and N. I. Kaliteevsky, *Opt. Spektrosk.*, 1956, **1**, 606.

[70] Kh. I. Zil'bershtein, *Zavodsk. Lab.*, 1980, **46**, 1095.

[71] O. A. Grigor'eva, E. A. Karpova and Yu. I. Turkin, *Zh. Prikl. Spektrosk.*, 1980, **33**, 240.

[72] A. I. Drobyshev, E. V. Gorchakova and Yu.I Turkin, *Zh. Prikl. Spektrosk.*, 1984, **40**, 140.

[73] B. V. L'vov, *Atomic Absorption Analysis*, Nauka, Moscow, 1966, pp. 60-65.

[74] G. F. Kirkbright and M. Sargent, *Atomic Absorption and Fluorescence Spectroscopy*, Academic Press, London, 1971, pp. 101-145.

[75] E. S. Dobrosavljević, A. G. Zhiglinsky and T. N. Khlopina, *Bull. Boris Kidrič Inst. Nucl. Sci. Phys.*, 1968, **19**, 1.

[76] K. Sommer, A. Thorne and R. Learner, *J. Phys. D.*, 1983, **16**, 233.

[77] N. K. Rudnevsky, D. E. Maksimov and L. P. Lazareva, *Zh. Prikl. Spektrosk..*, 1978, **29**, 916.

[78] R. B. Djulgerova, *Ph. D. Thesis*, Sofia, 1980.

[79] R. B. Djulgerova, D. Z. Zhechev, S. Popova and E. Momchilova, *Spectrosc. Lett.*, 1983, **16**, 765.

[80] R. B. Djulgerova, D. Z. Zhechev, S. Popova, V. Kamenarova, J. Koseva, L. Mihaylova, S. Kolarova and V. Dragova, *Proc. 10th Natl. Conf. Atom. Spectrosc. V Tarnovo, Bulgaria*, 1982 (in the press).

Author Index

Subject Index